POINT DEFECTS IN METALS

Point Defects
in Metals

A. C. DAMASK

Brookhaven National Laboratory
Pitman-Dunn Research Institute, Frankford Arsenal

and

G. J. DIENES

Brookhaven National Laboratory

GORDON AND BREACH

Science Publishers

New York · London

PRINTED IN GREAT BRITAIN BY

W. S. COWELL LTD, BUTTER MARKET, IPSWICH

PREFACE

Point defects are crystalline irregularities of atomic dimensions. These simple imperfections play a central role in the atomic interpretation of many physical properties and processes in solids. The first intensive study of point defects was carried out on ionic crystals and culminated in the successful explanation of many properties of color centers. In turn, this development led to an interpretation of the more complex behavior of technically important substances, such as photographic emulsions and luminescent materials. Similar theoretical and experimental techniques showed that point defects play an important role in the understanding of semiconductors and in the development of semiconductor technology. A parallel effort on metals first led to an atomic interpretation of diffusion processes. Further effort was stimulated by the requirements of modern materials technology in dealing with the problems arising from radiation and mechanical damage. An understanding of the process of formation and the properties of point defects was found to be essential to a sound interpretation of a variety of phenomena in these areas.

In many respects point defects assume their simplest character in metallic solids, since they cause only minor disturbances in the system of electrons, at least in the simple metals. They have been studied rather extensively during the last decade, and theoretical and experimental techniques have been refined to the point where highly reliable information is now available for a few representative metals. The properties of point defects in thermodynamic equilibrium are quite well understood, and important advances have recently been made in the controlled production of defects, the understanding of their migration characteristics, and the study of their influence on physical properties. The point defects treated in this book are primarily the structural ones, that is, vacancies (vacant lattice sites), interstitials (an extra atom in a non-lattice position), and their clusters. Other imperfections, such as impurity atoms, dislocations etc., are discussed insofar as they interact with the structural point defects and influence their static or dynamic characteristics. Similarly, a detailed treatment of solid state diffusion is not given, although the theoretical and experimental aspects of diffusion that shed light on the characteristics of point defects have been included.

The purpose of this book is to present in a systematic way the theoretical and experimental methods employed in investigating the fundamental properties of point defects in metals and to summarize the basic properties of these imperfections as revealed by modern techniques. Representative investigations are discussed in detail. Complete coverage of the literature has not been attempted, but sufficient references are included for adequate and easy entry into the wide literature of this field. It is hoped that the treatment given will be of use to graduate students, to those interested in the broad science of materials, and to specialists in metallurgy and solid state physics who desire a systematic and integrated review of the role of point defects in metals.

The writers are indebted to their colleagues in the Solid State Physics Group at Brookhaven National Laboratory for many helpful discussions, to C. Erginsoy and R. A. Johnson for a critical reading of the manuscript, to G. H. Vineyard and A. Seeger for discussions on several important points, to Mrs. Dienes for editorial assistance, and to Mrs. H. Cannan and Mrs. V. Mead for dedicated assistance in the preparation of the manuscript.

June, 1963   A. C. DAMASK

                                                  G. J. DIENES

CONTENTS

Chapter III. Methods of Analysis of Annealing Curves

Chapter IV. Physical Properties and Point Defects

Chapter V. Some Basic Experiments

INTRODUCTION

All real crystals contain a variety of imperfections. Many of the imperfections, such as impurity atoms, dislocations, grain boundaries, etc., are produced during the preparation, treatment, and handling of the crystal. Structural point defects, i.e., irregularities of atomic dimensions in the crystal lattice, are the simplest imperfections and are in a class by themselves because they are present in a crystal in thermodynamic equilibrium. The basic structural point defects are the vacancy, a vacant lattice site, and the interstitial, an extra atom in a non-lattice position. The nature, behavior, and properties of these defects in metals form the central theme of this book. Other imperfections are also treated because they interact with the point defects, but the discussion is limited to these interactions.

Point defects are important because they influence many physical properties and are responsible for many diffusion controlled processes. The mechanical properties of metals are particularly sensitive to the presence of point defects because of their strong interactions with dislocations. Diffusion processes, which are responsible for many solid state reactions, are largely controlled by the migration characteristics of point defects, primarily vacancies. Thus both the static and dynamic properties of point defects are of crucial importance in many areas of materials science.

The presence of point defects can be determined by careful measurements of such physical properties as electrical resistivity and lattice parameter. Although it has recently become possible to observe point defects directly with the field ion microscope under special circumstances, most of the currently available information is derived indirectly from studying changes in physical properties as a function of defect concentration and from investigating rate processes which mirror the migration of defects.

The ultimate aim of research in this field is the quantitative description and understanding of the properties of point defects, their mode of production and migration, their interaction with each other and with other imperfections, and their role in influencing physical properties and controlling diffusion processes. These aims can be achieved only by a combination of theoretical and experimental investigations.

This book starts with the basic thermodynamic description of point defects, which leads naturally to the concept and calculation of energies and entropies of formation and migration. The rest of Chapter I is devoted to a discussion of some of the important properties of defects, their interactions with each other and with other imperfections, and their modes of production by both reversible and irreversible processes. The migration properties of defects must be derived from various observable rate processes, most prominently from the disappearance of an excess concentration of defects brought about by a variety of annealing processes. The kinetic theory of annealing processes is treated in Chapter II. In many ways this is the most detailed chapter because much of this information is very recent and has never been summarized systematically. The usual mathematical procedures needed to derive the characteristic kinetic parameters from experiment are given in Chapter III. Up to this point in the book it has been assumed that the concentration of the defects is known from some appropriate experiment. In order to carry out an experiment, however, the relation between some physically measurable quantity and the defect concentration must be known. The relations of physical property changes to defect concentrations are the subject of Chapter IV. This chapter, therefore, is essentially an introduction to the experimental sections. Primarily the results, rather than the details, of theoretical calculations are presented, in order to permit interpretation of the currently available basic experiments.

Finally, a comparison of theory and experiment is presented in Chapter V. The treatment is not exhaustive but is limited to basic experiments that have been carried out under sufficiently well controlled conditions to be interpretable. The principal aim of Chapter V is to illustrate the modern experimental techniques that have led to highly reliable results, at least for a few typical metals, and to summarize the best available quantitative data.

The organization of this book reflects personal preferences to some extent, since the thermodynamic proof of the existence of the phenomena was considered to take precedence over the description and study of the effects of the phenomena. A conscious effort has been made, however, to render each chapter essentially self-contained. Hopefully this effort was successful enough to permit a reader, not immediately interested in all the details of point defect research, to find and understand specific items of interest.

The extensive literature on point defects in metals is not completely covered, but the references are sufficient for the purposes of the book and for easy entry into the literature. Immediately below is a general bibliography listing books, conference proceedings, and review articles on the topics treated in this book and related fields.

General Bibliography

Books

J. Frenkel, *Kinetic Theory of Liquids*, Oxford University Press, Oxford, 1946.

R. H. Fowler and E. A. Guggenheim, *Statistical Thermodynamics*, Cambridge University Press, Cambridge, 1939.

C. Kittel, *Introduction to Solid State Physics*, Wiley, New York, 1956.

R. A. Swalin, *Thermodynamics of Solids*, Wiley, New York, 1962.

H. G. van Bueren, *Imperfections in Crystals*, North-Holland Publishing Co., Amsterdam, 1961.

A. H. Cottrell, *Dislocations and Plastic Flow in Crystals*, Oxford University Press, Oxford, 1953.

W. T. Read, *Dislocations in Crystals*, McGraw-Hill, New York, 1953.

J. Friedel, *Les Dislocations*, Gauthier-Villars, Paris, 1956.

G. J. Dienes and G. H. Vineyard, *Radiation Effects in Solids*, Interscience, New York, 1957.

D. S. Billington and J. H. Crawford, *Radiation Damage in Solids*, Princeton University Press, 1961.

W. Jost, *Diffusion in Solids, Liquids and Gases*, Academic Press, New York, 1960.

P. G. Shewmon, *Diffusion in Solids*, McGraw-Hill, New York, 1963.

K. Lintner and E. Schmid, *Werkstoffe des Reaktorbaues*, Springer-Verlag, Berlin 1962.

T. J. Gray, Editor, *The Defect Solid State*, Interscience, New York, 1957.

Conference Proceedings and Recent Review Articles

Phase Transformations in Solids, R. Smoluchowski, Editor, Wiley, New York, 1951.

Imperfections in Nearly Perfect Crystals, W. Shockley et al., Editors, Wiley, New York, 1952.

Report of the Conference on Defects in Crystalline Solids, The Physical Society, London, 1955.

Atom Movements, American Society for Metals, Cleveland, 1951.

Vacancies and Other Point Defects in Metals and Alloys, The Institute of Metals, London, 1958.

Radiation effects in inorganic solids, *Discussions Faraday Soc.* **No. 31** (1962).

Radiation Damage in Solids, Vols. I and II, International Atomic Energy Agency, Vienna, 1962.

Proceedings of the International Conference on the Peaceful Uses of Atomic Energy, UN, New York, 1956.

Proceedings of the Second UN International Conference on the Peaceful Uses of Atomic Energy, UN, Geneva, 1958.

International Conference on Crystal Lattice Defects, J. Phys. Soc. Japan **18**, Suppl. I–III (1963).

Recovery and Recrystallization of Metals, L. Himmel, Editor, A.I.M.E., 1962 (in press).

Dislocations and Mechanical Properties of Crystals, J. C. Fisher, et al., Editors, Wiley, New York, 1957.

Direct Observations of Imperfections in Crystals, J. B. Newkirk and J. H. Wernick, Editors, Interscience, New York, 1962.

F. Seitz and J. S. Koehler, Displacement of atoms during irradiation, in *Solid State Physics*, Vol. II, pp. 307–449, F. Seitz and D. Turnbull, Editors, Academic Press, New York, 1956.

D. Lazarus, Diffusion in metals, *Ibid.*, Vol. 10, pp. 71–114, 1960.

A. N. Goland, Atomic displacements in solids by nuclear radiation, *Ann. Rev. Nucl. Sci.* **12**, 243 (1962).

J. Friedel, Point defects and irradiation, in *Low Temperature Physics*, C. DeWitt et al., Editors, Gordon and Breach, New York, 1962.

A. Seeger, Recent advances in the theory of defects in crystals, *Physica Status Solidi* **1**, 669 (1961).

W. M. Lomer, Defects in pure metals, *Progr. Metal Phys.* **8**, 255–321 (1959).

Nuclear Metallurgy (Vol. III), *IMD Special Report Series*, No. 3, A.I.M.E., 1956.

Radiation Damage in Solids Course 18 (*Proceedings of the International School of Physics, "Enrico Fermi", 1960*), D. S. Billington, Editor, Academic Press, New York (1962).

Strengthening Mechanisms in Solids, American Society for Metals, Metals Park, Ohio, 1962.

Perspectives in Materials Research, L. Himmel et al., Editors, ACR-61, Office of Naval Research, 1963.

Effects of Radiation on Materials, J. J. Harwood et al., Editors, Reinhold, New York, 1958.

Impurities and Imperfections, American Society for Metals, Cleveland, 1955.

A. Seeger, in *Handbuch der Physik*, VII/1, Springer-Verlag, Berlin, 1955.

G. H. Kinchin and R. S. Pease, The displacement of atoms in solids by radiation, *Rept. Progr. Phys.* **18**, 1 (1955).

H. B. Huntington, Point defects – an evaluation, *Dallas Meeting of A.I.M.E., 1963* (in press).

Properties of Reactor Materials and the Effects of Radiation Damage, D. J Littler Editor, Butterworths, London (1962).

CHAPTER ONE

GENERAL THEORY

1. Definitions and Description

In a perfect crystal the atoms are arranged in an absolutely periodic array. In real crystals this periodic array is disturbed by imperfections. It is convenient to classify these imperfections as point defects and extended defects. The point defects, as the name indicates, are highly localized and are characterized by the disturbance around a single atomic site. It will be shown in section I–2 that a perfect crystal is thermodynamically stable only at the temperature of absolute zero, and at any higher temperature the crystal must contain a certain number of point defects.

The most elementary structural defects in a pure crystal are the vacancy and the interstitial. Although a substitutional impurity atom (atom A in Fig. I–1.1) is a point defect in a real crystal, such defects will be treated only insofar as they interact with the structural point defects. The vacancy is a missing atom in the array as shown by point C in Fig. I–1.1. The interstitial is an atom located in a non-lattice position in the array, such as the atom indicated by B in the figure. Point defects can interact with each other. If a vacancy and an interstitial combine, the two defects are annihilated with the interstitial reoccupying a normal lattice site. Two vacancies can combine into a divacancy (indicated by D in the figure) to form the simplest of the defect clusters. The clustering process of vacancies can continue until a small void is formed. Recent calculations have indicated that interstitials can also combine to form clusters.

All real crystals also contain extended defects, i.e., disturbances in the regular array which extend over many lattice distances. Such defects are accidents of growth and are not in thermodynamic equilibrium; the most obvious such defect is the external surface where the growth has stopped. A similar role is played by internal surfaces such as grain boundaries, twinning, and stacking faults.

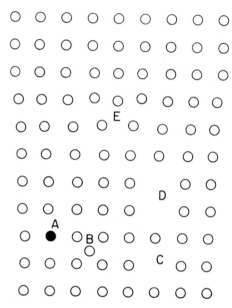

Fig. I–1.1 Schematic illustration of the basic crystalline defects. A: Substitutional impurity atom; B: interstitial atom; C: lattice vacancy; D: divacancy; and E: edge dislocation.

A very important type of extended defect is the dislocation, which was thought up as an explanation for the mechanical yielding of crystals and was later experimentally shown to exist. The simplest dislocation is the edge dislocation, which consists of an incomplete plane of atoms. Such an incomplete plane, normal to the page, is represented in Fig. I–1.1 by the row of atoms starting at the top of the figure and terminating at point E. The properties of this and other types of dislocations will not be described in detail but will be discussed insofar as they interact strongly with point defects and can serve as sources, sinks, and traps for them.

2. Thermodynamics

Formation of point defects in a crystal, since it requires a certain amount of positive work, increases the internal energy of the crystal. However, the configurational or mixing entropy is also increased because there are many ways of distributing the point defects on the available lattice sites. At any given temperature, T, above absolute zero, the free energy will be a minimum for a certain concentration of defects determined by the balance of the energy and entropy terms. The number of ways, W, in which n defects can be arranged on N lattice sites is

$$W = \frac{N(N-1)(N-2)\ldots(N-n+2)(N-n+1)}{n!}.$$

Multiplication of both the numerator and denominator by $(N-n)!$ and rearrangement gives

$$W = \frac{N!}{(N-n)!\,n!}, \qquad\qquad \text{I–2.1}$$

and the configurational entropy, S, is given from statistical mechanics as

$$S = k \ln W = k \ln \frac{N!}{(N-n)!\,n!}. \qquad\qquad \text{I–2.2}$$

Application of Stirling's approximation for the logarithm of the factorial of a large number,

$$\ln x! \cong x \ln x - x,$$

gives

$$S = k\,[N \ln N - (N-n)\ln(N-n) - n \ln n]. \qquad \text{I–2.3}$$

The free energy, F, of a crystal containing n defects, if the energy to form one defect is E_F, is given by

$$F = nE_F - TS. \qquad\qquad \text{I–2.4}$$

B

Minimizing the free energy with respect to the number of defects gives

$$\frac{\partial F}{\partial n} = 0 = E_F - kT\left(\ln\frac{N-n}{n}\right). \qquad \text{I–2.5}$$

Thus

$$n/(N-n) = e^{-E_F/kT}, \qquad \text{I–2.6}$$

and for $n \ll N$ the atomic fraction of any isolated defect is given by

$$n/N = e^{-E_F/kT}. \qquad \text{I–2.7}$$

The defect concentration is clearly zero at absolute zero and increases rapidly as the temperature is increased.

A similar thermodynamic calculation may be made for simple clusters of point defects. As a specific example, and to show the relation between the concentrations of two types of defects, the formula for divacancy concentration, V_2, and its relation to single vacancy concentration, V_1, are derived below.

If the coordination number (number of nearest neighbors in a perfect crystal lattice) is z, then there are $zN/2$ adjacent pairs of lattice sites in the crystal. If larger clusters are ignored, then n_2 divacancies can be distributed in the following number of ways:

$$W = \frac{(zN/2)!}{[(zN/2)-n_2]!\,n_2!}. \qquad \text{I–2.8}$$

The procedure used in equations I–2.1 to I–2.7 gives

$$n_2/N = V_2 = \tfrac{1}{2}ze^{-E_F^{(2)}/kT}, \qquad \text{I–2.9}$$

where $E_F^{(2)}$ is the energy of formation of a divacancy. If B is the binding energy of two vacancies to form a divacancy and $E_F^{(1)}$ is the formation energy of a single vacancy, then

$$E_F^{(2)} = 2E_F^{(1)} - B \qquad \text{I–2.10}$$

and equation I–2.9 may be rewritten as

$$V_2 = \tfrac{1}{2}ze^{-2E_F^{(1)}/kT}e^{B/kT} = \tfrac{1}{2}zV_1^2 e^{B/kT}. \qquad \text{I–2.11}$$

For a face-centered cubic lattice, where $z = 12$, the ratio of the two concentrations may be written as

$$V_2/V_1 = 6V_1 e^{B/kT} \qquad \text{I-2.12}$$

where the combinatory number 6 is the number of independent orientations of a cluster in the lattice. It is very easy to make a mistake in the calculation of the combinatory numbers for multiple defects and, in fact, the writers themselves have erred occasionally. A simple procedure is given below for obtaining these numbers, the use of which, it is hoped, will prevent future errors.

The procedure of equations I-2.9 to I-2.12 can be applied to any cluster of vacancies or interstitials with the general result

$$n_2/N = C_2(n_1/N)^2 e^{B_2/kT} ,$$
$$n_3/N = C_3(n_1/N)^3 e^{B_2/kT} e^{B_3/kT} , \qquad \text{I-2.13}$$

etc., where B_2 and B_3 are the incremental binding energies (i.e., B_3 is the binding energy for a cluster of three defects relative to a cluster of two). The combinatory numbers C_2 and C_3 are obtained by computing the number of independent orientations of each cluster. This is done most simply by first considering the defects to be distinguishable and computing the number of orientations possible, and then making the defects indistinguishable by dividing by the number of possible permutations. Thus, for a divacancy in a face-centered cubic lattice

$$C_2 = \frac{12}{2!} = 6 ,$$

the number obtained previously by a correct but riskier method. If a trivacancy in the f.c.c. lattice lies in one plane in an equilateral triangle of nearest neighbors, C_3 would be the number of orientations of a divacancy times the number of ways of attaching the third vacancy, divided by the number of permutations of the three vacancies,

$$C_3 = \frac{12 \times 4}{3!} = 8 .$$

However, theoretical calculations, to be discussed later, have shown the trivacancy to be in a tetrahedral configuration with an atom in the center and, therefore, the accepted combinatory number for the trivacancy is

$$C_3 = \frac{12 \times 4}{4!} = 2 .$$

Equations I–2.11 to I–2.13 are also derivable from the law of mass action. Consider the simplest case of the interaction between vacancies and divacancies, which may be represented by the chemical equation

$$V_1 + V_1 \overset{K_1}{\underset{K_2}{\rightleftharpoons}} V_2 . \qquad\qquad \text{I–2.14}$$

At equilibrium the law of mass action gives

$$V_2/V_1 = (K_1/K_2)V_1 . \qquad\qquad \text{I–2.15}$$

Comparison with the thermodynamically derived equation, I–2.12, shows immediately that

$$K_1/K_2 = C_2\, e^{B_2/kT} . \qquad\qquad \text{I–2.16}$$

Therefore, from the kinetic equations, the ratio of the number of ways two defects can come together to the number of ways they can separate must be equal to the number of independent orientations which the cluster can have in the lattice.

3. Vibrational Frequencies and Entropy

In the derivation of the basic formulas for defect concentration all entropy changes other than that in the configurational entropy were neglected. Thus, equation I–2.7 should be written in the more general form

$$n/N = Ae^{-E_F/kT} , \qquad\qquad \text{I–3.1}$$

where A is usually referred to as the pre-exponential factor and contains all the entropy terms other than the previously considered configurational entropy.

Two main contributions to the value of A have been considered in the literature. First, the vibrational frequencies around a defect are altered. This change contributes to the entropy of formation. Second, the energy of formation depends on the interatomic distance and, hence, on the temperature via the volume expansion. However, a detailed thermodynamic analysis[1] shows that energy terms which depend only on the volume do not contribute to the entropy of formation, and these are the entropy terms which have often been incorrectly included in the past. According to this analysis, the entropy of formation depends only on the lattice frequencies before and after the formation of the defect and can be represented by a temperature independent simple multiplicative exponential term. The derivation requires a knowledge of statistical mechanics somewhat greater than that used in the preceding section and the details may be omitted by the reader willing to accept the results. The argument runs as follows.

Consider a perfect crystal lattice of the Born-von Karman type, i.e., one in which the thermal oscillations are of sufficiently small amplitude that the potential energy is a quadratic function of the atomic displacements. The internal partition function of the N-atom perfect crystal is given by

$$Z_p = e^{-\Phi_p/T} \prod_j e^{-\nu_{pj}/2T} (1 - e^{-\nu_{pj}/T})^{-1} \qquad \text{I–3.2}$$

where ν_p is the frequency of one of the $3N - 6 = j$ oscillators, measured in energy units; T is the temperature in energy units (and therefore contains k); Φ_p is the equilibrium potential energy; and the product is taken over the entire set j, of oscillator frequencies. It is important to note that in this partition function Φ_p and ν_p are functions of the volume only and of no other thermodynamic variable. The entropy, S_p, may now be written as

$$S_p = \sum_j [-\ln (1 - e^{-\nu_{pj}/T}) + (\nu_{pj}/T) (e^{\nu_{pj}/T} - 1)^{-1}]. \qquad \text{I–3.3}$$

At temperatures appreciably above the Debye characteristic temperature of the crystal, the entropy can be expressed in the following simplified form by expansion to first order in ν/T:

$$S_p \cong \sum_j [1 - \ln (\nu_{pj}/T)]. \qquad \text{I–3.4}$$

Consider next a crystal identical with the perfect crystal just treated, except that it contains one defect. This imperfect crystal constitutes a second mechanical system describable by a volume-dependent potential energy of equilibrium, Φ_i, and a set of independent simple harmonic lattice oscillators characterized by the volume-dependent frequencies, ν_i. All the preceding formulas for thermodynamic quantities apply to the imperfect lattice simply upon replacement of the subscript p by the subscript i throughout.

In the statistical mechanical derivation of defect concentration given in I–2 all entropy terms other than the mixing entropy were neglected and, therefore, the contribution to the free energy consisted of an internal energy term, E_F, and the mixing entropy, S. If other entropy changes are taken into account, the Gibbs free energy for the defect, g, must be substituted for E_F. On this basis the derivation is unchanged but the defect concentration is given by

$$n/N = e^{-g/T} . \qquad\qquad \text{I–3.5}$$

This equation is equivalent to equation I–3.1, where the entropy terms were included in A. Clearly, g is given by

$$g = G_i - G_p , \qquad\qquad \text{I–3.6}$$

where G_i and G_p are the Gibbs free energies of the imperfect and perfect crystals respectively.

Experimentally defect concentrations are always determined over a restricted range of temperatures, and an equation of the type of I–3.1 is employed to analyze the data. In most cases a plot of $\ln{(n/N)}$ vs. $1/T$ proves to be very nearly linear over the entire experimental range, which suggests that the most useful form in which to elaborate equation I–3.5 is the following.

Let T_1 be a temperature near the middle of the experimental range. Development of g in Taylor series about T_1 gives

$$g(T) = g(T_1) + (\partial g/\partial T_1)_p (T - T_1) + \tfrac{1}{2}(\partial^2 g/\partial T_1^2)_p (T - T_1)^2 + \ldots . \qquad \text{I–3.7}$$

As long as the experimental data can be represented by a straight line in the usual plot, the first two terms of equation I–3.7 must

vacancies and interstitials has been done by Huntington et al.[3] for a face-centered cubic lattice, based on an approximate evaluation of equation I–3.11 with an Einstein model used for the localized vibrations. In this way the calculations can be simplified by separate consideration of the contributions of three important regions to the entropy: the nearest neighbors of the defect, the elastic stress field of the defect, and the surface effect. (In earlier calculations Dienes[4] considered only the local term and Zener[5] considered only the long-range elastic contribution.) It is apparent that in the immediate neighborhood of the defect, whenever a crowding of the atoms occurs, as in the case of the interstitial, the vibrational frequencies will rise and, therefore, the corresponding local contribution to the entropy will be negative (equation I–3.10). Conversely, this entropy term for a vacancy is expected to be positive since the vacancy creates a region of lower density in the lattice. The long-range interactions, such as elastic and surface effects, may be comparable in magnitude with the local terms, may even be of opposite sign, and may render invalid the simple argument given above for the sign of the entropy change. However, it still remains true that defects which cause a local crowding of the lattice have a lower specific entropy than those which cause an expansion. As specific examples, the numerical results given by Huntington et al.[3] for an interstitial and a vacancy in copper may be cited. The entropy for an interstitial was calculated to be 0.8 k and that for a vacancy 1.47 k. The actual numerical values should not be considered too reliable because of the approximations and the oversimplified force model used in the calculation. However, the relative magnitudes and the underlying physical approach are considered to be reliable. Since the calculated result for the entropy is approximately one, this number will be used throughout this book unless stated otherwise, but the reader should be aware that these calculations are only approximate. For example, a recent calculation by Nardelli and Tettamanzi[6] indicated that the contribution to the self-entropy of a vacancy arising from the loss of coupling with the neighbors, a term considered unimportant by Huntington, may be a significant part of the total vacancy entropy. Thus, theoretical and experimental entropies cannot be expected to agree precisely.

4. Formation Energies

The simplest way to estimate the energy of formation of a vacancy is to consider a crystal held together by central forces and to assume that there is no electronic or atomic rearrangement around the vacancy. In this case the energy of formation of a vacancy is equal, as will be shown, to the lattice energy per atom of the solid. Let $V(r)$ be the potential energy of interaction of an atom with another lattice atom at a distance r. The lattice energy, or cohesive energy, per atom, E_c, is given by

$$E_c = -\tfrac{1}{2} \sum_k V(r_k) , \qquad\qquad \text{I–4.1}$$

where k is the summation over all lattice atoms and the factor $\tfrac{1}{2}$ is necessary to prevent the counting of pairwise interactions twice. E_c is also the average energy necessary to remove an atom from the surface, i.e., the sublimation energy. If E_∞ is the energy required to remove an atom from the interior to infinity, then

$$E_\infty = - \sum_k V(r_k) . \qquad\qquad \text{I–4.2}$$

It should be noted that the creation of a vacancy requires the removal of an atom from the interior to the surface. The energy of formation, E_F, is calculated by removing the atom from the interior to infinity and then placing it on the surface. Thus,

$$E_F = E_\infty - E_c = 2E_c - E_c = E_c . \qquad\qquad \text{I–4.3}$$

The same conclusion is reached by counting the breakage and formation of atomic bonds. For example, the formation of a single vacancy requires the breakage of 12 bonds and the formation of 6 bonds (on the average) on the surface in a face-centered cubic material. The energy of formation may be expressed as

$$E_F = (12 - 6)\,(E_c/6) = E_c .$$

The energy of formation is greatly overestimated by this simple argument because it neglects the energy gained by the rearrangement of the electrons and the atoms around the vacancy. If W denotes the sum of all these relaxation energies, then

$$E_F = E_c - W.$$

The central problem in calculating the energy of formation of defects is the theoretical determination of W. Several efforts have been made in this direction, and the major contributions for metals are discussed below.

A number of terms must be considered. The creation of a vacancy causes an increase in the number of lattice sites but does not change the number of electrons; therefore, the effective radius of the sphere occupied by each electron is increased. The density change per vacancy is $1/N$, where N is the number of atoms; therefore, for small concentrations, the effective sphere radius is increased by $1/(3N)$ per vacancy. From this change in the effective electron radius Huntington and Seitz[7] calculated the changes in the Fermi energy, the exchange energy, and the correlation energy for copper. They also calculated the change in the electrostatic self-energy for the electrons and the energy arising from the removal of a positive ion from the site of the vacancy. The redistribution of the electrons around the vacancy requires three terms: (1) the energy of interaction of the electrons with the positive ion hole, (2) the self-energy of the modified charge distribution, and (3) the kinetic energy of the non-uniform charge distribution. The change in the closed-shell repulsion energy resulting from the removal of an ion core and the rearrangement of the atoms around the defect also must be taken into account. On the basis of this calculation, Huntington and Seitz arrived at a value of between 1 and 2 eV for the formation energy of a vacancy in copper. A further refinement by Huntington[8] gave a value of 1.8 eV. A correction to this latter calculation by Brooks[9] and Fumi[10] placed the best value between 1.0 and 1.2 eV. Although many approximations are involved, this value, as will be seen later, is in remarkably good agreement with experiment.

The type of calculation performed by Huntington and Seitz is an exceedingly difficult one and is very hard to generalize for other metals. Fumi[10] proposed a simpler method which can be applied quite generally to the noble and alkali metals. In this model the positive charge of the ions is uniformly distributed within a sphere and the electrons are free to move. When an ion is removed from the center of the sphere, the energy of the free electrons changes because the electron waves undergo phase shifts in order to screen the vacancy. This change in energy was calculated with use of the Friedel[11] sum rule for the phase shifts. The change in volume of the sphere was also taken into account. Fumi found the change in electronic energy to be proportional to the Fermi energy of the metal. He used essentially the same repulsive term for the noble metals as Huntington and Seitz but neglected this contribution in the case of the alkali metals since the latter are characterized by an open lattice and a weak repulsive interaction. Seeger and Bross[12] performed a calculation for the noble metals by a method similar to that of Fumi but with some simplification. The results from different types of theoretical calculations for the energy of vacancy formation in metals are summarized in Table I–4.1. The general agreement is reasonable. These theoretical

TABLE I–4.1

Theoretical Energies of Vacancy Formation, E_F, in Metals

Metal	E_F (eV)	Reference
Cu	1–1.2	Huntington and Seitz[7]
Cu	0.9	Fumi[10]
Cu	0.81	Seeger and Bross[12]
Cu	1.0	Seeger and Mann[55]
Ag	~0.6	Fumi[10]
Ag	0.92	Seeger and Bross[12]
Au	~0.6	Fumi[10]
Au	0.77	Seeger and Bross[12]
Li	0.55	Fumi[10]
Na	0.53	,,
K	0.36	,,
Rb	0.31	,,
Cs	0.26	,,

approaches are still being refined,[13–15a] but no drastic changes in the quoted numbers have appeared.

While the vacancy always resides on a lattice site in any metal, more than one possible configuration for the interstitial must be considered. Huntington and Seitz,[7] and Huntington[8] have applied their general techniques, discussed earlier, to the calculation of the energy of formation of an interstitial in copper. They considered two configurations, illustrated in Fig. I–4.1 and referred to as the body-centered (a) and the "split" configuration (b). They calculated the energy of formation of an interstitial in copper to be 5 to 6 eV but could not decide, within the accuracy of their calculations, which was the more stable configuration.

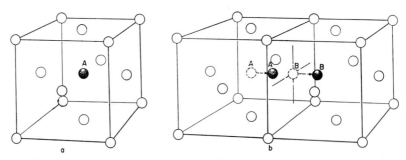

Fig. I–4.1 The two configurations of an interstitial atom in a face-centered cubic lattice. (a) The interstitial, marked A, is at the body-centered position in the cube. (b) The interstitial in the "split" configuration: two atoms, A and B, share an empty lattice site.

The configurations of the interstitial have also been studied recently by high-speed computing machine calculations[16,17] (these techniques are discussed in detail in I–5 and I–12). Three configurations were investigated, the body-centered and split configurations discussed above and also the "crowdion" configuration. This last configuration, originally proposed by Paneth[18] for body-centered lattices, is an interstitial located in a close-packed line of atoms with linear outward distortion, with its motion restricted to this line of atoms. In dynamic machine calculations the motion of many deliberately disturbed atoms can be followed to their final equilibrium positions. The body-centered configuration of the interstitial, Fig. I–4.1 (a), was found to be unstable: an atom placed in this position moved rapidly away from the cube center toward one of its nearest neighbors and settled down in the split configuration of Fig. I–4.1 (b), sharing a lattice site with an original lattice atom across one of the cube faces. For the potentials simulating copper, which were used in these calculations, the split interstitial atoms were 0.6 of a lattice constant apart. The stability of the split configuration in face-centered metals has been confirmed by a number of other theoretical calculations.[19,20] The calculations also showed that the energy difference between the split and the body-centered configurations is small, of the order of 0.1 eV. Unless otherwise stated, the interstitial in this book will be assumed to be in the split configuration, but it should be kept in mind that, since the energy difference is so small, theoretical calculations cannot be considered conclusive. The formation energy of an interstitial is not known with high accuracy. The best value for copper is about 3 eV,[15,19] somewhat smaller than the value obtained in the early calculations.[7,8]

The theoretical calculations[15–19] done to date have shown that the crowdion configuration, described earlier, is unstable in copper, a face-centered cubic lattice. Recent dynamic machine calculations[21] indicate that it is also unstable in iron, a body-centered cubic crystal. The stable form of the interstitial in this metal, according to the dynamic calculations,[22] is again a split configuration, as illustrated in Fig. I–4.2. It should be noted that the orientation of this configuration is different from that in copper shown in Fig. I–4.1 (b).

Detailed quantum mechanical calculations are difficult to make and are hard to generalize to different metals. Brooks[9] has suggested a relatively simple semi-empirical type of calculation for the energy of formation of defects. The energy of formation is correlated with the specific surface free energy by considering the formation of a vacancy to be equivalent to creating a new surface equal to the area of one atomic volume. The elastic energy associated with distortion around the vacancy is then calculated from elasticity theory, and the reduction of surface energy arising from contraction around the vacancy is also taken into account. By minimizing the total energy with respect to the strain, Brooks obtained an expression for the energy of formation in terms of the atomic radius, surface energy, and elastic moduli. Since these quantities are generally known, the vacancy formation energy

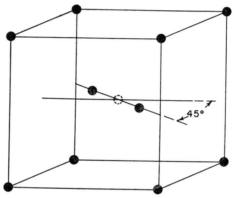

Fig. I–4.2 Interstitial configuration found to be stable in iron by dynamic machine calculations. (From reference 22.)

can be estimated for many metals. This method of calculation, in comparison with the more detailed theoretical calculation and also with experiment, generally overestimates the vacancy energy of formation by about a factor of 1.5 to 2.0. The results for interstitial formation energies are also high, perhaps by about a factor of 3. This is not surprising, since the distortions around the interstitial are large (see I–9), and, therefore, linear elasticity theory is a very poor approximation. In spite of its shortcomings, the Brooks method is useful in giving a rough estimate of the energies involved in defect formation in different metals.

5. Configuration and Binding Energy of Clusters

Detailed calculations have shown that clusters of vacancies and clusters of interstitials are stable. A simple argument can be given for the divacancy which illustrates the mechanism of vacancy binding.[23]

As discussed in the preceding section, the formation of a single vacancy in an f.c.c. lattice requires the breakage of 12 bonds in the interior and the formation of 6 (on the average) on the surface. Thus, the vacancy formation energy is

$$E_F = (12 - 6)\,(E_c/6)\,,$$

where E_c is the cohesive energy. Now let a second atom be removed which is a nearest neighbor of the vacancy. One of the bonds of this atom is already broken so that only 11 bonds have to be broken in removing it to the surface. On this basis the energy of formation of a divacancy $E_F^{(2)}$ is given by

$$E_F^{(2)} = (11 - 6)\,(E_c/6) + (12 - 6)\,(E_c/6) = 11\,E_c/6\,. \qquad \text{I–5.1}$$

The energy of divacancy formation is twice the energy of formation of a single vacancy minus the divacancy binding energy, B_2 (see I–2). Thus,

$$E_F^{(2)} = 2E_F - B_2\,,$$

or

$$B_2 = 2E_c - (11/6)E_c = E_c/6\,. \qquad \text{I–5.2}$$

For copper E_c is 3.52 eV; therefore, via this estimate, B_2 would be about 0.6 eV. If the electronic and atomic rearrangement energies are assumed to be distributed among the bonds in the same way as the cohesive energy, then a simple subtractive correction can be made to obtain a better value for B_2. On this basis Bartlett and Dienes[23] arrived at a value of about 0.3 eV for B_2. Seeger and Bross[12] treated the electronic rearrangement in a more sophisticated way using the techniques discussed in I–4. They found that in the noble metals the binding energy, B_2, is approximately 0.06 times the Fermi energy. B_2 values are, therefore, typically about 0.3 eV for these metals. However, Corless and March[24] have pointed out that some terms omitted by Seeger and Bross can seriously affect the quantitative results. In fact, they suspect

that the whole point charge model may be inadequate for calculating the interaction between point defects. A calculation has
also been carried out for the divacancy binding energy in copper
by Weizer and Girifalco[25] using a Morse function for the interaction potential. They found a value of 0.64 eV, which seems
rather high in comparison with recent experimental results (see
Chapter V). Their calculations also showed that two vacancies
attract one another at separations of less than about 7 Å but do
not interact appreciably at larger separations. It is generally
agreed that divacancies are stable, but the corresponding binding
energies are rather poorly known theoretically.

Larger clusters of vacancies are also expected to form, but their
configuration and energy of stabilization are not well known. A
few detailed calculations indicating the relative stability of
various configurations have been made. The first calculation of
this type was for the trivacancy in copper with a Morse function
used for the potential.[26] Three possible configurations were considered, as shown in Fig. I–5.1. In the linear array (a), all three

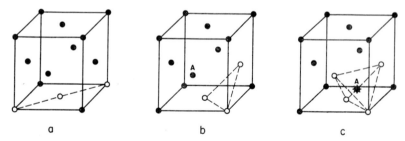

Fig. I–5.1 Three possible configurations of the trivacancy in the face-
centered cubic lattice. (a) Linear array. (b) Planar configuration. (c) Tetrahedral configuration, in which atom A has relaxed into the center of the
tetrahedron. Configuration (c) is the stable one.[26,27]

vacancies are not nearest neighbors of each other; therefore, since
there is a positive binding energy of one vacancy to another, this
configuration is energetically the least stable. Configuration (b)
might be thought stable since all the vacancies are nearest neighbors of each other and full advantage is taken of the binding

between them. Intuition turns out to be misleading in this case, since the detailed calculations showed that atom A relaxes into the center of the tetrahedron shown in (c) and the trivacancy exists as three vacancies shared equally on four atomic sites in a tetrahedral configuration with an interstitial (the starred atom) in the middle. This relaxation results in a large contribution to the binding energy.

The many-body features of vacancy clustering were evaluated by means of a computer calculation by Vineyard and co-workers[16,27] using a lattice array of 450 atoms. For the interaction between the atoms they employed a Born-Mayer repulsive potential and a constant inward force on the boundary atoms to simulate the binding caused by the conduction electrons. The formation energies calculated with this model appear to be somewhat lower than indicated by experiments (see Chapter V), but the relaxations of the atoms and the relative energies of the configurations are considered trustworthy. The Vineyard[27] calculation verified the stability of the divacancy and also of configuration (c) for the trivacancy. The results of similar calculations for the tetra- and pentavacancies are shown in Figs. I–5.2 and I–5.3. Atoms which have suffered gross displacements are shown in their new positions by starred dots, but the smaller relaxations are not shown. Binding energies against separation into isolated vacancies are given as B in the figures. It is to be noted that the tetrahedral form of the tetravacancy in this model is unstable although, as previously mentioned, a form similar to this is stable in the trivacancy case. It appears that the relaxation of one or more atoms into a vacancy cluster tends to stabilize the configuration. This situation occurs again in the octahedral form of the tetravacancy, where the pair of grossly relaxed atoms in its center cause it to have a much larger stabilization energy than the tetrahedral form. A similar situation occurs for the octahedral form of the pentavacancy with a single relaxed atom. In both cases the grossly relaxed atoms are in asymmetrical positions, approximately as indicated in the figures. The asymmetry is shared by the surroundings (although not shown) and is believed

c

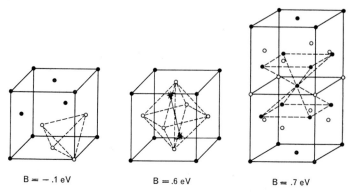

$$B = -.1 \text{ eV} \qquad B = .6 \text{ eV} \qquad B = .7 \text{ eV}$$

Fig. I–5.2 Three configurations of the tetravacancy. $B = $ binding energy relative to isolated vacancies. Note that the tetrahedral configuration (left) is unstable. (From reference 27.)

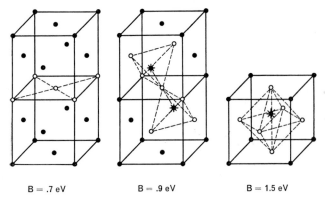

$$B = .7 \text{ eV} \qquad B = .9 \text{ eV} \qquad B = 1.5 \text{ eV}$$

Fig. I–5.3 Three configurations of the pentavacancy. $B = $ binding energy relative to isolated vacancies. (From reference 27.)

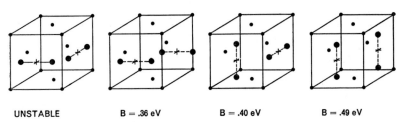

$$\text{UNSTABLE} \qquad B = .36 \text{ eV} \qquad B = .40 \text{ eV} \qquad B = .49 \text{ eV}$$

Fig. I–5.4 Di-interstitial configurations. $B = $ binding energy relative to isolated interstitials. (From reference 27.)

to be a real effect, despite one's natural inclination to doubt it. The large number of stable clusters and the high binding energy of all but one of them shown by this model are significant indications of the importance of clustering reactions. Undoubtedly many other stable configurations of clusters of a small number of vacancies exist; the calculations that have been made do not exhaust the possibilities.

The configuration and stability of the di-interstitial has been investigated by Vineyard[27] and by Johnson and Brown[17] using the technique of machine calculation discussed above. Several configurations of the di-interstitial were investigated, three of which were found to be stable.[27] These configurations and their binding energies, relative to isolated interstitials, are shown in Fig. I–5.4. The energies of the three stable configurations are seen to be quite close to one another so that the dominant configuration cannot be selected with accuracy. Larger clusters of interstitials have not yet been investigated.

The formation entropies of divacancies and higher clusters have not been calculated in any detail, although a brief discussion has been given by Schottky.[28]

6. Impurity-Defect Binding

Whenever there is a positive binding energy between vacancies and impurity atoms, some of the vacancies will be bound to the impurities. The concentration of such complexes in thermal equilibrium can be calculated by statistical mechanics by a procedure analogous to that used for single and divacancies discussed in I–2. If z is the coordination number of the impurity atom, then, because multiple complexes are excluded, each complex considered in the calculation pre-empts z lattice sites and, therefore, the number of ways of arranging C complexes on zI_0 sites (where I_0 is the impurity concentration) is given by

$$W = \frac{(zI_0)!}{(zI_0 - zC)!\, C!} .$$

I–6.1

Application of Stirling's formula and minimization of the free energy, as in I–2, gives

$$C/(I_0 - C) = ze^{-E_F(c)/kT} \qquad \text{I–6.2}$$

where $E_F(c)$ is the energy required to remove an atom which is nearest neighbor to an impurity and place it on the surface. $E_F(c)$ can also be expressed as the difference between the energy of formation of a vacancy, E_F, and the binding energy, B, of a vacancy to an impurity atom. Thus,

$$E_F(c) = E_F - B. \qquad \text{I–6.3}$$

Formula I–6.2 may therefore be rewritten as

$$C/(I_0 - C) = ze^{B/kT}e^{-E_F/kT} = zVe^{B/kT}, \qquad \text{I–6.4}$$

where V is the free vacancy concentration in the crystal. In deriving equation I–6.4 it has been assumed that the number of free vacancies is independent of the number of bound vacancies. This assumption is valid up to $I_0 = $ about 10^{-3} atomic fraction of impurity atoms; when I_0 is larger, the correction to the free vacancy concentration becomes significant (i.e., $> 1\%$). The vacancy is excluded from occupying the position of the impurity and the z nearest-neighbor sites of the impurity. The total number of sites available to the vacancy in a face-centered cubic lattice is, therefore, $N - 12I_0'$ where N is the number of solvent lattice sites and I_0' the number of impurity atoms (while I_0 is the atomic fraction). The total number of vacancies and complexes, V_t', is then given (by using equation I–6.2) by

$$V_t' = (N - 12I_0')e^{-E_F/kT} + 12I_0e^{-E_F/kT}e^{B/kT}(N + I_0')$$

$$= (N + I_0')e^{-E_F/kT}\left[\frac{N}{N + I_0'} - \frac{12I_0'}{N + I_0'} + 12I_0e^{B/kT}\right]. \quad \text{I–6.5}$$

If $I_0' \ll N$, then equation I–6.5 may be written as

$$\frac{V_t'}{N + I_0'} \cong \frac{V_t'}{N} = V_t = e^{-E_F/kT}[1 - 12I_0 + 12I_0e^{B/kT}] \quad \text{I–6.6}$$

where V_t and I_0 are expressed in atomic fractions.

Formula I–6.4 can also be derived from the law of mass action by considering equilibrium between the complexes and vacancies in the following reaction:

$$V + I \underset{K_2}{\overset{K_1}{\rightleftharpoons}} C \qquad\qquad \text{I–6.7}$$

where I is the concentration of unbound impurities. The equilibrium constant of this reaction is given by

$$\frac{C}{VI} = \frac{C}{V(I_0 - C)} = \frac{K_1}{K_2}. \qquad\qquad \text{I–6.8}$$

By comparison with I–6.4,

$$K_1/K_2 = ze^{B/kT}. \qquad\qquad \text{I–6.9}$$

It should be noted that equation I–6.4 is analogous to equation I–2.12, which gives the divacancy concentration in terms of the single vacancy concentration, although the numerical pre-exponential differs by a factor of 2 for face-centered cubic lattices. This difference in the pre-exponential term arises because there are no permutations of the vacancy-impurity complex, since the vacancy and impurity are distinguishable entities. The corresponding difference, by the method of counting the number of independent orientations given in I–2, is a factor of 2. It should also be noted that the general thermodynamic formulas derived above are equally valid for the binding of a vacancy to an interstitial impurity atom and for the binding of an interstitial atom to an impurity, with appropriate evaluation of the pre-exponential factors.

Two important energy terms are expected to give rise to the binding energy of a defect to an impurity, namely, the change in the strain energy around the impurity and the electrostatic interaction between the defect and the impurity. If the impurity atom differs in size from the host atom, the strain surrounding the impurity atom may be relieved by placing a defect adjacent to the impurity. It seems intuitively clear that the strain interaction between an oversized atom and a vacancy can be an important part of the binding energy; in general, one expects vacancies to be bound in regions of compression and interstitials in regions of dilation in a manner similar to that calculated for strain relief around a dislocation (see I–13). However, no specific calculations have been made for the binding of a vacancy to an impurity atom by strain relief.

Since the distortion around an interstitial is quite large (see I–9), the strain relief obtained upon trapping an undersized impurity can be considerable. An attempt to estimate the magnitude of such interactions has been made by Hasiguti[29] on the basis of elasticity theory as applied to point defects by Eshelby.[30] For an undersized impurity atom, beryllium, in copper, he obtained a binding energy of 0.5 eV. Hasiguti also pointed out that an oversized atom can also be bound to an interstitial if the two defects are arranged in a suitable crystallographic orientation. For example, a gold atom placed at position 111 (with the interstitial at 000) in copper gave a binding energy, by his calculation, of 0.17 eV. It should be recognized, of course, that elasticity theory is applicable only in the region outside a radius of several lattice parameters from the point source of the dilation. Elasticity calculations, therefore, neglect the very important local interaction terms and must be taken as a very crude estimate of the interaction energies. A careful local calculation has not been made.

The first approach to the electrostatic bonding of a vacancy to an impurity was given by Lazarus,[31] based on Mott's treatment of the screening of an impurity atom by the Fermi electrons. Lazarus' calculations are for a substitutional impurity atom in a monovalent metal with all atomic distortions neglected. According to Mott,[32] the excess ionic charge, Z, of the impurity atom will be screened on the basis of the linearized Thomas-Fermi equation by an interaction potential of the form

$$\Phi(r) = \frac{Ze}{r} \exp\left(-qr\right), \qquad \text{I–6.10}$$

where r is the distance from the center of the impurity, e the electronic charge, and q the screening constant, which is a characteristic number for any given solvent metal. The neighboring solvent atoms around an impurity will, therefore, be repelled by a Coulomb force in addition to the usual closed-shell repulsive forces. Consequently, the binding energy of these atoms is decreased and therefore it takes less energy to remove one of these neighboring atoms from the lattice. The decrease in the binding energy of these atoms is equal to the change in the energy, ΔE_F, required to form a vacancy at a site adjacent to the impurity. Thus,

$$\Delta E_F = -e\Phi(r_0) = -\frac{Ze^2}{r_0}\exp\left(-qr_0\right), \qquad \text{I--6.11}$$

where r_0 is the impurity-vacancy separation. It should be noted that the valence difference between the impurity and the solvent is explicitly defined as Z and therefore the binding energy is proportional to the excess valency. A typical value for the electrostatic part of the binding energy is 0.06 eV for a divalent impurity in a monovalent metal.

The reliability of this calculation has been investigated further.[13,24,33-35] March and co-workers[24,33] and Fujiwara[34] have shown that, if the exact solutions of the Thomas-Fermi equation, instead of the linearized form, are used, then the interaction energy is still given by equation I–6.11 but with a multiplicative constant, α. α is a function of Z, but is of the order of unity and does not seriously influence the values calculated by equation I–6.9 for electropositive impurities. Blatt[35] further refined this type of calculation by considering the variation of q with Z under the Friedel[11] sum rule. His procedure gives better values for the screening potential at close distance to the impurity atom. For electropositive impurities the asymptotic form, equation I–6.11, is accurate at interatomic distances, but for electronegative impurities Blatt finds that the screening parameter, q is not a characteristic of the solvent alone but depends on Z rather strongly. This conclusion is supported by an approximate solution of the Thomas-Fermi equation for electronegative impurities by Alfred and March.[33] Thus, equation I–6.11 cannot be used for electronegative impurities without the modifications suggested by Blatt and by Alfred and March.

7. Mobility of Single Point Defects

a) Statistical mechanical treatment

Vacancies and interstitials in a solid are mobile at a sufficiently high temperature. In order to change its position, the defect has to surmount a potential barrier. This process is usually treated on the basis of absolute reaction rate theory,[36] although some attempts have been made recently at a dynamical approach.[37] The approximations inherent in any rate theory are that well-defined states exist for the original system (atom near its starting point) and the transition system (atom near the saddle point). This requires any interactions that are not a part of the phase space under consideration to be sufficiently weak.

In general individual defect jump rates, Γ, are given by the equation

$$\Gamma = \tilde{\nu}e^{-G/kT} \qquad\qquad \text{I--7.1}$$

where G is the free energy needed to carry the defect from an initial equilibrium position to a saddle point, T is the absolute temperature, k is Boltzmann's constant, and $\tilde{\nu}$ is an effective frequency associated with vibration of the defect in the direction of the saddle point. Even though only one atom jumps in the elementary process, the problem is essentially one of many bodies because the jumping atom is surrounded by other atoms with which it interacts. The derivation of equation I--7.1, and its equivalent form I--7.17, is based on statistical mechanical arguments, the details of which may be omitted by the reader without loss of continuity.

In the derivation of equation I--7.1 the problem has usually been oversimplified by reducing an inherently many-body problem to a one-body model. In such treatments the frequency either remains loosely defined or is reduced inaccurately to an Einstein frequency. Vineyard[38] has shown that the many-body aspects are readily incorporated in the absolute rate theory and that $\tilde{\nu}$ and G can be completely defined by appropriate statistical mechanical generalizations. He considered the particular case of a vacant lattice site in a crystal. Γ is then the average rate at which a neighboring atom jumps into the vacancy. If there are $N/3$ atoms in the crystal, the number of degrees of freedom is N, denoted by $x_1 \ldots x_n$. The mass associated with x_j is m_j and new coordinates are defined as $y_j = m_j^{1/2} x_j$. The potential energy of the entire crystal is expressed in terms of these new coordinates as $\Phi(y_1 \ldots y_n)$. In Fig. I–7.1 the N-dimensional configurational space is illustrated schematically. The solid contour lines represent hypersurfaces of constant potential energy. Point A represents a minimum in Φ corresponding to a lattice atom adjacent to a vacancy, with all

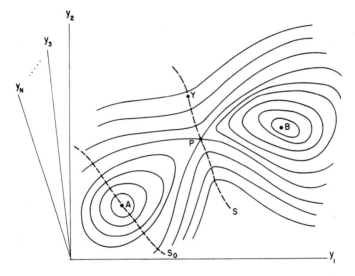

Fig. I–7.1 N-dimensional configuration space showing, schematically, hypersurfaces of constant potential energy (solid lines) and imaginary constraining hypersurfaces (dotted lines). The saddle point is at P. (From reference 38.)

other atoms in their equilibrium positions. If this atom has exchanged with the vacancy, and all other atoms have been relaxed back to their equilibrium positions, then an equivalent minimum exists in Φ at point B. In order to pass from point A to point B the atom must surmount a potential barrier through a saddle point. In Fig. I–7.1 this saddle point is indicated by point P, and the dotted line drawn through point P represents a unique $(N - 1)$-dimensional hypersurface S. S passes through point P and is perpendicular to the contours of constant Φ everywhere else and therefore separates region A from region B. The dotted line S_0 represents a similar surface through A.

A system in thermal equilibrium has a definite number of representative points, Q_A, in the region to the "left" of S, and a definite number, Q_A', crossing S from "left" to "right" per second. The average lifetime, τ, of representative points in region A, and the rate, Γ, of transition from A to B are related as follows:

$$\Gamma = 1/\tau = Q_A'/Q_A .\qquad\qquad \text{I–7.2}$$

The quantities Q_A' and Q_A were evaluated by standard statistical mechanical methods and it was found that the jump rate Γ, can be expressed in the form of the ratio of two partition functions as

$$\Gamma = \sqrt{\frac{kT}{2\pi}} \frac{\int_S e^{-\Phi/kT}\, dS}{\int_A e^{-\Phi/kT}\, dv} ,\qquad\qquad \text{I–7.3}$$

where the integration in the numerator is over the hypersurface S and the integration in the denominator is over the configuration space to the left of S (around A). The influence of all the atoms and all degrees of freedom is taken into account in this formulation since the configuration space used in arriving at this formula is a many-body space.

In order to reduce equation I–7.3 to a useful expression the theory of small vibrations was employed, and Φ was expanded near point A in a Taylor series to second order, and a similar expansion was made about the saddle point P within the constraining surface S. By this procedure equation I–7.3 was finally reduced to

$$\Gamma = \left(\frac{\prod\limits_{j=1}^{N} \nu_j}{\prod\limits_{j=1}^{N-1} \nu_j'} \right) e^{-[\Phi(P)-\Phi(A)]/kT} .\qquad\qquad \text{I–7.4}$$

In this form the transition rate is displayed as the product of an effective frequency,

$$\nu^* = \frac{\displaystyle\prod_{j=1}^{N} \nu_j}{\displaystyle\prod_{j=1}^{N-1} \nu_j'} , \qquad \text{I–7.5}$$

and of an activation exponential. The activation energy for motion, E_M, is $\Phi(P) - \Phi(A)$, which is the isothermal work required to raise the system from point A to point P. In these formulas the ν_js are the normal frequencies for vibrations about point A and the ν_j's for the vibrations about the saddle point P.

The effective frequency, ν^*, is very different from a simple Einstein frequency or any single frequency exhibited in physical space. It is the ratio of the product of the N normal frequencies of the entire system at the starting point of the transition to the $N - 1$ normal frequencies of the system constrained in the saddle point configuration.

At this stage in the analysis a connection can be made between equations I–7.4 and I–7.5 and the thermodynamic formulation represented by equation I–7.1. The procedure is similar to that used earlier by Wert and Zener[39] and shows clearly the connection between the two differently defined effective frequencies ν^* (of equation I–7.5) and $\bar{\nu}$ (of equation I–7.1). In classical systems in equilibrium the position and velocity of a representative point in configuration space are independently distributed, and the density in configuration space, ρ, can be written as

$$\rho = \rho_0 \, e^{-\Phi/kT} \qquad \text{I–7.6}$$

where ρ_0 is a normalizing constant. Then

$$Q_A = \rho_0 \int_A e^{-\Phi/kT} \, dv , \qquad \text{I–7.7}$$

where the integration is over the portion of configuration space to the "left" of S. Vineyard defined the two constrained configurational partition functions corresponding to points A and P of Fig. I–7.1 as

$$Q_0 = \rho_0 \int_{S_0} e^{-\Phi/kT} \, dS_0 \qquad\qquad \text{I–7.8}$$

and

$$Q_S = \rho_0 \int_{S} e^{-\Phi/kT} \, dS \qquad\qquad \text{I–7.9}$$

where the integration in I–7.8 is over the hypersurface S_0 and in I–7.9 over the hypersurface S. Recognizing that the numerator in I–7.3 is Q_S and multiplying and dividing the latter by Q_0 gives

$$\Gamma = \sqrt{\left(\frac{kT}{2\pi}\right)} \frac{Q_0}{Q_A} \frac{Q_S}{Q_0} . \qquad\qquad \text{I–7.10}$$

Q_S/Q_0 is now the ratio of two partition functions of the same degree of freedom and is, therefore, equivalent to the thermodynamic expression

$$Q_S/Q_0 = e^{-G/kT} = e^{S/k} \, e^{-E_M/kT} , \qquad\qquad \text{I–7.11}$$

where G is the free energy change when the system, constrained to lie on the hypersurface, is carried from A to P by reversible motion of the constraining hypersurface. The remaining factors in I–7.10 define the effective frequency, $\tilde{\nu}$, as

$$\tilde{\nu} = \sqrt{\left(\frac{kT}{2\pi}\right)} \frac{Q_0}{Q_A} . \qquad\qquad \text{I–7.12}$$

This again is a ratio of partition functions, the denominator referring to a system of dimensionality one less than the numerator. The previously defined effective frequency, ν^*, is related to the present one by

$$\nu^* = \tilde{\nu} e^{S/k} . \qquad\qquad \text{I–7.13}$$

For the small vibration approximation,

$$S = k \ln \left(\frac{\prod_{j=1}^{N-1} \nu_j^0}{\prod_{j=1}^{N-1} \nu_j'} \right) \qquad\qquad \text{I–7.14}$$

where $\nu_j{}^0$ is the frequency of the jth normal mode for the system constrained to lie on surface S_0. Since in this approximation

$$\frac{Q_0}{Q_A} = \sqrt{\frac{2\pi}{kT}} \left(\frac{\displaystyle\prod_{j=1}^{N} \nu_j}{\displaystyle\prod_{j=1}^{N-1} \nu_j{}^0} \right), \qquad \text{I–7.15}$$

ν^* is given by

$$\nu^* = \left(\frac{\displaystyle\prod_{j=1}^{N} \nu_j}{\displaystyle\prod_{j=1}^{N-1} \nu_j{}'} \right),$$

which is the same as equation I–7.5.

Quantum mechanical corrections[40] arising from the finite width of the energy levels both in the starting and the saddle point configurations are small and can be neglected for point defects in metals. A discussion of these effects for the rare gas crystals may be found in the publications of Nardelli and co-workers.[6] Another problem, which has not been fully solved, arises from a consideration of the details of the energy dissipation of the activated atom after it has gone over the saddle point. If this energy is not dissipated rapidly enough, the atom could have sufficient energy to make a return jump.[41,42]

The equation for the jump rate is usually written in the form

$$\nu = \nu_0 \, e^{S_M/k} \, e^{-E_M/kT}, \qquad \text{I–7.17}$$

with ν equal to the Γ of equation I–7.1 and ν_0 equal to $\bar{\nu}$ as used in equations I–7.1 and I–7.12. ν_0 represents an effective frequency for the vibration of the defect in the direction of the saddle point and is usually taken as about 10^{13} sec^{-1}.

At this stage a direct connection can be made with the theory of atomic diffusion in solids.[31,41,43] If an atom is to diffuse via the vacancy mechanism, then the probability that an atom will move one unit is the probability that a vacancy is adjacent to the atom multiplied by the probability that the atom will jump into the vacancy. Thus, the atomic jump rate, J, is given by

$$J = \nu V$$

where V is the vacancy concentration expressed in atomic fraction. By combining equation I–7.17 and equation I–2.7, J may be written as

$$J = \nu_0 \, e^{S_M'/k} \, e^{-(E_M+E_F)/kT} = J_0 \, e^{-Q/kT} \, . \qquad \text{I–7.18}$$

Q is clearly equal to the sum of the vacancy formation and migration energies, and S_M' is the sum of the corresponding entropies. This type of expression, which relates a rate exponentially to the reciprocal of the absolute temperature, is often referred to as the Arrhenius equation. It can be shown that the diffusion coefficient, D, is related to J as

$$D = \gamma a^2 J,$$

where γ is a geometrical constant and a is the lattice parameter. Thus

$$D = D_0 \, e^{-Q/kT} \qquad \text{I–7.19}$$

where Q is the over-all activation energy for self-diffusion and $D_0 = \gamma a^2 \nu_0 e^{S_M'/k}$. It should be noted that these formulas are not limited to the vacancy mechanism but are valid for any thermally generated defect that causes diffusion.

b) *The activation energy for migration*

Activation energies for migration, E_M, have been estimated theoretically by methods analogous to those used in determining the energies of formation (see I–4). E_M is the difference in potential energy between the equilibrium configuration, a moving atom adjacent to a vacancy in the case of vacancy migration, and the saddle point configuration, the top of the potential barrier between two equivalent positions. In close-packed metals the moving atom must pass through a barrier of atoms at a distance closer than the nearest-neighbor distance, a 4-atom barrier in f.c.c. and

two 3-atom barriers in b.c.c. metals. Thus, the major contribution
to the activation energy is expected to come from the ion core
repulsive interactions. Huntington and Seitz[7] and Huntington[8]
carried out detailed calculations for vacancy migration in copper
and obtained a value of about 1 eV for the activation energy.
This result is not considered as reliable as the theoretical result
for the energy of formation because the saddle point configuration
has lower symmetry than the equilibrium configuration, which
renders the computation more complex. Fumi[10] has also applied
his technique to the determination of activation energy for
vacancy motion in copper and the alkali metals. He found that,
to a first approximation, the electronic contribution may be neglected and obtained a value of 0.6 eV for copper. Since the
repulsive contributions are very small in the alkali metals, the
activation energy for motion, according to Fumi's calculation, is
essentially zero in these metals.

TABLE I–7.1

Theoretical Activation Energies for the Migration of Single Defects

Metal	E_M (eV)	Reference
Vacancy		
Cu	1	Huntington and Seitz[7] and Huntington[8]
Cu	0.6	Fumi[10]
Cu	0.97	Bartlett and Dienes[23]
Cu	1.3	Damask, Dienes and Weizer[26]
Alkali metals	∼0.0	Fumi[10]
Interstitial		
Cu	∼0.1	Huntington[46]
Cu	∼0.05	Vineyard et al.[47]
Cu	∼0.05	Johnson and Brown[17]
Cu	∼0.5	Seeger et al.[19]

Two calculations were made for copper with a Morse function
used for the interatomic potential. In the first, Bartlett and

Dienes[23] used a set of constants for the Morse function given by Slater,[44] included nearest-neighbor interactions only, and obtained 0.97 eV for E_M. A more refined calculation was carried out by Damask et al.[26] including both first- and second-nearest-neighbor interactions. The constants in their Morse function were taken from the work of Girifalco and Weizer[45] as derived from the sublimation energy and the elastic constants of copper. They obtained a value of 1.3 eV for E_M.

A summary of the meager theoretical results to date is given in Table I–7.1.

Brooks[9] has applied his procedure (see I–4) also to the saddle point configuration. As in his formation energy calculations, the results for the saddle point energy appear to be too high. They do show very clearly, however, that the saddle point energy is very small in the alkali metals, of the order of 0.1 eV, in agreement with Fumi's results.

The concentration of interstitials in close-packed metals is expected to be negligibly small because of the high energy of formation, 3 to 4 eV for copper (see I–4). However, since interstitials can be produced by non-equilibrium processes such as irradiation and cold work, the energy of migration is an important parameter. The first calculation of interstitial mobility was done by Huntington[46] for copper using the techniques already discussed. He found the energy difference between the split interstitial configuration and the body-centered configuration to be very small, of the order of 0.1 eV. As a matter of fact, within the accuracy of his calculation he could not decide which of these configurations was the stable one. Whichever is the stable configuration, the other one corresponds to a possible saddle point configuration for interstitial motion, although not necessarily the true one, and therefore 0.1 eV is the maximum activation energy for interstitial migration. It should be mentioned that this type of interstitial migration, in which the interstitial displaces a normal atom into an interstitial position and occupies its site, is called "interstitialcy" motion. This name is used to distinguish this type of replacement migration from the type of interstitial

migration usually associated with the motion of a small interstitial impurity moving from one interstitial position to another
without replacing a lattice atom.

Recent machine calculations have confirmed the small energy
difference between the stable split interstitial configuration and
the unstable body-centered configuration for copper. Both Vineyard et al.[47] and Johnson and Brown[17] found this energy difference
to be about 0.08 eV. The machine calculations also showed that
the body-centered position is not the saddle point configuration.
With reference to Fig. I–4.1 (b), the motion into the right-hand
cell may be described as follows. Atom A moves towards atom
position B while atom B moves towards one of the faces to
establish, for example, the split configuration perpendicular to the
front face. During its motion atom B comes near to but does not
pass through the body-centered configuration. The activation
energy for migration along this path was found to be 0.05 eV.
The absolute magnitude of these energies should not be taken too
seriously, but the machine calculations indicate quite strongly
that the interstitial in copper is far more mobile than the vacancy.*

Recently Seeger et al.[19] have attempted to improve the calculation for interstitial formation and migration energies in copper
by allowing for the anisotropy of the elastic displacement field, for
the large relative displacements of neighboring atoms, and for
various cutoff and correction procedures. The migration energy
for the interstitial was found to be fairly high in this calculation,
about 0.5 eV (still less than that for a vacancy), but the actual
numerical value is quite sensitive to the correction procedures
employed. As already mentioned in I–4, their value for the interstitial formation energy in copper is 2.8 eV, in reasonable agreement with other calculations.

A summary of the results is included in Table I–7.1.

---

* Recent machine calculations by R. A. Johnson (to be published) on
b.c.c. iron indicate that the migration energies for the vacancy and interstitial are 0.6 and 0.3 eV, respectively. Although these absolute values are
not to be taken too seriously at this stage, the indications are clear that the
interstitial is more mobile than the vacancy in b.c.c. metals also.

D

c) The entropy of activation for migration

The entropy of activation, S_M, of equation I–7.17 is fully defined by equation I–7.14. The calculation of S_M from this equation is a difficult matter, however. The problem has been treated several times in the literature, not always from a consistent viewpoint. In particular, the effect of thermal expansion has been included by several authors, but, as shown in I–3, thermal expansion of the lattice does not contribute to the entropy of a defect either in its equilibrium position or at the saddle point. Individual aspects of this problem have been treated correctly. Zener,[41] for example, employed the standard thermodynamic relationship

$$S_M = - (\partial G/\partial T)_P \qquad \text{I–7.20}$$

to evaluate S_M. He assumed that the major contribution to the free energy, G, comes from the strains caused by the distortion of the atoms around the saddle point. This distortion arises because the migrating atom is closer to the surrounding atoms than the normal interatomic distance. Zener approximated the strain by equating it to the elastic shear strain, a procedure which is valid only at some distance away from the center of the defect. The temperature dependence of this stored elastic energy is determined principally by the temperature dependence of the shear moduli. Equation I–7.20 may be rewritten, at constant pressure, as

$$S_M = - G_0 \, d(G/G_0)/dT , \qquad \text{I–7.21}$$

where G_0 is the value of G at $T = 0$ and may be replaced, to good approximation, by E_M. On the basis of the above argument the derivative in equation I–7.21 can be replaced by $d(\mu/\mu_0)/dT$, where μ is the shear modulus. The final result is

$$S_M = - E_M \, d(\mu/\mu_0)/dT . \qquad \text{I–7.22}$$

Since the elastic moduli have a negative temperature coefficient, the resulting entropies of migration by this treatment would always be positive. The above arguments apply equally well to vacancy, interstitial, and interstitialcy motion.

Dienes[48] considered the alteration of vibrational frequencies of the nearest neighbors both in the equilibrium and the saddle point positions arising from the interactions with the defect. This is the region neglected by Zener because of the inapplicability of elastic theory. Dienes found that both positive and negative entropies are possible on the basis of such a local calculation. The physical basis for his arguments is that a local expansion of the lattice permits greater freedom of atomic movement and hence a larger entropy, while compression of the lattice will result, of course, in a negative contribution to the entropy.

The most detailed calculation is that by Huntington et al.[3] using the same methods as those employed for the calculation of the entropy of formation discussed in I–3. They calculated the entropy of the saddle point configuration of the vacancy taking into account the local interactions, the elastic contribution, and the surface effect. They also included some of the relaxations of the barrier atoms. They obtained 0.93 k for the specific entropy of formation of the saddle point configuration relative to the perfect crystal. As shown in I–3, the corresponding value for the entropy of formation of a vacancy in an equilibrium position is 1.47 k. Thus, the entropy of motion, S_M, is -0.4 k. This negative value for S_M is physically reasonable, since a crowding of the lattice occurs upon moving an atom adjacent to the vacancy into the saddle point configuration. A similarly complete calculation has not been made for either interstitial or interstitialcy motion.

8. Mobility of Simple Clusters

It was first suggested by Seitz[49] that divacancies in close-packed metals may be highly mobile because the number of repulsive interactions that must be overcome is reduced. In the case of single vacancy migration in f.c.c. lattices the moving atom must pass through a barrier of four atoms at a distance closer than the nearest-neighbor distance. The corresponding repulsive energy terms represent the major contribution to the activation energy. If one of these barrier atoms is removed to form a divacancy, not only is one of the four large repulsive terms eliminated but also

the moving atom can choose a path further away from the remaining three barrier atoms.

Two calculations of divacancy mobility in copper have been
made with a Morse function used for the interatomic potential. In
the first, Bartlett and Dienes[23] used a set of Morse function constants given by Slater[44] and included nearest-neighbor interactions only. They obtained a value of about 0.35 eV for the
activation energy of motion of the divacancy in copper in comparison with 0.97 eV for single vacancy motion with the same
potential. A more refined calculation was carried out by Damask
et al.[26] which included both first- and second-nearest-neighbor
interactions. The constants in their Morse function were taken
from the work of Girifalco and Weizer[45] as derived from the
sublimation energy and the elastic constants of copper. They
obtained a value of 0.2 eV for the activation energy of motion of
the divacancy in comparison with 1.3 eV for single vacancy
motion with the same potential. Neither atomic relaxation nor
electronic rearrangements were taken into account in either calculation. These theoretical calculations indicate that divacancies in
f.c.c. metals are more mobile than single vacancies, but the
absolute magnitudes are not to be considered reliable. Lomer[50]
performed a similar calculation including more neighbors and used
two atomic interaction potentials, the Morse function and a pure
exponential repulsion. He obtained what he considered to be a
high value with his Morse function and a low value with the purely
repulsive interaction and concluded that the 0.35 eV value
suggested by Bartlett and Dienes is as good a value as can be
obtained by such techniques.

It will be recalled (I–5) that the trivacancy in f.c.c. metals is
highly stable and has the tetrahedral configuration.[26] In order to
migrate, the trivacancy must partially dissociate. The geometry
of the configuration is illustrated in Fig. I–8.1. The V's identify
the vacancies. In the initial stable configuration, atom R, shown
at $10\bar{1}$, is in its relaxed position in the center of the tetrahedron,
i.e., near the head of the arrow. This initial configuration is the
tetrahedral one in which a central atom R is surrounded by four

partial vacancies. If M is the moving atom, for example, it migrates to $01\bar{1}$ along the line indicated. During this motion of M, atom R is driven back from the center of the tetrahedron to $10\bar{1}$ and the atom at 101 relaxes into the center of the new tetrahedron formed by the lattice sites 000, 110, 011 and 101. The energy changes in this process were calculated by Damask et al.[26] using

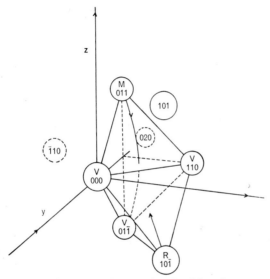

Fig. I–8.1 Schematic diagram of atoms involved in trivacancy motion in f.c.c. lattice. The V's are vacancies, M is the moving atom, and R is the relaxing atom. The line from M, including the lower dashed portion, shows the path of the moving atom. (From reference 26.)

the same potential as in their mono- and divacancy calculation. The migration energy was found to be 1.9 eV, which is approximately 1.5 times the migration energy of the single vacancy for the same potential and method of calculation.

Schottky[28] has made a rough estimate of the trivacancy migration energy with another potential. He took this energy to be the sum of the energy for atom R to be driven back to position $10\bar{1}$ and for atom M to move into the divacancy located at 000 and 110 of Fig. I–8.1. He used a potential similar to that of Fumi[10] and estimated the value of the trivacancy migration energy to be between 0.5 and 1.0 eV in copper. Fumi's use of this potential in copper gave 0.6 eV for the migration energy of a single vacancy. The ratio of the trivacancy migration energy to that for a single vacancy is in the range of 1 to 1.5, in reasonable agreement with the more detailed calculation of Damask et al.

Thus, the theoretical calculations indicate strongly that the trivacancy migration energy is considerably higher than that of single vacancies and much higher than that of divacancies. The trivacancy, therefore, is the smallest vacancy cluster which has both high stability and low mobility. The calculations of Vineyard et al. (I–5) showed that the large atomic relaxations made a major contribution to the activation energy of trivacancy migration. Similarly, the large atomic relaxations found by Vineyard et al. for the larger vacancy clusters should inhibit their motion. Thus the trivacancy is probably the smallest nucleus for void formation.

One method of migration for the di-interstitial has been investigated by Johnson and Brown[17] by means of high-speed computing techniques (I–7). The initial configuration was taken to be the right-hand one shown in Fig. I–5.4, one of the parallel arrangements of the di-interstitial. It was assumed that the two di-interstitials moved simultaneously and parallel to the two nearest edges of the cube thereby becoming two adjacent body-centered interstitials (i.e., no longer in the split configuration). The relative energy difference between the equilibrium configuration and this possible saddle point position was found to be 0.26 eV. Since the assumed saddle point may not be the actual one. the 0.26 eV value is an upper bound to the migration energy of a di-interstitial.* However, these calculations indicate that the di-interstitial is less mobile than the single interstitial. While the migration path of a di-interstitial is not known, the motion of the more stable configuration may possibly be restricted to one dimension, similar to that proposed for the crowdion (I–4).

---

* Another migration path for the di-interstitial with an activation energy of 0.08 eV has recently been found by R. A. Johnson (to be published).

TABLE I–8.1

Theoretical Migration Energies (in eV) for Defect Clusters
in Copper

$E_M^{(1)}$	$E_M^{(2)}$	$E_M^{(3)}$	$E_M^{(2)}/E_M^{(1)}$	$E_M^{(3)}/E_M^{(1)}$	Reference
Vacancy	Di-vacancy	Tri-vacancy			
0.97	0.35		0.35		Bartlett and Dienes[23]
1.3	0.20	1.9	0.15	1.5	Damask et al.[26]
	0.20–1.0		<1.0		Lomer[50]
0.6		0.5–1.0		1–1.5	Schottky[28]
Inter-stitial	Di-inter-stitial				
0.05	<0.26		<5.2		Johnson and Brown[17]

The theoretical results are summarized in Table I–8.1. There is clearly a great deal of uncertainty in these calculations and the absolute magnitudes are not to be taken too seriously. However, the relative values obtained in any given calculation should be fairly reliable.

9. Distortions Around Defects

Whenever a defect is introduced into a crystal lattice, the atoms in its immediate neighborhood rearrange themselves into a configuration of minimum energy. This shift in the atomic positions is the lattice distortion associated with the defect and is an important property of the defect itself. As indicated in previous sections, the distortion, also called atomic relaxation, contributes in a significant way to the lowering of the energy of formation and the energy of motion of defects. The same techniques that have been used to calculate the energies of formation and migration of point defects have also been used to estimate the distortions.

In order to perform an accurate calculation of the relaxation of the atoms surrounding a defect, not only must the shift of the nearest neighbors to the defect be considered, but also the shift of their nearest neighbors, etc., and the effect of the new positions of the second-nearest neighbors on the calculated positions of the first-nearest neighbors, etc. Thus, the relaxation calculation is the minimization of the energy of position of all the neighbors close enough to make a significant contribution to the total energy.

TABLE I–9.1

Atomic Distortions Around Defects

(Relaxation of the shells around defects expressed as fraction of the nearest-neighbor atomic distance)

Metal	Type of defect	Potential used	Shell around defect			Reference
			1st	2nd	3rd	
Face-centered cubic						
Cu	vacancy	Born-Mayer	−0.021	0.002	−0.002	Seeger and Mann[55]
,,	,,	,,	−0.023	−0.001	−0.004	Tewordt[15]
,,	,,	Morse	−0.022	0.004		Girifalco and Weizer[
,,	,,	Born-Mayer	−0.021	0.001	−0.007	Vineyard et al.[47]
,,	,,	,,	−0.021	0.001	−0.007	Johnson[53]
,,	interstitial (body-centered)	,,	0.149		0.032	Huntington[46]
,,	,,	,,	0.154	0.007	0.019	Seeger and Mann[55]
,,	,,	,,	0.174	−0.011	0.029	Tewordt[15]
,,	,,	,,	0.174	−0.016	0.045	Johnson[53]
Pb	vacancy	Morse	−0.014	0.004		Girifalco and Weizer[
Ni	,,	,,	−0.021	0.004		,, ,,
Ca	,,	,,	−0.027	0.004		,, ,,
Body-centered cubic						
Fe	vacancy	Morse	−0.061	0.021	0.003	Girifalco and Weizer[
Ba	,,	,,	−0.079	0.027	−0.007	,, ,,
Na	,,	,,	−0.108	0.031	−0.034	,, ,,
,,	interstitial (body-centered)	,,	$\sim$0.3			Dienes[56]
Mo, Cr, W	vacancy	5–7 inverse power	−0.05	0.01		Girifalco and Streetman[57]

The earliest calculations were done on copper with a Born-Mayer type of repulsive potential and with only the nearest-neighbor relaxations included.[7,8,46] The results indicated that the nearest neighbors around the vacancy relaxed inward about 2%, while the outward relaxation of the nearest neighbors around an interstitial, assumed to be in the body-centered position, was about 10%. A number of more sophisticated calculations have been carried out during the last few years. It is difficult to evaluate the quantitative accuracy of these calculations because a variety of interatomic potentials and computational approximations have been used. There is agreement on one important point, however, namely the strong departure from any systematic decrease of the distortion with distance. Thus, while the distortion of the second shell around a vacancy is small compared to that of the first shell, it is in the opposite direction, i.e., outward rather than inward. This anisotropy of the distortion around the vacancy was first pointed out by Kanzaki[51] in a calculation for the face-centered cubic argon crystal, and by Hall[52] in a general calculation for face-centered cubic metals. The sign of the displacement of the second shell around an interstitial in the body-centered position is not certain because it is small and therefore subject to computational uncertainties. What is significant, however, is that the second shell is displaced much less than either the first or the third shell. A summary of the more recent calculations for defects with the symmetry of the lattice is given in Table I–9.1. All the detailed calculations for f.c.c. metals (Cu, Pb, Ni, Ca), except that by Tewordt,[15] verify the general findings of Kanzaki and Hall that the second shell around a vacancy in f.c.c. metals moves outward. Some calculations have also been made for the distortions around defects that do not have the symmetry of the lattice. In these cases the distortions are generally anisotropic and the positions of many atoms have to be specified to describe the strain pattern. As might be expected, the distortions are large around the split interstitial and the di-interstitial[53] and are rather small around the divacancy.[25]

It has already been indicated that these distortions play an important role in the theory of the energies of formation and motions of defects. The distortions are also propagated elastically to the surface of the crystal, and the lattice parameter and the specific volume are altered thereby (see also IV–4). The volume change can be calculated from the knowledge of the local distortion

TABLE I–9.2

Theoretical Estimates of the Volume Change, ΔV, per Defect in Copper

Defect	ΔV per defect (in units of the atomic volume)	Reference
Vacancy	-0.53	Tewordt[15]
,,	-0.29	Seeger and Mann[55]
,,	-0.48	Johnson and Brown[17]
,,	-0.57	Vineyard et al.[47]
Vacancy saddle point	-0.23	Johnson and Brown[17]
Divacancy	~ -1.0	,, ,,
Trivacancy	~ -1.5	Vineyard et al.[47]
Tetravacancy	-1.5 to -2.0	,, ,,
Pentavacancy	-2.6 to -2.9	,, ,,
Septavacancy	~ -3.6	,, ,,
Interstitial, body-centered	1.72	Tewordt[15]
,,	1.39	Seeger and Mann[55]
,,	2.46	Johnson and Brown[17]
Interstitial, split config.	1.73	Vineyard et al.[47]
,,	2.20	Johnson and Brown[17]
Interstitial, saddle point	2.19	,, ,,
Di-interstitial, parallel	~ 4.0	,, ,,
,,	~ 2.7	Vineyard et al.[47]

by treating the strain propagation on the basis of elasticity theory, a procedure discussed in detail by Eshelby.[30] A proper treatment of this problem is intricate because the elastic solutions have to be matched to the local distortions, and different authors have used somewhat different procedures. Further, as shown by Eshelby,[58] the condition of vanishing stress at the surface of the specimen

results in an increase of about 50% in the volume change associated with a local distortion, and thus an image force correction
is required. Huntington and Johnson[59] have shown that such
image force corrections are even more important for asymmetric
defects.

The theoretically determined volume changes, ΔV, associated
with various defects in copper are shown in Table I–9.2. The
values are given as fractional changes, per defect, of the atomic
volume and have all been corrected for the image force effect. It
should be noted that the difference between the formation volume
of a defect in its equilibrium position and in the saddle point configuration is the activation volume for migration. If the activation
volume for a defect is known, it is possible to calculate the activation entropy from the coefficients of thermal expansion and com-
pressibility through a relation given by Lawson.[60] The formation
volume and the corresponding activation volume for vacancies are
in good agreement with experiment, as will be shown in Chapter V.
Entropies of activation for defects have not yet been accurately
measured.

10. Production of Defects by Quenching

Point defects exist in metals at all temperatures above absolute
zero, as shown in section I–2, but the number of defects in
equilibrium is usually quite small at ambient temperatures. In
order to study the properties of defects and their effects on the
properties of the metal, it is desirable to produce them in large,
non-equilibrium concentrations.

Three important techniques have been used to produce large
concentrations of point defects, namely, quenching, plastic deformation, and high energy radiation. In this section production by
quenching is discussed.

The equilibrium concentration of a defect as a function of
temperature was derived as

$$n = e^{-E_F/kT} , \qquad\qquad \text{I–3.10}$$

where the entropy term has been set equal to 1; clearly, it increases rapidly with increasing temperature. The equilibrium concentration of defects is achieved and maintained in a crystal by diffusion to and from internal and external surfaces. The defects, since they are highly mobile at high temperatures, are continually being produced and annihilated at these surfaces, and therefore their concentration is maintained in the crystal in dynamic equilibrium. At any temperature the rate of establishing a new equilibrium defect concentration is determined by the mean free path between defect sources and sinks, the migration energy of the defects, and the temperature. Equilibrium is always established faster when the temperature is raised than when it is lowered, since the mobility of the defects increases exponentially with increasing temperature (I–7). The purpose of the quenching procedure is to allow a specimen to come to equilibrium at a high temperature, referred to as the quench temperature, T_q, and then to cool it to a lower temperature, T_L, quickly enough to retain the high temperature defect concentration.

A number of considerations enter into the choice of T_q, T_L, and the rate of quenching, R. T_L must be sufficiently low to prevent appreciable loss of defects before the desired measurements are completed. T_q must be high enough so that the equilibrium concentration of defects is large enough to be measured. From the equations for the equilibrium concentration of defect clusters (I–2 and I–5) it is known that the fraction of defects in clusters increases as the temperature is increased. If primarily single defects are desired, this association sets an upper limit on the quench temperature, while the requirement of a measurable amount sets a lower limit. The situation is further complicated by possible aggregation of the defects during the quench itself.

As an example of the simplest clustering reaction at high temperature, the calculations of Koehler et al.[61] for gold may be cited. These authors have calculated the equilibrium concentrations of monovacancies, V_1, and divacancies, V_2, at various quench temperatures. They used the basic equations for mono- and divacancy concentration, equations I–2.7 and I–2.12, modified by a pre-exponential term corresponding to an estimate of the entropy changes.* For gold they used the relations

$$V_1 = 3.8e^{-E_F/kT} \qquad \qquad \text{I–10.1}$$

and

$$V_2 = 18V_1^2 e^{B/kT} , \qquad \qquad \text{I–10.2}$$

where V_1 and V_2 are expressed in atomic fractions; the energy of formation, E_F, was taken as 0.98 eV, and three values of the binding energy, B, 0.1, 0.2, and 0.3 eV, were used in the calculations. The equilibrium concentrations are given in Table I–10.1 and are shown graphically in Fig. I–10.1. Since the energy of formation of V_2 is higher than that of V_1, the corresponding slope in Fig. I–10.1 is steeper. Thus, although at low temperatures V_2 is much smaller than V_1, it approaches V_1 as the temperature is increased. The fraction of V_2 therefore increases with increasing temperature, as shown in Fig. I–10.1 for three different divacancy binding energies. For example, if the quench is made from a temperature higher than that corresponding to the intersection of the V_2/V_1 and the 10^{-2} concentration lines in the figure, then more than 1% of the quenched-in defects will be divacancies.

Higher clusters may also be produced if their binding energy is sufficiently large, but since their concentration, in general, depends on an increasing power of V_1 (see, for example, equation I–2.13) they can usually be neglected. Furthermore, complications due to the presence of interstitials are not expected because their theoretical formation energy is so high (I–4) that their concentration in any quench experiment is expected to be negligible.

Since the vacancies are mobile during the early stage of the quench, association of the vacancies can occur. Koehler et al.[61] carried out an approximate calculation of the association during quench under the assumption that the total number of vacancies remains constant, i.e., no defects are lost by diffusion to internal

---

* It should be noted that, although their combinatory terms are incorrect (I–2), this error is unimportant because of the uncertainty in the entropy itself.

or external surfaces. They also assumed that the temperature varies linearly with the quenching time and that the change in the fraction of monovacancies caused by association during the quench is small. The corresponding differential equation can be solved

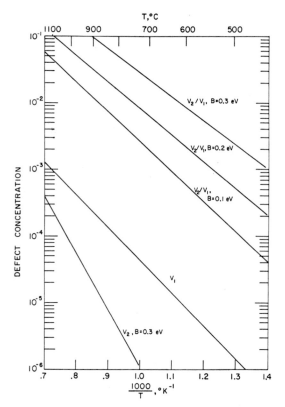

Fig. I–10.1 Equilibrium concentrations of mono- and divacancies as a function of temperature. The ratio of di- to monovacancy concentration as a function of temperature is shown for three different binding energies, B. The monovacancy formation energy was taken to be 0.98 eV.

only in terms of a series, but this solution has been evaluated numerically for some typical parameters applicable to gold. Some representative results are given in Table I–10.2 for two quenching

TABLE I–10.1

Equilibrium Concentration of Mono- and Divacancies in Gold (atomic fractions)

(*from reference 61*)

$T,°C$	V_1	$B = 0.3$ eV		$B = 0.2$ eV		$B = 0.1$ eV	
		V_2	V_2/V_1	V_2	V_2/V_1	V_2	V_2/V_1
600	8.40×10^{-6}	6.85×10^{-8}	8.15×10^{-3}	1.81×10^{-8}	2.16×10^{-3}	4.80×10^{-9}	5.71×10^{-4}
700	3.20×10^{-5}	6.59×10^{-7}	2.06×10^{-2}	2.00×10^{-7}	6.26×10^{-3}	6.08×10^{-8}	1.90×10^{-3}
800	9.52×10^{-5}	4.19×10^{-6}	4.40×10^{-2}	1.42×10^{-6}	1.49×10^{-2}	4.82×10^{-7}	5.06×10^{-3}
900	2.35×10^{-4}	1.93×10^{-5}	8.23×10^{-2}	7.19×10^{-6}	3.06×10^{-2}	2.68×10^{-6}	1.14×10^{-2}
1000	5.03×10^{-4}	7.04×10^{-5}	1.40×10^{-1}	2.82×10^{-5}	5.61×10^{-2}	1.13×10^{-5}	2.25×10^{-2}

TABLE I–10.2

Fraction of Monovacancies Before and After Quench

($E_F = 0.98$ eV, $E_M = 0.80$ eV)

(*from reference 61*)

	Quench temp., T_q (°C)	Fraction of monovacancies		Quench rate (°C/sec)
		$B = 0.1$ eV	$B = 0.2$ eV	
Fraction of mono-vacancies at T_q in equilibrium $f = V_1/(V_1 + 2V_2)$	900	0.9777		
	800	0.9900		
	700		0.9877	
	600		0.9957	
Fraction of mono-vacancies at 40°C after quench	900	0.7581		6×10^4
	800	0.8860		6×10^4
	700		0.5542	3×10^4
	600		0.8544	3×10^4
Fraction of mono-vacancies in equilibrium at 40°C if association goes to completion	900	0.7435		
	800	0.8774		

speeds and two binding energies. The monovacancy concentrations after the quench are underestimated because the integration was carried to $0°K$. The most noteworthy feature of the data is that, even with the fast quenches used, a high percentage of the monovacancies formed divacancies. It is clear that divacancies and possibly higher clusters must be taken into account when studying the quenched state of a metal, particularly for high quench temperatures and/or low quench rates.

Also, because of the high mobility of vacancies at high temperatures, vacancies may be lost during the quench at vacancy sinks (dislocations and internal and external surfaces). Lomer[50] has treated this process theoretically, neglecting vacancy association, and has given some typical computer solutions. The rate of loss of vacancies by diffusion to a fixed number of sinks at any temperature, T, is given by

$$dV/dt = - (V - V_0)\Gamma/n , \qquad \text{I–10.3}$$

where V is the vacancy concentration at any time t during the quench; V_0 is the thermodynamic equilibrium concentration of vacancies at the temperature T associated with time t; Γ is the jump frequency of the vacancy at temperature T; and n is the average number of jumps a vacancy has to make to reach a sink and is assumed to be independent of the temperature. V_0 can be calculated from equation I–2.7. If the entropy term is neglected, Γ can be expressed from equation I–7.17 as

$$\Gamma = \nu_0 e^{-E_M/kT} , \qquad \text{I–10.4}$$

where ν_0 is an average vibrational frequency. Substitution into I–10.3 gives the differential equation

$$dV/dt = - (V - e^{-E_F/kT}) (\nu_0/n)e^{-E_M/kT} . \qquad \text{I–10.5}$$

Lomer assumed an exponential cooling law of the form

$$dT/dt = - \beta(T - T_L) , \qquad \text{I–10.6}$$

where T_L is the temperature to which the sample is quenched and

β is the cooling constant. By using equation I–10.6, the independent variable, t, in equation I–10.5 can be changed to the variable T. Thus,

$$\frac{dV}{dT} = \frac{(V - e^{-E_F/kT})}{n\beta(T - T_L)} \nu_0 e^{-E_M/kT} , \qquad \text{I–10.7}$$

from which V at any temperature can be obtained by integration between the quench temperature, T_q, and any temperature, T. Lomer evaluated this integral numerically in terms of a constant γ, equal to $\beta n/\nu_0$, for several quench temperatures. The results are shown in Fig. I–10.2. The equilibrium concentration is indicated by the solid straight line, and the amount of vacancies present during the quench is shown by the various lines identified by the

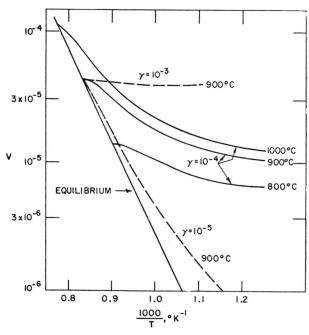

Fig. I–10.2 Calculated vacancy concentrations during quenching for various cooling rates (γ's) and several quench temperatures. (From reference 50.)

E

γ's. Curves are shown for three quench temperatures at a γ of 10^{-4} and for three γ's at a quench temperature of 900°C. The energies used in this calculation were $E_M = 0.7$ eV and $E_F = 1.0$ eV. It is apparent from the figure that for a quench from 900°C almost complete retention of vacancies is obtained for a high value of γ, which corresponds to a high cooling rate and/or a high value of n. A large n implies a well-annealed crystal, i.e., low sink concentration. An approximate analytical treatment of this process has been given by Mori, Meshii and Kauffman[62] and will be discussed in connection with their experiments in section V–3.

The above calculations are approximate also in the sense that the distribution of quenched-in vacancies is not truly random immediately after the quench. Koehler et al.[61] have discussed this problem and have obtained an expression for the spatial distribution of vacancies for the case in which the vacancies diffuse to cylindrical dislocations only. Their results indicate that after fast quenches from high temperatures the deviation from random distribution is not an important complication. The influence of nonrandom defect distribution on the annealing kinetics is discussed in II–2 and V–8.

The general conclusion so far is that the fastest quench is most desirable because it achieves the greatest retention and the least association of vacancies during the quench. However, a quench always produces some thermal stresses since the interior and exterior parts of any specimen cool at different rates. If the thermal stresses become sufficiently large to cause plastic deformation, moving dislocations will be generated in the specimen. During dislocation motion defects are generated in a non-thermodynamic way, and the equilibrium treatment given above may be seriously in error. The dislocations themselves are also sinks for defects and may thereby decrease the efficiency of the quench as well as influence the subsequent annealing. Avoidance of these complications is highly desirable and can be accomplished by limiting the quench rate to a value below which no plastic deformation occurs.

Van Bueren[63] has given approximate formulas, based on the theory of thermal stresses, for the maximum quenching rate and specimen size which can be used without producing plastic deformation. The conditions to be obeyed either by the quenching rate $(-dT/dt \equiv R)$ or by the radius, r, of the wire are

$$R < R_{max}; \quad R_{max} = 5(1 - \nu)\delta\sigma_{cr}/\alpha Gr^2, \qquad \text{I-10.8}$$

$$r < r_{max}; \quad r_{max} = \sqrt{5(1 - \nu)\delta\sigma_{cr}/\alpha GR}, \qquad \text{I-10.9}$$

where R is the quench rate, r is the radius of the wire, and ν is Poisson's ratio; and δ is the thermal diffusivity, α the coefficient of thermal expansion, σ_{cr} the critical shear stress, and G the shear modulus of the material. Using these formulas, van Bueren calculated some typical values for R_{max} and r_{max} for different metals; these are shown in Table I-10.3.

TABLE I-10.3

Maximum Allowable Quenching Rates and Wire Radii

(from reference 63)

Metal	R_{max} at $r = 0.1$ mm (10^4 °C/sec)	r_{max} at $R = 10^4$ (mm)
Cu	1.7	0.13
Au	2.4	0.16
Ag	2.4	0.16
Al	1.0	0.10
Ni	0.8	0.09
Pt	2.1	0.15
Fe	0.6	0.08
Mo	1.9	0.31
W	1.1	0.33

It will be recalled from Fig. I-10.2 that complete retention for a 900°C quench is not to be expected for E_M and E_F of 0.7 eV and 1.0 eV, respectively, unless γ is as high as 10^{-3}. Experimentally these energy values are reasonable for gold, and therefore a comparison may be made with van Bueren's maximum permissible quenching rate, R_{max}. The two quenching rates, γ and R, are not the same because two different cooling laws have been used. However, a suitable comparison can be made by equating the constant cooling rate with the initial rate of the exponential cooling law. If a gold wire of 0.1-mm radius is quenched from 900° to 0°C then

$$\beta = R_{max}/(T_q - T_L) = 26 \ . \qquad\qquad \text{I–10.10}$$

Since $\gamma = n\beta/\nu_0$, and ν_0 is about 10^{13}, a minimum value of n for complete retention may be estimated. The calculated value for $\gamma = 10^{-3}$ is about 4×10^8. This number of jumps to disappearance requires a specimen of very low dislocation content, i.e., a well-annealed wire. From these and previous considerations it is evident that a clean-cut experiment can be achieved only within very narrow limits with respect to quench temperature, quench rate, specimen size, and specimen preparation. These conditions have apparently been met in a number of experiments discussed in section V–7.

11. Production of Defects by Plastic Deformation

During plastic deformation dislocations are moved as well as generated by the applied stress. The motion of dislocations can generate point defects by several mechanisms, a variety of which have been discussed in the literature.[64,65] Two mechanisms are considered at present to be particularly important because they predict the right order of magnitude of defect production as judged by comparison with experiment. Several variations of these mechanisms have been proposed, but only the basic features will be described here.

An edge dislocation was described in section I–1 as an incomplete plane of atoms. Incomplete planes emerging on opposite sides of a crystal can arbitrarily be called positive and negative dislocations. Thus, in Fig. I–11.1 (left) the upper extra row of atoms represents a positive edge dislocation and the lower extra row a negative one. If moving positive and negative edge dislocations come together and terminate on adjacent planes, as in

Fig. I–11.1 (*a*), they will annihilate one another leaving a complete plane of atoms. However, if they terminate one plane apart,
as in Fig. I–11.1 (*b*), then when they come into registry the resulting geometrical configuration of the two partial planes of extra

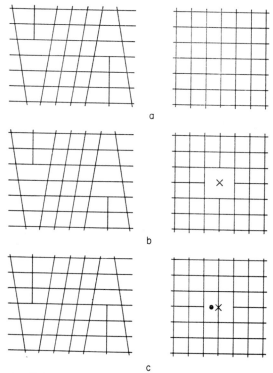

a

b

c

Fig. I–11.1 Annihilation of positive and negative edge dislocations with
the formation of (*a*) perfect lattice, (*b*) row of vacancies, and (*c*) row of
interstitials.

atoms is equivalent to one complete plane with a row of vacancies
located perpendicular to the page at point X. Thus, annihilation
of the two dislocations has occurred with the creation of a row of
vacancies. If the two partial planes terminate on the same plane,
as shown in Fig. I–11.1 (*c*), the final configuration will be a complete plane of atoms through point X plus a row of interstitials

adjacent to this plane, normal to the page, indicated by the dot. (The precise position of this row of interstitials is not known; the line is broken to indicate that the plane it represents is not periodic at this point.) This purely geometrical mode of generation does not favor the production of one defect over another, even though the energy required to produce them is unequal, because the energy is supplied by the outside force that induces the plastic deformation. Edge dislocations, necessary for the operation of the above mechanism, are produced during plastic deformation by several mechanisms. Semiquantitative estimates[49] indicate that the atomic fraction of defects produced by the geometrical mode of generation is proportional to the plastic strain with a proportionality constant of 10^{-4} to 10^{-5}. The rows of vacancies produced this way may be dispersed thermally, but it has been suggested that in the resulting distribution divacancies and larger clusters may be favored over single vacancies.[66,67]

An edge dislocation is an extra partial plane of atoms. If its terminal row of atoms (within the crystal) is incomplete, the edge dislocation is said to have a jog. The lateral view of such a jog is shown in Fig. I–11.2. When this dislocation moves slowly in a

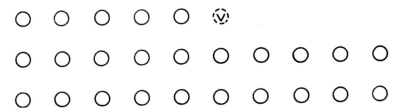

Fig. I–11.2 Schematic diagram of an edge dislocation jog. V is the site of the incipient vacancy.

direction normal to the plane of the diagram the jog will move along with it. At high dislocation velocities, however, dynamical instabilities are expected to develop, and the atom which is to move into the site denoted by V in Fig. I–11.2 may fail to do so. Thus a vacancy is left behind, and site V may be described as an incipient vacancy.[49,68,70] It is clear that by a symmetrically opposite geometry interstitials could also be created by this mechanism. Since the creation of the defect by this mechanism depends upon the local agitation of the atoms, the defect with the lower energy of formation is expected to be formed preferentially. In face-centered cubic metals, therefore, primarily vacancies will be produced.

During plastic deformation, jogs on dislocations can be produced by a variety of mechanisms. One simple example is the production of a jog by the crossing of two edge dislocations.[64] In Fig. I–11.3 the edge dislocation denoted by $ABCD$ has passed

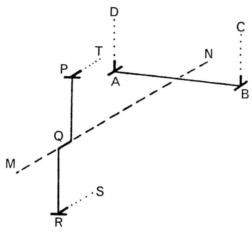

Fig. I–11.3 Schematic diagram showing the production of a jog by the crossing of two edge dislocations. (From reference 64.)

through the perpendicular edge dislocation $RPTS$ in the direction M to N. The relative displacement of the two parts of the crystal above and below plane $AMBN$, caused by the passing of dislocation $ABCD$, has created step Q, a jog in the terminal row of dislocation $RPTS$. Jogs can be formed by the crossing of dislocations in many other ways, which are fully described elsewhere.[64,65,68,69] The most important mechanism of jog formation isn ot the simple one described above as an example but a more complicated one involving the intersection of screw dislocations.[71] The number of vacancies produced by this double mechanism, the formation of jogs plus the subsequent generation of vacancies by the moving jogs, is not known with any certainty. In fact, it is not even known whether the concentration of vacancies produced is proportional to the strain or to some power of the strain, because this functional dependence is very sensitive to the detailed geometry of the moving dislocation.

In summary, it is quite certain that point defects are produced during plastic deformation, but very little is known either about the number of defects produced per unit strain or about the final distribution and configuration of the defects. Furthermore, since dislocations and point defects interact, the introduction of a large number of dislocations by plastic deformation renders the interpretation of experiments very difficult.

Dislocations also serve as sinks for point defects by processes essentially the reverse of defect creation by jogs on moving dislocations. For example, the defect can migrate to the dislocation, the reverse of dispersal, and subsequently disappear at a jog, the reverse of defect formation.

12. Production of Defects by Radiation

The two methods of defect production already discussed have certain limitations. At present, all indications are that only vacancies and their aggregates can be quenched into metals, and therefore interstitials cannot be studied by this technique. Furthermore, the fraction of vacancies that can be quenched in is small, because the fraction of vacancies at the melting point is small, and because there are theoretical limitations to the quenching rate, which have already been discussed. Although it appears that considerably higher concentrations of both vacancies and interstitials may be introduced by plastic deformation, the structural changes produced by the plastic deformation itself represent a serious complicating factor. The dislocation content and distribution are altered during plastic deformation, and, since the defects themselves interact with the dislocations, their environment is not representative of that in a well-annealed crystal. In addition, both these production processes depend strongly on the temperature. Another method of producing point defects is irradiation by high energy particles, which is the subject of this section. This method overcomes some of the above limitations, for example, it allows temperature independent introduction of a high concentration of vacancies and interstitials, but it has some limitations of its own.

The most important basic processes[72–74] arising from the interaction of high energy radiation with solids may be classified as follows: (1) production of displaced electrons, i.e., ionization; (2) production of displaced atoms by elastic collision; and (3) production of fission and thermal spikes.

The passage of charged particles through a solid causes extensive ionization and electronic excitation. In metals, where the electrical conductivity is high, the ionization produced by irradiation is very rapidly neutralized by the conduction electrons, and no observable changes in the physical properties result from this process. This conclusion can be supported by the following simple argument.[75] A solid, considered as a conducting medium, is characterized by conductivity σ and dielectric constant ϵ. Any initial charge distribution (produced by non-ohmic forces such as radiation) decays exponentially to zero, with a time constant τ given by

$$\tau = \epsilon/\sigma. \qquad \text{I–12.1}$$

For copper, a typical metal, one finds $\tau = 1.5 \times 10^{-19}$ seconds, if the value of ϵ for free space is used. The above is a rather crude calculation, but it is clear that the relaxation time for charge redistribution in a typical metal is exceedingly short. Therefore, ionization effects in metals are not observable.

If in an elastic collision with a bombarding particle a lattice atom receives an energy E_p in excess of the energy E_d, defined as the displacement threshold energy, the atom will be displaced from its lattice position. In most cases the displaced atom has enough recoil energy to travel a few atomic distances from its initial position

before coming to rest in an interstitial position. Thus the fundamental displacement pair is produced: the displaced atom or interstitial, and the lattice site it vacated, the vacancy. In most solids
E_d has a value between 10 and 30 eV. This is several times larger
than the 3 to 6 eV generally required to create an interstitial-vacancy
pair in a reversible thermodynamic process. If E_p is only slightly
larger than E_d, then only one interstitial-vacancy pair is created
per primary collision. This case is illustrated in Fig. I–12.1, which
shows the results of a machine calculation by Gibson et al.[16] applying the techniques discussed in section I–5 to the dynamics of

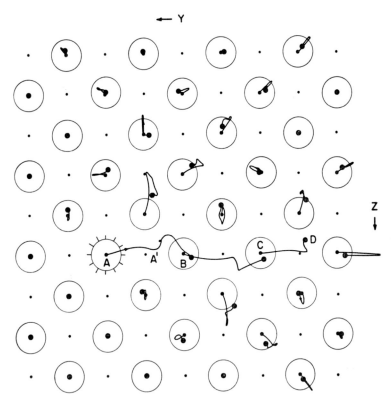

Fig. I–12.1 Atomic paths, calculated dynamically, produced by a 40-eV
knock-on in copper. The primary knock-on collision was at lattice position
A. (From reference 16.)

defect production by energetic collisions. In the low energy event illustrated, atom A, called the primary knock-on, is assumed to have been struck by a bombarding particle and to have been given an initial energy of 40 eV (in this model E_d is about 25 eV). By subsequent collisions an interstitial has been produced at location D and a vacancy left behind at position A. Another important effect, the replacement collision, is also illustrated here. This type

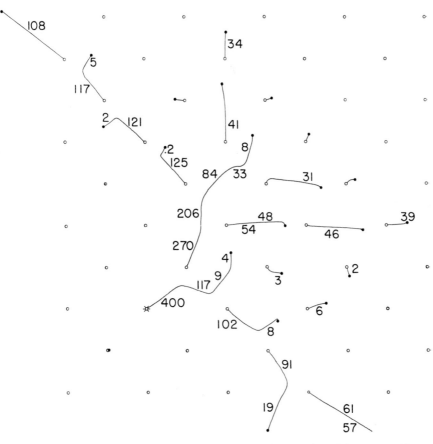

Fig. I–12.2 Atomic paths, calculated dynamically, produced by a 400-eV knock-on in copper. The open circles represent the starting positions, the filled circles represent the positions at a later time, and the numbers give the energies of the various atoms along their paths. (From reference 16.)

of event occurred at locations B and C, where atom A replaced
atom B and, in turn, atom B replaced atom C. Focusing collisions, preferential propagation of energy along rows of close-
packed atoms, are also clearly seen in this diagram.

As E_p increases, two or more pairs of vacancies and interstitials
will be created. Such an event is shown in Fig. I–12.2. In this case
the primary knock-on, originally at the starred position, was given
an initial energy of 400 eV. Much more disturbance of the lattice
is evident. At this higher energy the focusing collisions transport
matter as well as energy.[76,77] Thus interstitials are produced at
some distance from the point of original impact by means of a
series of replacement collisions. The vacancies, not having such a
dynamic mode of propagation, are left in the neighborhood of the

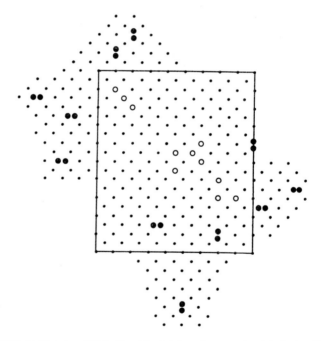

Fig. I–12.3 Split interstitials (double dots) and vacancies (circles) estimated
to result from the 400-eV event of Fig. I–12.2. The atoms shown in
Fig. I–12.2 are enclosed in the rectangle. (From reference 16.)

point of original impact in a rather compact configuration. The end result of the 400-eV event is shown in Fig. I–12.3, and may be described as the formation of essentially isolated interstitials in the split configuration, and of a variety of vacancy clusters.

When E_p has a high value, many of the displaced atoms have sufficient energy to displace additional atoms and thus to cause a cascade of displacements. Such an event, based on a cascade theory calculation, is shown in Fig. I–12.4.[78] This particular calculation is for an E_p of 10,000 eV in germanium with an assumed displacement energy of 25 eV; 231 interstitials and the same number of

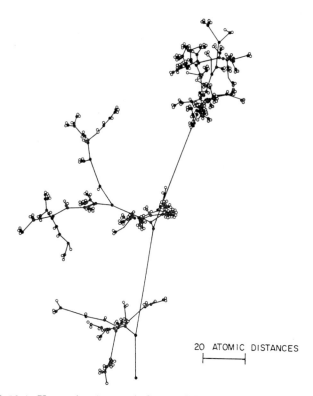

Fig. I–12.4 Vacancies (open circles) and interstitials (filled circles) produced by a 10,000-eV knock-on in germanium, based on a cascade theory calculation. (From reference 78.)

vacancies were produced. This illustration represents a transient condition because a number of the vacancies and interstitials are adjacent to one another and would be expected to recombine.

Another type of long-range transport of atoms has been shown, by some machine calculations,[79,80] to occur at rather high energies. A knock-on may travel long distances in a crystal along channels, bordered by close-packed atomic planes, inherent in the crystal. Recent theoretical investigations[81] have indicated that the range can be very large in copper, of the order of 10^3 lattice parameters for a 10-keV knock-on. Experimental results on aluminum bombarded with rare gas ions tend to confirm this effect.[82] However, the occurrence of channeling has not been demonstrated in radiation damage events in which a lattice atom rather than a bombarding ion would have to be deflected into a channel.

When bombardment is performed with heavy particles, the energy, E_p, received by a lattice atom can be very large, and near the end of the path of the primary knock-on the collision mean free path in many close-packed solids would be about equal to the mean distance between the atoms. In this situation nearly every atom in the path of a knock-on would be displaced and a transient region of high turbulence, called a displacement spike,[83] would be formed. A transient of very high temperature, referred to as a thermal spike,[27,72] can be formed along the path of the primary knock-on. Obviously fission fragments can cause a similar, but in general more severe, local damage.[74] Materials irradiated in a reactor, or with massive charged particles, are likely to have been exposed to thermal spikes and to contain displacement spikes in addition to many regions of cascaded displacements. Since no accurate theoretical description of these spikes exists, they represent unwanted complications in the controlled production of defects.

Theoretical studies of the type described above will lead eventually to a detailed understanding of the dynamics of defect production by high energy radiation. In spite of the lack of a complete theory incorporating collective processes and lattice effects, the average number of displaced atoms can be estimated to a good approximation by means of a very simple model based on binary collisions.

The most important characteristic of a collision is the energy transferred to the struck atom. This may range from zero in a glancing collision to a maximum, $E_{p\ max}$, transferred in a head-on collision. From energy and momentum conservation in an elastic collision, $E_{p\ max}$ is given by the equation

$$E_{p\ max} = 4EMm/(M + m)^2 \qquad\qquad I{-}12.2$$

where E and m are energy and mass of the incident particle and M is the mass of the struck atom. This relation is applicable to nonrelativistic particles and is valid for neutrons, protons, etc., in the energy range of interest here. For electrons in the MeV range

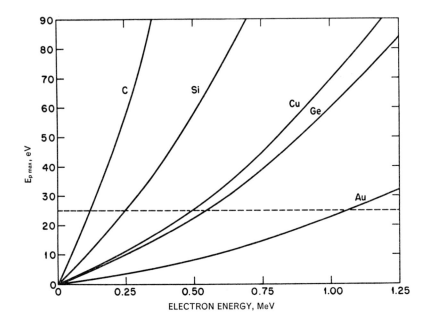

Fig. I–12.5 The maximum energy transferred to various atoms as a function of the energy of the bombarding electron. Dashed line indicates approximate threshold for atomic displacements. (From reference 72.)

relativistic effects must be taken into account, and equation I–12.2 is therefore modified to

$$E_{p\ max} = 2E(E + 2mc^2)/Mc^2, \qquad I–12.3$$

where m is the rest mass of the electron and c is the velocity of light. The maximum energy transferred to various atoms by high energy electrons is shown graphically in Fig. I–12.5.[72] The dashed horizontal line in this figure represents the approximate threshold energy. If it is assumed that 25 eV is required to displace an atom in a solid (i.e., $E_d = 25$ eV), then the above formulas can be used to calculate the minimum energy, E, that a bombarding particle must have in order to cause a displacement. Typical values are given in Table I–12.1 for various bombarding particles and various atomic weights of the target atoms.[73]

TABLE I–12.1

Threshold Radiation Energy for Producing Displacements
with $E_d = 25$ eV

(*from reference 73*)

Bombarding particles	Atomic weight of stationary atoms			
	10	50	100	200
Neutrons, protons (eV)	76	325	638	1263
Electrons, γ rays* (MeV)	0.10	0.41	0.68	1.10
α Particles (eV)	31	91	169	325
Fission fragments of mass 100 (eV)	76	28	25	28

* In the case of γ rays the radiation effect is primarily caused by the Compton electrons or photoelectrons, and therefore the electron threshold energy is used.

The order of magnitude of the threshold energy of an atom in a solid can be estimated by the following simple argument given by Seitz.[84] The energy of sublimation (cohesive energy), E_c, of most tightly bound solids is of the order of 5 to 6 eV. However, during sublimation an atom is removed from the surface where only half the bonds are effective. Therefore, to remove an atom from the interior of a crystal in a reversible manner requires an energy of about $2E_c$. In a collision process the atom is removed from its position and forced into the lattice in a highly irreversible way and should, therefore, require an energy at least of the order of $4E_c$. This would correspond to a threshold energy of 20 to 30 eV.

In the above estimate all crystallographic effects have been neglected. The machine calculations have shown[16] that the threshold energy depends quite strongly on the crystallographic direction of the knock-on. The results of a recent detailed study for iron are shown in Fig. I–12.6.[85] The threshold energy clearly varies greatly with the knock-on direction. These effects have not

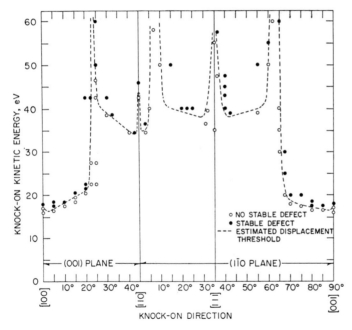

Fig. I–12.6 Directional dependence of the displacement threshold energy in α-iron, a body-centered crystal. The direction of easiest displacement is the [100], giving a minimum threshold of ∼17 eV in this model. (From reference 85.)

F

yet been incorporated into the cascade theories of displacement production.

In the case of collisions with high energy heavy particles, cascades of displacements are expected, such as the one shown in Fig. I–12.4. The average number of atomic displacements made in such events has been estimated theoretically to various degrees of sophistication,[72–74] but only a much simplified discussion is given here. The average number of atoms displaced per unit volume, N_d, is given by

$$N_d = \phi t n_0 \sigma_d \bar{\nu} , \qquad\qquad \text{I–12.4}$$

where ϕ is the bombarding flux density, t the time of bombardment, n_0 the number of atoms per unit volume in the specimen, σ_d the cross section per atom for collisions that produce displacements, and $\bar{\nu}$ the mean number of displacements per primary displaced atom. All these terms are known except $\bar{\nu}$, which is given approximately by the formula

$$\bar{\nu} = E_{p\ av}/2E_d , \qquad\qquad \text{I–12.5}$$

where E_p $_{av}$ is the mean energy transferred by the bombarding particle, which for a neutron is $\frac{1}{2}E_p$ $_{max}$ but for charged particles is given by a more complicated expression. Some typical $\bar{\nu}$ values are given in Table I–12.2 for a mean neutron energy of 1 MeV, the average energy expected in reactor irradiations.[73,74]

TABLE I–12.2

Calculated Mean Number of Displaced Atoms per Primary Knock-on, $\bar{\nu}$, for a 1-MeV Neutron in Various Substances

(*from reference 73*)

Substance	Atomic weight	$\bar{\nu}$
Iron	56	390
Copper	64	380
Germanium	93	290
Gold	197	140

With electrons in the energy range conveniently available, 1 to 3 MeV, $\bar{\nu}$ for most metals is close to one; therefore, one, or at most a few vacancy-interstitial pairs are created per primary knock-on. Electron bombardment results in the simplest distribution of vacancies and interstitials because the knock-ons do not have sufficient energy to cause thermal or displacement spikes. These conclusions also apply to irradiation by γ rays because the displacements are produced by internal bombardment by the Compton electrons or photoelectrons created by the γ rays. Bombardment by γ rays is far less efficient than electron bombardment in producing defects but, because of the high penetration of γ rays in contrast to electrons, a very uniform irradiation of a sample can be obtained.

13. Interaction of Point Defects and Dislocations

The formation of point defects by the interaction of dislocations was discussed in section I–11. The distortions around the point defect and the dislocations cause an interaction between their respective stress fields. A part of the energy of a point defect in a crystal arises from the strain energy created in the system by the expansion or contraction of the medium surrounding the defect. If the medium is otherwise free of stress, this strain energy is due entirely to the elastic resistance of the material. If the dilation occurs in a region already subjected to a stress field, work will also be done against the forces acting on the defect from this field. The total strain energy of the system will be altered by the amount of the energy of interaction of the defect and the stress field. The defect will experience a force which attracts it to the region where it can relieve the most stress. As illustrated in Fig. I–1.1, the region immediately below the terminal row of atoms of the partial plane of an edge dislocation is a region of dilation, while the region immediately above is one of compression. Thus, a vacancy will be attracted to a region of compression and an interstitial to one of dilation. Three important factors determine this interaction energy: (1) the elastic interaction of the two stress fields, (2) the electrical interaction arising from the redistribution of electrons caused by any volume dilation, and (3) the interaction with the nonelastic distortions in the dislocation core region (the region immediately surrounding the terminal row of atoms). The first two have been estimated theoretically but no calculations have been made of the third.

The elastic interaction is calculated in the following manner. If $r(1 + \epsilon)$ is the radius of a defect and r is the radius of the available space for this defect in the parent crystal, then, as shown by Cottrell[86] and by Cottrell and Bilby,[87] the interaction energy of the defect with any stress field is given by the expression

$$U = -\tfrac{4}{3}\pi\epsilon r^3(\sigma_x + \sigma_y + \sigma_z) \qquad \text{I–13.1}$$

where the σ's are the normal stresses at the site of the defect. The normal stresses associated with an edge dislocation (for a positive edge dislocation lying along the z axis) at any point x,y are given by Koehler[88] as

$$\sigma_x = -\frac{G\lambda}{2\pi(1 - \nu)}\, y\, \frac{3x^2 + y^2}{(x^2 + y^2)^2},$$

$$\sigma_y = \frac{G\lambda}{2\pi(1 - \nu)}\, y\, \frac{x^2 - y^2}{(x^2 + y^2)^2},$$

$$\sigma_z = \nu(\sigma_x + \sigma_y), \qquad \text{I–13.2}$$

where G is the shear modulus, ν is Poisson's ratio, and λ is the slip distance in the dislocation. Substitution into equation I–13.1 and conversion to cylindrical coordinates, with the defect position given by radius vector R and angle α, yields the expression for the interaction energy,

$$U = \frac{4G\epsilon r^3 \lambda}{3R}\frac{(1 + \nu)}{(1 - \nu)}\sin \alpha . \qquad \text{I–13.3}$$

It should be noted that U is negative for a negative ϵ for values of α between 0 and π, that is, on the upper side of the dislocation. Thus, in accordance with the qualitative discussion given above, a defect which is smaller than the host atoms, such as a vacancy,

will be attracted to the upper part of the dislocation since a negative U represents a positive binding energy. Just the opposite is
the case for a positive ϵ. Although some refinements have been
given to this theory, they are all within the framework of elasticity
theory, and therefore the whole treatment is inapplicable very
close to the dislocation core. Recent calculations[89] indicate that
the elastic treatment becomes increasingly inaccurate with increasing proximity to the core, the error being about 10% at two
atomic distances and about 50% at one atomic distance. For a
rough estimate equation I–13.3 may still be used at one atomic
distance. For most metals, the quantity

$$\frac{4Gr^3\lambda}{3}\frac{(1+\nu)}{(1-\nu)}$$

is about 5×10^{-20} dyne-cm². The maximum value of U occurs at
$\alpha = \pi/2$. For R equal to 3 Å (one atomic distance), the numerical
magnitude of U expressed in eV is of the order of ϵ. Some estimates
of this elastic binding energy for vacancies and interstitials are
given in Table I–13.1 for a range of ϵ values.

The second contribution to the binding energy of a point defect
to a dislocation, that arising from the electrical interaction, has
been estimated by Cottrell et al.[90] The dilation field alters the
Fermi energy and the ground state of the conduction electrons.
Thus, since the Fermi level must be constant everywhere, a charge
shift occurs by a redistribution of the electrons, and an electric
dipole is formed on the dislocation. Mott's[91] estimate of the effective charge on a defect can be used to calculate the electrical
interaction of a defect with the dislocation. The electrical interaction is generally much smaller than the elastic interaction and
is typically of the order of 0.02 eV for vacancies and interstitials
in the monovalent metals at one atomic distance from the dislocation.

As mentioned before, the third contribution, i.e., the nonelastic interaction in the core of the dislocation, has not yet been
estimated theoretically.

A summary of the available theoretical estimates is given in

Table I–13.1, with the ϵ values taken from the distortions listed in Table I–9.1. It should be remarked that these estimates are very rough indeed.

TABLE I–13.1

Theoretical Estimates of the Binding Energy, U, Between
Point Defects and Edge Dislocations

	U elastic (eV)	U electric (eV)	U total (eV)
Interstitial atoms			
$\epsilon = 0.1$	0.1	0.02	0.12
$\epsilon = 0.2$	0.2	0.02	0.22
Vacancies			
$\epsilon = 0.02$	0.02	0.02	0.04
$\epsilon = 0.05$	0.05	0.02	0.07

According to the discussion of this section, dislocations can act as traps for point defects and/or their clusters. It was shown in I–11 that dislocations are also sources and sinks for point defects. Thus, dislocations play a central role in bringing the defect concentration in any crystal to thermodynamic equilibrium, and it has been shown[92] that for all practical purposes the dislocations in this respect are equivalent to free surfaces.

References

1. G. H. Vineyard and G. J. Dienes, *Phys. Rev.* **93**, 265 (1954).
2. N. F. Mott and R. W. Gurney, *Electronic Processes in Ionic Crystals*, pp. 29–30, Oxford University Press, Oxford, 1948.
3. H. B. Huntington, G. A. Shirn and E. S. Wajda, *Phys. Rev.* **99**, 1085 (1955).
4. G. J. Dienes, *Phys. Rev.* **89**, 185 (1953).
5. C. Zener, *J. Appl. Phys.* **22**, 372 (1951).
6. G. F. Nardelli and N. Tettamanzi, *Phys. Rev.* **126**, 1283 (1962); see also G. F. Nardelli and A. R. Chiarotti, *Nuovo Cimento* **18**, 1953 (1960).
7. H. B. Huntington and F. Seitz, *Phys. Rev.* **61**, 315 (1942).

8. H. B. Huntington, *Phys. Rev.* **61**, 325 (1942).
9. H. Brooks, in *Impurities and Imperfections*, pp. 1–27, American Society for Metals, Cleveland, 1955.
10. F. G. Fumi, *Phil. Mag.* **46**, 1007 (1955).
11. J. Friedel, *Phil. Mag.* **43**, 153 (1962); *Advan. Phys.* **3**, 446 (1954).
12. A. Seeger and H. Bross, *Z. Physik* **145**, 161 (1956); see also A. Seeger, *Z. Physik* **144**, 637 (1956) and reference 14.
13. C. P. Flynn, *Phys. Rev.* **125**, 881 (1962).
14. A. Seeger, *J. Phys. Radium* **23**, 616 (1962).
15. L. Tewordt, *Phys. Rev.* **109**, 61 (1958).
15a. K. H. Bennemann, *Phys. Rev.* **130**, 1757, 1763 (1963).
16. J. B. Gibson, A. N. Goland, M. Milgram and G. H. Vineyard, *Phys. Rev.* **120**, 1229 (1960).
17. R. A. Johnson and E. Brown, *Phys. Rev.* **127**, 446 (1962).
18. H. Paneth, *Phys. Rev.* **80**, 708 (1950).
19. A. Seeger, E. Mann and R. V. Jan, *J. Phys. Chem. Solids* **23**, 639 (1962).
20. P. Hoekstra and D. R. Behrendt, *Phys. Rev.* **128**, 560 (1962).
21. C. Erginsoy, G. H. Vineyard and A. Englert, *Phys. Rev.* (in press).
22. G. H. Vineyard, *J. Phys. Soc. Japan* **18**, Suppl. III (*Intern. Conf. Crystal Lattice Defects*), 144 (1963).
23. J. M. Bartlett and G. J. Dienes, *Phys. Rev.* **89**, 848 (1953).
24. G. K. Corless and N. H. March, *Phil. Mag.* **6**, 1285 (1961).
25. V. G. Weizer and L. A. Girifalco, *Phys. Rev.* **120**, 837 (1960).
26. A. C. Damask, G. J. Dienes and V. G. Weizer, *Phys. Rev.* **113**, 781 (1959).
27. G. H. Vineyard, *Discussions Faraday Soc. No.* **31**, 7 (1961).
28. G. Schottky, *Z. Phys.* **159**, 584 (1960).
29. R. R. Hasiguti, *Proc. Japan Acad.* **36**, 335 (1960); *J. Phys. Soc. Japan*, **15**, 1807 (1960).
30. J. D. Eshelby, in *Solid State Physics*, F. Seitz and D. Turnbull, Editors, Vol. 3, pp. 79–107, Academic Press, New York, 1956.
31. D. Lazarus, *Phys. Rev.* **93**, 973 (1954); and in *Solid State Physics*, F. Seitz and D. Turnbull, Editors, Vol. 10, pp. 71–114, Academic Press, New York, 1960.
32. N. F. Mott, *Proc. Cambridge Phil. Soc.* **32**, 281 (1936).
33. L. C. R. Alfred and N. H. March, *Phys. Rev.* **103**, 877 (1956); *Phil. Mag.* **2**, 985 (1957).
34. H. Fujiwara, *J. Phys. Soc. Japan* **10**, 339 (1955); **13**, 250, 935 (1958).
35. F. J. Blatt, *Phys. Rev.* **99**, 600 (1955).
36. S. Glasstone, K. J. Laidler and H. Eyring, *The Theory of Rate Processes*, McGraw-Hill, New York, 1941.
37. S. A. Rice, *Phys. Rev.* **112**, 804 (1958).
38. G. H. Vineyard, *J. Phys. Chem. Solids* **3**, 121 (1957).
39. C. A. Wert and C. Zener, *Phys. Rev.* **76**, 1169 (1949).
40. E. P. Wigner, *Phys. Rev.* **40**, 749 (1932).
41. C. Zener, in *Imperfections in Nearly Perfect Crystals*, W. Shockley et al., Editors, p. 295, Wiley, New York, 1952; *J. Appl. Phys.* **22**, 372 (1951).
42. J. Frenkel, *Kinetic Theory of Liquids*, Oxford University Press, 1946.
43. A. D. LeClaire, *Progr. Metal Phys.* **4**, 265–333 (1953).
44. J. C. Slater, *Introduction to Chemical Physics*, McGraw-Hill, New York, 1939 (particularly chapter XXVII).
45. L. A. Girifalco and V. G. Weizer, *Phys. Rev.* **114**, 687 (1959).

46. H. B. Huntington, *Phys. Rev.* **91**, 1092 (1953).
47. G. H. Vineyard, J. B. Gibson, A. N. Goland and M. Milgram (unpublished results).
48. G. J. Dienes, *Phys. Rev.* **89**, 185 (1953); see also reference 1.
49. F. Seitz, *Advan. Phys.* **1**, 43 (1952).
50. W. M. Lomer, *Progr. Metal Phys.* **8**, 255–321 (1959).
51. H. Kanzaki, *J. Phys. Chem. Solids* **2**, 24 (1957).
52. G. L. Hall, *J. Phys. Chem. Solids* **3**, 210 (1957).
53. R. A. Johnson, Thesis, Rensselaer Polytechnic Institute, 1962.
54. L. A. Girifalco and V. G. Weizer, *J. Phys. Chem. Solids* **12**, 260 (1960).
55. A. Seeger and E. Mann, *J. Phys. Chem. Solids* **12**, 326 (1960).
56. G. J. Dienes, *Phys. Rev.* **86**, 228 (1952).
57. L. A. Girifalco and J. R. Streetman, *J. Phys. Chem. Solids* **4**, 182 (1958).
58. J. D. Eshelby, *Acta Met.* **3**, 487 (1955).
59. H. B. Huntington and R. A. Johnson, *Acta Met.* **10**, 281 (1962).
60. A. W. Lawson, *J. Phys. Chem. Solids* **3**, 250 (1957).
61. J. S. Koehler, F. Seitz and J. E. Bauerle, *Phys. Rev.* **107**, 1499 (1957).
62. T. Mori, M. Meshii and J. W. Kauffman, *J. Appl. Phys.* **33**, 2776 (1962).
63. H. G. van Bueren, *Imperfections in Crystals*, pp. 276–81, North-Holland Publishing Co., Amsterdam, 1961.
64. A. H. Cottrell, *Dislocations and Plastic Flow in Crystals*, Oxford University Press, 1953.
65. J. Friedel, *Les Dislocations*, Gauthier-Villars, Paris, 1956.
66. R. R. Hasiguti, *J. Phys. Soc. Japan* **8**, 798 (1953).
67. A. C. Damask and G. J. Dienes, *Acta Met.* **7**, 818 (1959).
68. W. T. Read, *Dislocations in Crystals*, McGraw-Hill, New York, 1953.
69. A. Seeger, in *Handbuch der Physik*, VII/1, Springer-Verlag, Berlin, 1955.
70. N. F. Mott, *Proc. Phys. Soc.* **64B**, 729 (1951).
71. N. F. Mott, *Phil. Mag.* **43**, 1151 (1952); **44**, 741 (1953).
72. F. Seitz and J. S. Koehler, in *Solid State Physics*, F. Seitz and D. Turnbull, Editors, Vol. 2, pp. 307–449, Academic Press, New York, 1956.
73. G. J. Dienes and G. H. Vineyard, *Radiation Effects in Solids*, Interscience, New York, 1957.
74. D. S. Billington and J. H. Crawford, *Radiation Damage in Solids*, Princeton University Press, 1961.
75. J. A. Stratton, *Electromagnetic Theory*, p. 15, McGraw-Hill, New York, 1941.
76. R. M. Silsbee, *J. Appl. Phys.* **28**, 1246 (1957).
77. G. Leibfried, *J. Appl. Phys.* **30**, 1388 (1959).
78. M. Yoshida, *J. Phys. Soc. Japan* **16**, 44 (1961).
79. M. T. Robinson, D. K. Holmes and O. S. Oen, *Bull. Am. Phys. Soc.* **7**, 171 (1962).
80. M. T. Robinson and O. S. Oen, *Appl. Phys. Letters* **2**, 30 (1963).
81. C. Lehmann and G. Leibfried, *J. Appl. Phys.* **34**, 2821 (1963).
82. G. R. Piercy, F. Brown, J. A. Davies and M. McCargo, *Phys. Rev. Letters* **10**, 399 (1963); J. A. Davies, J. D. McIntyre, R. L. Cushing and M. Lounsbury, *Can. J. Chem.* **38**, 1535 (1960).
83. J. A. Brinkman, *J. Appl. Phys.* **25**, 961 (1954); *Am. J. Phys.* **24**, 246 (1956).
84. F. Seitz, *Discussions Faraday Soc.* No. 5, 271 (1949).

85. C. Erginsoy, in *ASTM Symposium on the Chemical and Physical Effects of High Energy Radiation, Atlantic City, June, 1963*; see also reference 21.
86. A. H. Cottrell, in *Report of a Conference on Strength of Solids*, p. 30, The Physical Society, London, 1948.
87. A. H. Cottrell and B. A. Bilby, *Proc. Phys. Soc.* **62A**, 49 (1949).
88. J. S. Koehler, *Phys. Rev.* **60**, 397 (1941).
89. A. Englert and H. Tompa, *J. Phys. Chem. Solids* **21**, 306 (1961).
90. A. H. Cottrell, S. C. Hunter and F. R. N. Nabarro, *Phil. Mag.* **44**, 1064 (1953).
91. N. F. Mott and H. Jones, *Theory of the Properties of Metals and Alloys*, pp. 263–89, Dover Publications, New York, 1958.
92. J. Bardeen and C. Herring, in *Atom Movements*, pp. 87–111, American Society for Metals, Cleveland, 1951.

CHAPTER TWO

ANNEALING THEORY

1. Introduction

It has been shown in previous sections how point defects may be produced in a metal in excess of the thermodynamic equilibrium concentration. In such a crystal, there exists a thermodynamic driving force to reduce the concentration of the defects to the equilibrium concentration characteristic of the crystal temperature. Annealing is the process of disappearance of a defect from a super-saturated crystal. Whether a sufficient number of defects disappear at any given temperature to be experimentally observable in a reasonable length of time depends upon their mobility. It has been shown already that the mobility of point defects increases rapidly with increasing temperature, and a suitable temperature interval can always be found in which the disappearance of a given defect can be observed. However, the disappearance of a defect cluster may not be controlled by its own migration but may arise from its decomposition into simpler and more mobile defects.

Excess defects may disappear from a crystal by two different mechanisms, migration to sinks and recombination. If defects of only one type are present, for example vacancies and their simple clusters, they disappear only at sinks, the simplest of which is, of course, the external surface. However, in real crystals there are internal surfaces such as grain boundaries and dislocations. Even in a perfect crystal defects may generate their own dislocation at which they can then disappear. For example, as already indicated, these may be created by the clustering of vacancies and the subsequent collapse of a large cluster into a dislocation ring. The addition of further vacancies will cause the ring to grow. If two types of defects that can annihilate each other are present then they can disappear by direct recombination. The most important example is that of an interstitial falling into a vacancy, which eliminates both defects.

The rate of disappearance of a defect from a crystal is influenced by trapping of the defect or by association of like defects. The equilibrium properties of these reactions have been discussed in Chapter I. These processes are important in any kinetic consideration and will be treated in detail in this chapter. Most of the kinetic problems have been treated in the literature but have not been formulated consistently and systematically. The chemical scheme for reaction rates was selected in this book as an appropriate uniform formulation for defect interaction and annealing. In order to render the development readily comprehensible in this formulation, the derivations are presented in considerable detail.

2. Random Diffusion to Sinks

The simplest annealing process is that in which defects of one species diffuse to a fixed number of unfillable sinks with no associated stress field.* The mathematical description of this process is a problem in classical diffusion whose general solution is well known.[1,2] The concentration at each point r, and also the total amount of the diffusing defect, decays as a sum of damped exponentials in time with the decay time inversely proportional to the diffusion coefficient of the defect.[3] The long-time solution is always a simple exponential, since the higher-order terms, the

---

* An example of diffusion of defects in a stress field has been treated by Cottrell and Bilby.[4] They have shown that if the imperfections are uniformly distributed about an edge dislocation at time = 0, and have a drift velocity proportional only to the gradient of the stress-induced potential energy, the number of defects that have arrived at the dislocation at time t is proportional to $t^{2/3}$. For some recent theoretical work on the diffusion to dislocations and to disk clusters in a stress field see the studies by Sines et al.[4a]

transients, decay more rapidly. In many experimental observations the simple exponential form is valid during the entire course of the observations. Such a time dependence is equivalent to that of a first-order chemical reaction, that is, the number of defects remaining in the metal, n, changes according to the relation

$$dn/dt = -Kn \qquad\qquad \text{II–2.1}$$

where K is a rate constant independent of n and proportional to the diffusion coefficient, D, for the annealing species. Thus,

$$n = n_0 e^{-Kt} \qquad\qquad \text{II–2.2}$$

where

$$K = \alpha D . \qquad\qquad \text{II–2.3}$$

The importance of the transients, and hence the time required to reach the simple exponential decay of equation II–2.2, depends on the initial defect distribution and the sink distribution. If the initial defect distribution is uniform, the transients are less important than if it is highly localized, and the exponential form is reached sooner. If both the initial concentration and sink distributions are random, equation II–2.2 is valid from the beginning. In practice the simple exponential form appears to be quite satisfactory, although its limitations must be kept in mind. Annealing reactions other than simple migration to fixed sinks appear to be far more important than non-uniformities in the initial distribution in leading to more complicated kinetics.

The coefficient α in equation II–2.3 is easily evaluated for simple geometrical shapes by solving the diffusion equation with appropriate boundary conditions.[3,5,6] If the crystal contains no sinks except the external surface, then for a sphere of radius R

$$\alpha = \pi^2/R^2 ; \qquad\qquad \text{II–2.4}$$

for a rectangular parallelopiped of dimensions A by B by C

$$\alpha = \pi^2(1/A^2 + 1/B^2 + 1/C^2) ; \qquad\qquad \text{II–2.5}$$

and for an infinite cylinder of radius R

$$\alpha = X_1^2/R^2 , \qquad\qquad \text{II–2.6}$$

where X_1 = the first root of the zeroth order Bessel function. An important corollary of these results is that if one dimension, L, is much smaller than the others, this small dimension, L, determines α, and hence α is of the order of $1/L^2$.

The appropriate values of α can also be worked out for internal sinks.[3] Let N_0 be the number per unit volume of spherical sinks of radius r_0 distributed randomly in the crystal. By partitioning the crystal into imaginary spherical cells with the spherical sink precisely at the center of the cell one can reduce the problem to diffusion in one sphere. The appropriate boundary condition is that of perfect absorption at the concentric inner surface, r_0, and perfect reflection at the outer surface, r_1, with $r_1 \gg r_0$. The result is

$$\alpha = 3r_0/r_1{}^3 = 4\pi r_0 N_0 \ . \qquad \text{II–2.7}$$

As already discussed in Chapter I, dislocations are sinks for point defects. In a similar way α can be evaluated for a random distribution of edge dislocations. Let the crystal contain N_0 dislocation lines per unit area in the crystal, and let each dislocation be represented by an infinite absorbing circular cylinder of radius r_0. The problem can thus be reduced to diffusion between concentric circular cylinders with the outer cylinder being a perfect reflector of radius r_1, where $\pi r_1{}^2 = 1/N_0$. The result (again for $r_1 \gg r_0$) is

$$\alpha = 2\pi N_0/\ln(r_1/r_0) \ . \qquad \text{II–2.8}$$

The various formulas for α are listed in Table II–2.1.

In bulk material the dislocations are the major sinks for point defects. Their concentration is expressed as the number of dislocation lines per unit area. In kinetic formulations of an annealing step it is convenient to express α of equation II–2.3 in atomic concentration of sinks. For absorption at dislocations α is given by equation II–2.8. In practice, the logarithmic term varies very slowly over a wide range of N_0, and hence r_1, values and approximately cancels the factor 2π (where r_0 is taken to be about two atomic diameters). Thus

$$\alpha \cong N_0 \ .$$

N_0 may be converted to atomic fraction of sinks by the following argument. The concentration of sinks is N_0 times the number of lattice sites per centimeter of line. Thus α in atomic fraction is

$$\alpha = \frac{N_0 \times \text{lattice sites/cm}}{\text{lattice sites/cm}^3}.$$

It may be assumed that, on the average, lattice sites/cm of line = (lattice sites/cm^3)$^{1/3}$ and, with this substitution

$$\alpha \text{ (atomic fraction)} = N_0 \times \text{(number of lattice sites/cm}^3)^{-2/3}$$

TABLE II–2.1

The Value of α of Equation II–2.3 for Simple Geometrical Shapes

	Sphere	Rectangular parallelopiped	Infinite cylinder
Migration to external surfaces	π^2/R^2	$\pi^2(1/A^2 + 1/B^2 + 1/C^2)$	X_1^2/R^2

	Random distribution of spherical sinks		Random distribution of dislocations
Migration to internal sinks	$4\pi r_0 N_0$		$2\pi N_0/\ln (r_1/r_0)$

A quantity frequently evaluated in annealing experiments is the mean number of jumps, $\bar{n}$, a defect makes before it gets destroyed at a sink. For randomly distributed sinks, $\bar{n}$ can be evaluated by a random walk calculation and also by the above diffusion approach. The random walk calculation is the more basic one and will be described first. Consider a random walk on a lattice of coordination number z, and assume that the walker steps only to nearest-neighbor sites, and to each of these with probability $1/z$. It can be shown[7] that the average number of distinct sites visited in n steps, S_n, is given by

$$S_n = a + bn \qquad\qquad \text{II–2.9}$$

and, therefore, for large n,

$$S_n = bn . \qquad\qquad \text{II–2.10}$$

A calculation of b has been carried out for cubic lattices and gave 0.7437 for the face-centered and 0.7178 for the body-centered cubic lattice.[7] Let the system contain C atomic fraction of sinks, with the sinks assumed inexhaustible and of atomic size (i.e., occupying one lattice point). Let $P(n)$ be the probability of survival through n jumps. The rate of destruction per jump is then the product of P, of the probability of jump to a fresh site, b, and of the probability that there is a sink at that site, C. Thus,

$$-dP/dn = PbC \qquad\qquad \text{II–2.11}$$

and, therefore,

$$P = e^{-bCn} . \qquad\qquad \text{II–2.12}$$

The average number of jumps to destruction, $\bar{n}$, is then given by

$$\begin{aligned}
\bar{n} &= \int_1^0 n(-dP) \\
&= \int_0^\infty bCn e^{-bCn} dn \\
&= 1/bC . \qquad\qquad \text{II–2.13}
\end{aligned}$$

Thus, the average number of jumps to destruction is

$$\begin{aligned}
\bar{n} &= 1.345 \,(1/C) \quad \text{for face-centered cubic ,} \\
&= 1.393 \,(1/C) \quad \text{for body-centered cubic .} \quad \text{II–2.14}
\end{aligned}$$

$\bar{n}$ can also be calculated from diffusion theory, since it is given by the product of $\bar{v}$, the mean jump frequency in a particular direction, the coordination number, z ($z\bar{v}$ is the jump frequency in any direction), and the characteristic decay time, $\bar{\tau}$, of the annealing curve, i.e.,

$$\bar{n} = z\bar{v}\bar{\tau} .$$

For the simple exponential kinetics represented by equations II–2.2 and II–2.3,

$$\bar{\tau} = 1/K \ . \qquad\qquad\qquad \text{II–2.15}$$

Since the relation between a mean jump frequency in a particular direction and the corresponding diffusion coefficient, D, for the migrating defect (derivable from diffusion theory as discussed in I–7 for the equivalent case of atomic diffusion) is given by

$$\bar{\nu} = D/\gamma a^2 \ , \qquad\qquad\qquad \text{II–2.16}$$

and from equation II–2.3

$$K = \alpha D \ ,$$

then

$$\bar{n} = z/\alpha \gamma a^2 \ . \qquad\qquad\qquad \text{II–2.17}$$

Thus $\bar{n}$ is inversely proportional to α and is independent of the temperature but does depend upon the nature of the sink and the crystal structure of the metal.

For the case of destruction at randomly distributed spherical sinks, α is given by equation II–2.7 and $\bar{n}$ becomes

$$\bar{n} = z/4\pi r_0 N_0 \gamma a^2 \ . \qquad\qquad\qquad \text{II–2.18}$$

For all cubic lattices, $\gamma = 1$. If σ is the number of atoms per unit cell (2 for body-centered cubic and 4 for face-centered cubic) and the concentration of sinks, in atomic fractions, is $C\,[= N_0/(\sigma/a^3)]$, the expression for $\bar{n}$ becomes

$$\bar{n} = (za/4\pi r_0 \sigma)\,(1/C) \ . \qquad\qquad\qquad \text{II–2.19}$$

In order for the diffusion calculation to agree with the random walk calculation, the sink radius, r_0, must have the values

$$r_0 = 0.178a \quad \text{for face-centered cubic} \ ,$$

$$r_0 = 0.229a \quad \text{for body-centered cubic} \ , \qquad \text{II–2.20}$$

where a is the lattice parameter. The effective r_0 values are somewhat smaller than half the nearest-neighbor distances ($0.35a$ for f.c.c. and $0.433a$ for b.c.c.). This discrepancy between the two treatments is in the expected direction, since diffusion theory

G

departs from transport theory in this direction. The random walk treatment is generally considered to be the more precise one.

For all practical purposes the coefficient b in equation II–2.10 may be taken as one. Thus, approximately, the probability that any given jump takes the defect to a sink is simply the probability that the site visited is a sink. This probability is the atomic fraction of sinks, and therefore the average number of jumps to visit a sink is approximately the reciprocal of the atomic fraction.

3. Recombination of Vacancies and Interstitials

If a crystal contains two types of defects that can annihilate each other, they can disappear by direct recombination in addition to being absorbed at sinks. The most important physical process of this type is the vacancy-interstitial annihilation. In this section the recombination reaction itself is discussed with the assumption that no complicating side reactions occur, such as annealing to sinks or trapping. There are essentially two limiting cases of this process, namely, random recombination of vacancies and interstitials, and recombination of correlated vacancies and interstitials, i.e., annihilation of close pairs.

In order to calculate the rate of random recombination, consider a crystal that contains V vacancies and i interstitials with concentrations expressed in atomic fractions. In metals, as seen in earlier sections, the interstitial is the faster moving defect and therefore its jump rate is the rate controlling term. Let the jump frequency in any direction be ν_i. Suppose the vacancy is surrounded by z sites from which a jump of the interstitial toward the vacancy means certain annihilation, where z depends on the crystal structure and the configuration of the interstitial. If i' is the probability that an interstitial is on one of these z sites, then the rate of vacancy loss by recombination with interstitials is

$$-dV/dt = z\nu_i V i' . \qquad \text{II–3.1}$$

The simplest approximation with which this equation may be further developed is to assume that the interstitials are randomly distributed in the beginning and that diffusion continually re-distributes the remaining ones. Thus the sites bordering on an unreacted vacancy will first be assumed to contain precisely the over-all average concentration of interstitials. In this case i' is equal to i, the atomic fraction of interstitials.

When interstitials and vacancies disappear only by recombination, the number of interstitials that have disappeared must equal the number of vacancies destroyed. Thus

$$i = i_0 - V_0 + V , \qquad\qquad \text{II–3.2}$$

where i_0 and V_0 are the initial concentrations. Equation II–3.1 now becomes

$$-dV/dt = z\nu_i V (i_0 - V_0 + V) , \qquad\qquad \text{II–3.3}$$

which is the equation for bimolecular recombination. In the special case when the initial concentrations are equal, the rate of decay of the defects is described by the simple second-order equation

$$-dV/dt = z\nu_i V^2 , \qquad\qquad \text{II–3.3}$$

which integrates to

$$1/V - 1/V_0 = z\nu_i t . \qquad\qquad \text{II–3.4}$$

The assumption that $i' = i$, used for the preceding derivation, is a good approximation if the migrating interstitial visits the neighborhood of several vacancies before it recombines with one of them, because only in this way can a closely uniform distribution of defects be maintained. This sampling of many vacancy sites requires frequent reflection from a vacancy site and therefore the existence of an energy barrier to recombination. The absence of such a barrier would cause the depletion of defect concentration in some regions, alter the distribution of the defects, and therefore disturb the simple bimolecular kinetics. The disturbance of the kinetics occurs primarily in the early stages of annealing. Detailed treatments of such transients have been given in the literature based on the general concepts of diffusion limited reactions.[3,8–15] These treatments show that after the transient the kinetics are again bimolecular.

The case of highly non-uniform initial concentration is of

interest because closely spaced vacancy-interstitial pairs are
created by some of the methods of defect production, e.g., by
electron irradiation near the threshold (I–12). If an interstitial
recombines primarily with its nearest-neighbor vacancy, then the
annealing is a simple first-order process, since the rate is a function
only of the remaining concentration of either defect. The integrated form for this situation is then the exponential decay given
by equation II–2.2 with $K = zv_i$.

In a typical experiment both the above processes may have to
be considered, i.e., a mobile interstitial either recombines with its
neighboring vacancy or diffuses away never to return to that
particular vacancy. The recombination of the liberated defects[11,12,16] can be described approximately by bimolecular
kinetics. It is of interest to know what fraction of defects would
escape annihilation at a neighboring vacancy as a function of their
distance of separation. If i_0 interstitials are located at a distance
r_i from the center of a vacancy, which is assumed to be a perfect
sink of radius r_0, and if the interstitials diffuse at random, one can
show by an appropriate solution of the diffusion equation[3] that
after a time t the number of interstitials remaining in the system
is given by

$$i = i_0 \left[1 - \frac{r_0}{r_i} + \frac{r_0}{r_i} \operatorname{erf}\left(\frac{r_i - r_0}{2\sqrt{Dt}}\right) \right], \qquad \text{II–3.5}$$

where $erf(x)$ is the error function,

$$\operatorname{erf}(x) = \frac{2}{\sqrt{\pi}} \int_0^x e^{-x^2} \, dx .$$

From equation II–3.5 the asymptotic solution for long time gives
the fraction of interstitials starting at r_i that become liberated as

$$\frac{i}{i_0} = 1 - \frac{r_0}{r_i}. \qquad \text{II–3.6}$$

Fletcher and Brown[11] have made lattice random walk calculations
for the diamond lattice, and Streetman[17] has carried out a Monte
Carlo calculation of this random walk process for a body-centered
cubic crystal, more applicable to metals. Streetman's machine

calculations are summarized in Table II–3.1, which also includes
for comparison the same quantities calculated by equation II–3.6.
Although the Monte Carlo calculation indicates some irregularity
of escapes at the 6th and 7th neighbor positions, it does show
that any interstitials beyond a distance of ten $a/2$ units can be
considered to escape because of the rapid decrease of the numbers
captured beyond this distance. The use of equation II–3.6 is
satisfactory, although the choice of r_0 can be somewhat arbitrary;
data for several r_0 values are given in the table. The middle
column has been normalized to the Monte Carlo calculations at
the 3rd neighbor, and agreement remains excellent out to the 7th
neighbor. At long distances the diffusion equation falls off more
slowly than the Monte Carlo results and leads to a larger separation distance between vacancies and interstitials before they can be
considered isolated.

Many experiments are performed with an atomic fraction of
defects of the order of 10^{-6} to 10^{-4}. The numbers in Table II–3.1
indicate that at these concentrations only a small fraction of the
defects anneal by correlated annihilation if their initial distribution is random. Streetman's machine calculation is representative

TABLE II–3.1

Percent Capture of Interstitial by Neighboring Vacancy in b.c.c.
Lattice as a Function of Initial Interstitial-Vacancy Separation

Distance in $a/2$ units	Neighbor	Monte Carlo calculation	Equation II–3.6		
			$r_0 = 1$	$r_0 = 1.165$	$r_0 = 1.414$
$\sqrt{5}$	3	52.0%	44.6%	52.0%	63.2%
$\sqrt{6}$	4	44.8	40.8	47.5	57.7
3	5	38.4	33.3	38.9	47.2
3	6	33.6	33.3	38.9	47.2
$\sqrt{10}$	7	35.2	31.6	36.9	44.8
10		13.1	10	11.6	14.1
11		7.6	9.1	10.6	12.9
12		4.0	8.3	9.7	11.8
13		1.6	7.7	9.0	10.9

of the recombination step for a dilute concentration of randomly distributed defects with no barrier to recombination. Since the fraction of correlated annihilation is low at these concentrations, the mobile interstitial is expected to visit the neighborhood of several vacancies prior to annihilation, and the bimolecular recombination law should be a valid approximation.

4. Annealing of Defects with Interaction with Impurities

In previous sections the two basic mechanisms for the disappearance of excess defects were discussed, namely, migration to sinks and annihilation by recombination. In this and subsequent sections the annealing kinetics will be treated on the basis of the above fundamental disappearance processes. The complicating features associated with each of these processes will be treated separately. The kinetics of the annealing of a single species will be considered first.

The most common complication and fortunately the simplest mathematically is that arising from the interaction of a vacancy or an interstitial with impurity atoms. Metals of high purity (but not zone refined) contain an atomic fraction of impurity atoms of about 10^{-4} to 10^{-5}. Experimental studies of the annealing of quenched-in vacancies indicate that in a well-annealed metal the average number of jumps to disappearance for a vacancy is of the order of 10^6 to 10^8. Consequently, every vacancy will encounter a large number of impurity atoms during its migration to a sink. According to the discussion of I–6, vacancies may be bound to impurity atoms. If the vacancy-impurity complex is immobile or has a much lower mobility than that of the free vacancy, the vacancy is trapped and the complex must dissociate before the vacancy can continue its migration towards a sink. The importance to the kinetics of this temporary trapping depends upon the magnitude of the binding energy. In this section the influence of the defect-impurity interaction on the kinetics of migration to sinks is derived on the basis of chemical rate theory. The discussion will

be given in terms of vacancies but is equally applicable to interstitials.

In the theoretical treatment[18] to be given it is assumed that the
defect concentration is sufficiently low to allow one to neglect the
interaction of vacancies with one another (formation of divacancies
and higher clusters) and with vacancy-impurity complexes (i.e.,
only one vacancy can be bound to a given impurity atom). It is
further assumed that the migration of the vacancy to the sinks is
adequately described by a first-order process (from II–2 this
requires an initial random distribution of vacancies and sinks).

With these assumptions the annealing process can be symbolized by the following two chemical equations:

$$V + I \underset{K_2}{\overset{K_1}{\rightleftharpoons}} C , \qquad\qquad \text{II–4.1}$$

$$V \overset{K_3}{\rightarrow} \text{sinks} , \qquad\qquad \text{II–4.2}$$

where V, I, and C are the concentrations (atomic fractions) of
vacancies, unbound impurities, and vacancy-impurity complexes,
respectively, and the K's are the corresponding rate constants.
The physical meaning of equation II–4.2 is that vacancies disappear by migration to a fixed number of sinks. The differential
equations for these reactions can be written (after the substitution $I = I_0 - C$) as

$$dC/dt = K_1 I_0 V - K_1 CV - K_2 C , \qquad\qquad \text{II–4.3}$$

$$dV/dt = - K_1 I_0 V + K_1 CV + K_2 C - K_3 V , \qquad \text{II–4.4}$$

where I_0 is the total impurity concentration, which is a constant
for any given experiment. The total vacancy concentration is
$N = C + V$, which, from equations II–4.3 and II–4.4, is described by the differential equation

$$dN/dt = d(C + V)/dt = - K_3 V . \qquad\qquad \text{II–4.5}$$

Equations II–4.3 and II–4.4 form a set of nonlinear coupled
differential equations which, when solved, will describe the complete annealing behavior of the system. The equilibrium concentration of vacancies at the annealing temperature is negligibly

small, and hence V and C approach zero as time approaches infinity. (The equilibrium concentration is easily included, if desired, by a simple change in variables.)

These equations have been solved on an analog computer for a wide variety of parameters (initial vacancy concentration and binding energy). The first general result of interest was that the number of complexes, C, increased very rapidly during the early stage of the annealing. During this same transient period the concentration of free vacancies decreased rapidly. These transients will be discussed later. After these fast transients, C and V decayed steadily. The physical basis for this behavior is as follows: The equilibrium concentration of complexes at the annealing temperature is much larger than at the quench temperature. The fast transient is therefore the establishment of the new equilibrium and is largely governed by the jump rate of the vacancies. The rapid elimination of these transient conditions suggested that an analytic approximation could be used for the bulk of the decay curve. Equilibrium for the first reaction, equation II–4.1, implies that

$$\frac{C}{V(I_0 - C)} = \frac{K_1}{K_2} \equiv K , \qquad \text{II–4.6}$$

or

$$C = KI_0V/(1 + KV) ,$$

which, incidentally, is also the condition for steady-state approximation on C, i.e., $dC/dt = 0$. Substitution into equation II–4.5 and integration gives*

$$\ln V + \frac{KI_0}{1 + KV} - KI_0 \ln\left(\frac{1 + KV}{V}\right) + A = - K_3 t , \qquad \text{II–4.7}$$

where A is the constant of integration.

---

* It should be noted that only substitution into equation II–4.5 yields a solution that matches the analog computer solutions. If the substitution is made into either equation II–4.3 or II–4.4, an incorrect answer is obtained. The reason probably is that the substitution of the equilibrium condition into equation II–4.5 is a much better approximation than substitution into the other two equations because several terms have cancelled in forming equation II–4.5.

Equations II–4.6 and II–4.7 were found to fit all the curves obtained in the machine calculations after the transients. Somewhat surprisingly, however, many of the decay curves (the change of N with time) were found to be simple exponentials in time, which implies that the ratio of C to V remained constant. This constancy of C/V arises from a further approximation in equation II–4.6, namely $C \ll I_0$, which is valid over a wide range of the physically interesting parameters. Substitution of

$$C/V = I_0 K_1/K_2 \qquad\qquad \text{II–4.8}$$

into equation II–4.5 and integration gives

$$C + V = N = V_0' [1 + (I_0 K_1/K_2)]e^{-K_e t} , \qquad \text{II–4.9}$$

where V_0' is the free vacancy concentration at the beginning of the exponential decay and

$$K_e = K_3 / [1 + (I_0 K_1/K_2)] . \qquad\qquad \text{II–4.10}$$

These equations can also be derived from equation II–4.7 with the approximation that $KV < 1$ and $V < 10^{-3}$. (The latter approximation allows one to neglect KI_0 with respect to $|KI_0 \ln V|$.)

Two things are immediately evident from these equations. First, K_e is a composite of all the rate constants and the impurity concentration and will therefore generally not obey a simple Arrhenius equation (see section I–7) even though the decay curves are purely exponential. Second, the pre-exponential term contains two of the rate constants and is therefore temperature dependent. It is thus obvious that the determination of activation energy by change of annealing temperature and calculation of the slope ratio is unsatisfactory (see III–2).

Clearly, the effective rate constant decreases with increasing impurity concentration. The physical basis for this behavior may be described as follows. The vacancies, in their random migration toward sinks, encounter impurity atoms at which they become trapped temporarily, i.e., the complexes must dissociate to furnish free vacancies for further annealing. Thus, the whole annealing process is slowed down.

The various rate constants, based on the discussions of I–2, I–6, and II–2, may be written as follows:

$$K_1 = 84\nu \exp(-E_M/kT) \,,$$
$$K_2 = 7\nu \exp[-(E_M + B)/kT] \,,$$
$$K_3 = \alpha\nu\lambda^2 \exp(-E_M/kT) \,, \qquad\qquad \text{II–4.11}$$

where 84 and 7 are the appropriate combinatory numbers for association and dissociation of complexes in the face-centered cubic lattice, E_M is the migration energy for vacancies, B is the binding energy of a vacancy to the impurity atom, α is the vacancy sink concentration, ν is the jump frequency, λ is the jump distance, and the values assigned to these two constants are $\nu = 10^{13}$ sec^{-1} and $\lambda^2 = 10^{-15}$ cm^2. The factor 7 in K_2 is the number of ways a vacancy attached to an impurity atom can jump away; the factor 84 in K_1 is the number of sites surrounding an impurity atom from which a vacancy in one jump can become attached to the impurity atom. It was shown in I–2 that the ratio of the number of ways two defects can come together to the number of ways they can separate must be equal to the number of independent orientations which the cluster can have in the lattice. Therefore, for impurity-vacancy interactions, via equation I–6.7, K_1/K_2 is given by

$$K_1/K_2 = 12e^{B/kT}.$$

The factor 84 in K_1 can be arrived at either by a rather laborious counting procedure or more simply by multiplying the factor 7 of K_2 by the factor 12* in the above equation.

Some typical annealing curves are shown in Fig. II–4.1 for conditions under which approximation II–4.8 is valid. The lower

---

* In the original paper[18] an error in counting was made and a factor of 42 was used instead of 84 for K_1. This error is of no consequence in the development of the theory. It can also be easily shown that at any given annealing temperature this error is equivalent to a modification of the value of B by $<10\%$.

four curves represent runs at the same quench temperature, T_q, but different impurity concentrations. The upper curve has the same parameters except for a different quench temperature. It is seen to be parallel to the curve at equivalent impurity concentration but of lower quench temperature. All these curves are straight lines, which indicates that each has a single decay constant, and

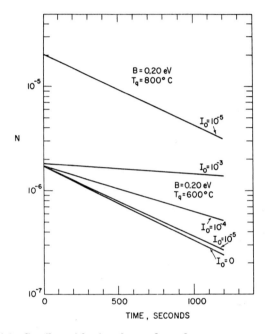

Fig. II–4.1 Semilogarithmic plots of analog computer curves for the decrease of N with time for selected values of T_q, B, and I_0. All curves in this figure are straight lines and obey equation II–4.9. (From reference 18.)

K_e read from these curves checked exactly the value calculated from equations II–4.9 and II–4.10. The important point demonstrated is that a good exponential plot of vacancy annealing data does not mean that the activation energy thereby determined is the activation energy of motion of the vacancy.

The approximation which applies in the above cases is that the number of complexes is small compared to the number of impurities. It is, therefore, expected that this approximation will become invalid at higher vacancy concentration, i.e., for higher quench temperatures, high binding energies, and low impurity concentrations. Deviation from linearity was observed in the computer curves under these conditions. In such cases the more complete solution of equation II–4.7 must be applied, and it has been found to be completely valid by direct comparison with the analog computer solutions.

It is of interest to calculate the temperature dependence of the new, complex rate constant, K_e, since it does not obey a simple Arrhenius equation. It is convenient to rewrite equation II–4.10 in the form

$$K_e = \frac{K_3}{1 + 12I_0 e^{B/KT}} \cdot \qquad \text{II–4.12}$$

Fig. II–4.2 shows K_e as a function of $1/T$ for a set of selected values of B and I_0 with E_M taken as 0.8 eV. All variations occur within the two limiting slopes of E_M and $E_M + B$. These two limits are shown in Fig. II–4.2 by curves 1 and 5. The limiting case of $E_M + B$ cannot be attained with a binding energy lower than 0.35 for an impurity concentration as low as 10^{-3}. Conversely, if the binding energy is 0.2 eV, then 10^{-6} impurity concentration will begin to cause deviation from the E_M limiting slope in the lower temperature region. This means that, if the binding energies of the impurities in a metal are not known, the measurement of vacancy migration energy cannot be guaranteed to be correct even with an impurity concentration of 10^{-7}. Although not shown in this figure, a binding energy of 0.35 will correspond to a slope larger than E_M for an impurity concentration as low as 10^{-7}. This may well be an extreme case, but the general picture given by this figure is that any measurement on metals that are less pure than zone-refining processes permit will contain a probable error of a considerable fraction of the unknown binding energy. Examples of the nonlinearlity of the Arrhenius plot are seen in curves 3 and 4. The change in slope with temperature is visually apparent in curve 3 and is calculated and labeled on curve 4. It is evident from this analysis that the influence of impurities is emphasized by low temperature annealing runs. It is also evident that the binding energy, B, is immediately derivable from the two limiting curves, curves 1 and 5.

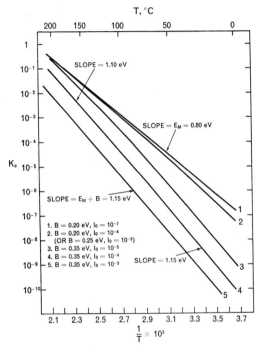

Fig. II–4.2 Plot of calculated K_e vs. $1/T$ for selected parameters. (From reference 18.)

The binding energy B can also be determined, if I_0 is known, by measurement of K_e and K_3 at the same temperature. K_3 is determined from an annealing experiment on a very pure sample, and K_e is determined during the same experiment on a sample containing a known amount of a given impurity.

Since annealing curves with an inflection point have been observed experimentally, it is of interest whether the N vs. t curve also can exhibit an inflection point. The necessary condition for the existence of an inflection point is that the second derivative, d^2N/dt^2 be negative at $t = 0$. By differentiating equation II–4.5, the second derivative is obtained as

$$d^2N/dt^2 = - K_3\,dV/dt = - K_3\,[-K_1V(I_0 - C) + K_2C - K_3V]\,.$$
II–4.13

At $t = 0$, I_0 and C are related by the equilibrium condition at the quench temperature, i.e.,

$$\frac{C}{V(I_0 - C)} = \frac{K_1'}{K_2'} = 12e^{B/kT_q}\,.$$
II–4.14

At $t = 0$, therefore,

$$\frac{d^2N}{dt^2} = K_3K_2 \left(\frac{K_3}{K_2}\,V_0 + \frac{K_1/K_2}{K_1'/K_2'}\,C_0 - C_0\right).$$
II–4.15

Since $T_q > T_a$ (the annealing temperature), $\exp(B/kT_q) < \exp(B/kT_a)$ and therefore $K_1'/K_2' < K_1/K_2$. Thus, $(K_1/K_2)/(K_1'/K_2') > 1$ and therefore d^2N/dt^2 is always positive. Consequently, the vacancy-impurity mechanism cannot explain those decay curves which show an inflection point.

The difficulty of zone refining a wire suitable for quenching, a necessary step to determine E_M via the measurement of K_3, can in principle be avoided by a careful measurement of the transient.[19] The transient arises from the forward reaction of equation II–4.1 due to the tendency of the free vacancies to combine with the available impurities. In the early part of the transient, particularly if $I_0 \ll V_0$, the back reaction may be neglected (this is favored by low temperature annealing since the activation energy for K_2 is larger than for K_1) and therefore $C \cong 0$ in equation II–4.4. With this approximation

$$dV/dt = - V(K_1I_0 + K_3)\,,$$
II–4.16

which is immediately integrable to

$$V = V_0 \exp\left[-(K_1I_0 + K_3)t\right].$$
II–4.17

Thus, there is an initial exponential decay of the free vacancies controlled by the rate constants K_1 and K_3, both of which have the same activation energy, E_M, i.e., the activation energy of migration of the free vacancy. Since a quenched wire has been heated to high temperature, it is of necessity an annealed wire and therefore has a rather low value of the sink concentration, α. Thus the dominating reaction during the transient is the migration of the free vacancies to the impurities, that is, $K_1 I_0 \gg K_3$. Therefore, during this transient there is essentially no change in the total vacancy concentration. The details of the transient can be properly observed only from analog computer solutions.[19]

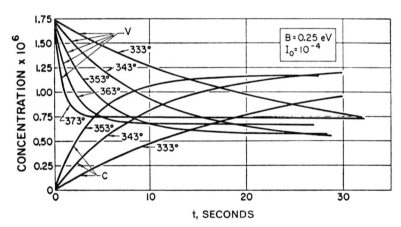

Fig. II–4.3 Isothermal decay of vacancy concentration, V, and growth of complex concentration, C, at the indicated temperatures (°K). (From reference 19.)

A typical series of isothermal annealing curves is shown in Fig. II–4.3, which illustrates clearly the decay of free vacancies, V, and the corresponding growth of the complexes, C. Some of the same curves and additional curves at lower temperatures are shown in Fig. II–4.4. They are quite clearly exponential at the very beginning, and the simple exponential decay persists to longer times at the lower temperatures, in accordance with the discussion given above. From the slopes of these exponential

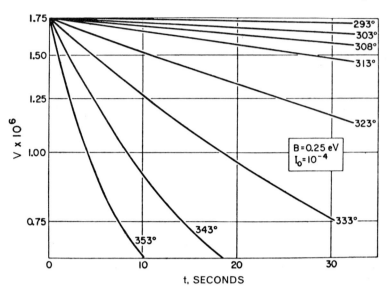

Fig. II–4.4 Logarithm of the vacancy concentration vs. time at the indicated temperatures (°K) during the early part of the transient. (From reference 19.)

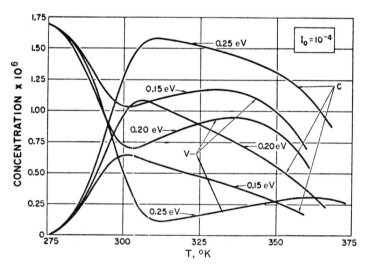

Fig. II–4.5 Constant rate of heating (1°K/minute) recovery curves for $I_0 = 10^{-4}$ and the indicated binding energies. (From reference 19.)

parts the activation energy of migrations of the vacancy can be determined via equation II–4.17.

The entire annealing process can be conveniently illustrated with curves obtained by increasing the annealing temperature at a constant rate and determining the concentration of a given defect as a function of the annealing temperature. A typical set of analog computer curves of this type is shown in Fig. II–4.5. The early parts of these curves clearly show the increase in the number of complexes at the expense of the free vacancies, with almost no effect due to sinks. In the middle temperature range V increases and C decreases because the complexes dissociate as a result of the shift in the equilibrium constant, K_1/K_2, with rising temperature. Finally migration to sinks dominates and V and C both decrease.

In order to distinguish quantitatively between the impurity-vacancy complex and the free vacancy plus impurity, one must choose a physical property that indicates a difference between these two types of defects. Electrical resistivity is probably a suitable property to measure, as will be shown in IV–6. If ρ_C, ρ_I, and ρ_V are the electrical resistivities of the complexes, impurities, and vacancies, respectively, then the resistivity is given by

$$\rho = \rho_V V + \rho_C C + \rho_I I \,. \qquad \text{II–4.18}$$

It is convenient to define a parameter β as

$$\beta = (\rho_C - \rho_I)/\rho_V \,. \qquad \text{II–4.19}$$

If $\beta = 0$, then a resistivity measurement follows directly the decrease of the free vacancy concentration because a trapped vacancy does not contribute to the resistivity. If $\beta = 1$, then no change occurs in the electrical resistivity of a vacancy upon being trapped and therefore its decay cannot be observed. The actual value of β probably lies somewhere between these two extremes.

One of the curves of Fig. II–4.5 ($B = 0.25$ eV) has been transformed in Fig. II–4.6 into resistivity vs. annealing temperature plots for several values of β. As indicated above, at $\beta = 0$ the decrease of free vacancies is being measured, whereas at $\beta = 1$ only the disappearance of complexes, i.e., vacancies going to

H

sinks, is observable. The two processes, the vacancies being
trapped at impurities and subsequently dissociating and migrating
to sinks, are clearly observable in the curves of Fig. II–4.6 for
realistic β's.

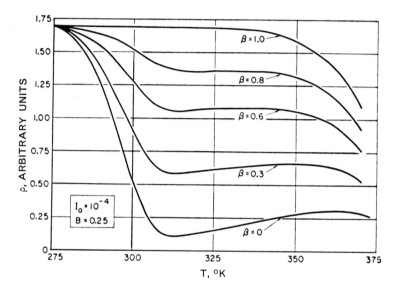

Fig. II–4.6 Constant rate of heating (1°K/minute) plots of resistivity recovery with the indicated values of β. β measures the relative electrical
resistivity contribution of free and bound vacancies. (From reference 19.)

If the resistivities, as given by equation II–4.18, are used in
equation II–4.9 instead of the concentrations, the exponential
form of equation II–4.9 remains unchanged in terms of $\Delta\rho$ vs.
time, where $\Delta\rho = \rho - \rho_I I_0$. This is because equation II–4.18 is
linear in the concentrations. Since K_e of equation II–4.9 is independent of β, both V and N decay exponentially with the same
decay constant regardless of the value of β.

In the above discussion it has been assumed that the vacancy-
impurity complex is immobile or at least migrates much more
slowly than the vacancy. The opposite may also happen if the
vacancy interchanges atomic positions both with the adjacent

impurity and with a lattice atom adjacent to both of them faster than with a normal lattice atom. In this case the complex will migrate to a sink faster than a vacancy and will give up the vacancy at the sink but will leave an impurity atom trapped at the sink, i.e., such a process is accompanied by impurity segregation. The corresponding kinetic scheme is

$$V + I \underset{K_2}{\overset{K_1}{\rightleftharpoons}} C , \qquad \text{II–4.20}$$

$$V \overset{K_3}{\rightarrow} \text{sinks} , \qquad \text{II–4.21}$$

$$C \overset{K_4}{\rightarrow} \text{sinks} + I_t , \qquad \text{II–4.22}$$

where I_t is the atomic fraction of trapped impurity atoms. The corresponding differential equations have not been solved on a computer. An approximate analytic solution can be given with the same equilibrium approximation that was used before and is expressed by equation II–4.8. The analog of equation II–4.5, applied to this problem, is

$$dN/dt = - K_3 V - K_4 C , \qquad \text{II–4.23}$$

which, upon substitution of equation II–4.8, integrates to

$$C = (V_0'I_0K_1/K_2)e^{-K_e t} , \qquad \text{II–4.24}$$

where

$$K_e = \frac{K_3K_2 + K_1K_4I_0}{K_2 + K_1I_0} . \qquad \text{II–4.25}$$

Since $N = V + C$ and $C = (I_0K_1/K_2)V$, the final expression for N is

$$N = V_0' [1 + (I_0K_1/K_2)]e^{-K_e t} . \qquad \text{II–4.26}$$

Thus, the decay is still exponential but with a K_e different from what it was before. Equations II–4.25 and II–4.26 reduce to equations II–4.9 and II–4.10 for $K_4 = 0$ and to the simple vacancy migration case (II–2.2) for $I_0 = 0$.

5. Annealing of Vacancies with Variable Sink Concentration

Another rather simple modification of the random diffusion mechanism of vacancy annealing at sinks in pure metals (no impurities present) takes into account the possibility that the sink concentration itself may be altered by the process of annealing. Theory indicates that vacancies can generate their own sinks by aggregating into disk-shaped clusters which can collapse and form sessile dislocation rings.[20] In the case of face-centered cubic metals such sessile dislocation rings cannot dissociate into partial dislocations and therefore are stable. Absorption of vacancies at the periphery of such a ring causes it to grow while remaining in its original plane. The periphery of the rings can be considered as a line of sinks for vacancies which grows with the increasing number of vacancies absorbed.

Kimura, Maddin and Wilsdorf[21] worked out the kinetic scheme based on the assumption that the nuclei for the ring-shaped sessile dislocation are formed during the quench and, therefore, that N_s (expressed in atomic fraction) sessile dislocation nuclei of zero radius are present at zero annealing time. They further assumed that N_s depends only on the quench temperature. They developed the equations for two types of decay schemes: (a) the number of fixed sinks is negligible compared to the number of variable sinks, and (b) the number of fixed sinks is comparable to the number of variable sinks.

a) Variable sink decay

The kinetic scheme for variable sink decay is

$$V_1 \xrightarrow{K_3} \text{variable sinks} , \qquad\qquad \text{II--5.1}$$

where V_1 = atomic fraction of quenched-in single vacancies. The corresponding differential equation is

$$dV_1/dt = - K_3 V_1 , \qquad\qquad \text{II--5.2}$$

where $K_3 = f(V_1)$ according to the assumptions stated. The periphery of the sessile dislocation ring of radius r is $2\pi r$ and, if the diameter of an atom is D, the number of sinks around the periphery is $2\pi r/D$. Thus, the atomic fraction of sessile dislocation sinks, n_v is given by

$$n_v = 2\pi r N_S/D . \qquad\qquad \text{II–5.3}$$

The N_s sessile rings of radius r have absorbed $(V_1{}^0 - V_1)$ vacancies (where $V_1{}^0 = V_1$ at $t = 0$). Thus,

$$4\pi r^2 N_S/\pi D^2 = V_1{}^0 - V_1 . \qquad\qquad \text{II–5.4}$$

From equations II–5.3 and II–5.4, n_v may then be written as

$$n_v = \pi N_S^{1/2}(V_1{}^0 - V_1)^{1/2} . \qquad\qquad \text{II–5.5}$$

The coefficient K_3 in equation II–5.2 is then given by

$$K_3 = n_v K_3' = \pi N_S^{1/2}(V_1{}^0 - V_1)^{1/2} K_3' ,$$

where

$$K_3' = \nu e^{-E_M/kT} .$$

Equation II–5.1 therefore becomes

$$dV_1/dt = -\pi K_3' N_S^{1/2} V_1 (V_1{}^0 - V_1)^{1/2} , \qquad\qquad \text{II–5.6}$$

which is immediately integrable to give

$$V_1 = V_1{}^0 [\cosh (\tfrac{1}{2}\beta t)]^{-2} , \qquad\qquad \text{II–5.7}$$

where

$$\beta = \pi K_3' \sqrt{N_S V_1{}^0} .$$

If divacancies, V_2, rather than single vacancies are the mobile units which become absorbed at the sessile rings, the equations remain the same with

$$n_v = \pi (N_S/2)^{1/2}(V_2{}^0 - V_2)^{1/2} \qquad\qquad \text{II–5.8}$$

and, therefore,

$$\beta = \pi K_3' \sqrt{N_S V_2{}^0/2} .$$

b) *Simultaneous decay to fixed and variable sinks*

If fixed sinks (i.e., concentration independent of annealing time) are also present, the decay scheme becomes

$$
V_1 \;
\begin{cases}
\xrightarrow{\;\alpha\lambda^2 K_3\;} & \text{fixed sinks} \\[2ex]
\xrightarrow[\;n_v K_3'\;]{} & \text{variable sinks}
\end{cases}
\qquad \text{II–5.9}
$$

where α = effective fixed sink concentration and $\lambda^2 = 10^{-15}$ cm^2 (see II–2 and II–4).

The corresponding differential equation is

$$
dV_1/dt = - K_3'(\alpha\lambda^2 + n_v)V_1 . \qquad \text{II–5.10}
$$

Substitution of $n_v = \pi\sqrt{N_s V_1{}^v}$ and $V_1 = V_1{}^0 - V_1{}^v - V_1{}^F$, where $V_1{}^v$ = atomic fraction of vacancies absorbed in sessile rings and $V_1{}^F$ = atomic fraction of vacancies absorbed in fixed sinks, gives

$$
dV_1{}^v/dt = n_v K_3' V_1 = n_v K_3'(V_1{}^0 - V_1{}^v - V_1{}^F) , \qquad \text{II–5.11}
$$

$$
dV_1{}^F/dt = \alpha\lambda^2 K_3' V_1 = \alpha\lambda^2 K_3'(V_1{}^0 - V_1{}^v - V_1{}^F) , \qquad \text{II–5.12}
$$

where

$$
dV_1{}^v/dt + dV_1{}^F/dt = - dV_1/dt .
$$

Division of equation II–5.11 by II–5.12 and use of equation II–5.5 gives

$$
dV_1{}^v/dV_1{}^F = n_v/\alpha\lambda^2 = (\pi/\alpha\lambda^2)\sqrt{N_s V_1{}^v} . \qquad \text{II–5.13}
$$

Integration yields

$$
V_1{}^v = \tfrac{1}{4}\pi^2 N_s (V_1{}^F)^2/(\alpha\lambda^2)^2 . \qquad \text{II–5.14}
$$

$V_1{}^v$ in equation II–5.12 can now be eliminated and the integration performed. After considerable reduction the result is

$$
V_1{}^F = \frac{2V_1{}^0(1 - e^{-Kt})}{1 + \sqrt{1 + 2\gamma V_1{}^0} - (1 - \sqrt{1 + 2\gamma V_1{}^0})e^{-Kt}} , \qquad \text{II–5.15}
$$

and

$$
V_1{}^v = \tfrac{1}{2}\gamma(V_1{}^F)^2 ,
$$

$$
V_1 = V_1{}^0 - V_1{}^F - V_1{}^v ,
$$

where

$$K = \alpha\lambda^2 K_3' \sqrt{1 + 2\gamma V_1^0} \, ,$$

$$\gamma = \tfrac{1}{2}\pi^2 N_s/(\alpha\lambda^2)^2 \, .$$

If divacancies are the mobile species, comparison of equations II–5.5 and II–5.8 shows that the same equations are valid for V_2 except that $N_s/2$ is to be substituted for N_s.

Several typical annealing curves based on the above equations are shown in Fig. II–5.1. Curves 1 and 2 are for variable sink decay only, for two different sessile dislocation concentrations. Curves 3 and 4 are representative of simultaneous decay to both variable and fixed sinks. For comparison, a typical curve for the vacancy-divacancy mechanism to be discussed in II–6 is shown as curve 5.

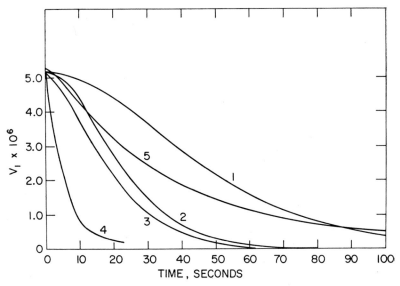

Fig. II–5.1 Representative annealing curves from the Kimura et al. theory.[21] Curves 1 and 2: variable sink decay for two different dislocation concentrations, 1.2×10^{-8} and 5×10^{-8}, respectively. Curves 3 and 4: simultaneous decay to variable and fixed sinks; fixed sink concentrations of $\alpha = 10^9$ and $\alpha = 10^{10}$ added to curves 1 and 2 respectively. Curve 5: a typical curve for vacancy-divacancy mechanism (see II–6) shown for comparison.

It will be noted that in curve 4 the initial delay and the corresponding inflection point, clearly observable in the other curves, have disappeared. The conditions for the presence of the delay and inflection can be stated analytically from the requirement that d^2V_1/dt^2 be negative (see II–4) at $t = 0$ (i.e., when $V_1{}^F = 0$, $V_1{}^v = 0$, where $V_1{}^v$ and $V_1{}^F$ are the single vacancies that migrate to variable and fixed sinks, respectively). Application of this requirement to the situation where

$$dV_1/dt = - dV_1{}^F/dt - dV_1{}^v/dt$$

$$= - (V_1{}^0 - V_1{}^F - V_1{}^v)[\alpha\lambda^2K_3{}' + K_3{}'\pi(N_sV_1{}^v)^{1/2}] \quad \text{II–5.16}$$

gives

$$(d^2V_1/dt^2)_{t=0} = V_1{}^0(K_3{}')^2\,[(\alpha\lambda^2)^2 - \tfrac{1}{2}V_1{}^0\pi^2N_s] \quad \text{II–5.17}$$

and, therefore, for the second derivative to be negative it is necessary that

$$\tfrac{1}{2}V_1{}^0\pi^2N_s > (\alpha\lambda^2)^2$$

or

$$N_sV_1{}^0/\alpha^2 > 2 \times 10^{-31} \qquad \text{II–5.18}$$

where $\alpha \cong N_0$ = number of dislocation lines/cm^2.

As α is increased, for example by cold work, the inflection point, and hence the initial delay, disappears, and the annealing process is speeded up (compare curves 2, 3, and 4 in Fig. II–5.1). Qualitatively the same thing happens to the curve (curve 5) representative of the vacancy-divacancy mechanism. It should also be noted that curves 1 to 4 decay rapidly without exhibiting a long tail, particularly in comparison with curve 5.

c) Tetrahedra as sinks for vacancies

De Jong and Koehler[22] have investigated a modification of the variable sink decay model which also results in a defect concentration vs. time curve with a characteristic inflection point (S-shaped curve). In this model the tetravacancies are assumed to be stable and to aggregate into tetrahedra by the capture of a divacancy, i.e., the six-vacancy cluster is the smallest tetrahedron. The tetrahedra are assumed to grow by the absorption of vacancies at the four corners, i.e., the number of sinks per tetrahedron is always four. The model is, therefore, different from that of Kimura et al., since in the de Jong-Koehler model the number of sinks per tetrahedron is constant, but the tetrahedra themselves are formed by the interaction of the mobile mono-, di-, and trivacancies and, therefore, the concentration of the tetrahedra increases during the annealing.

If it is assumed that the defects and the tetrahedra are uniformly distributed in the sample, and if the migration of trivacancies is neglected, then the rate of annealing of single and divacancies by means of disappearance at the corners of the tetrahedra is given by

$$\frac{dN}{dt} = - (D_1V_1 + 2D_2V_2) \frac{4\Gamma}{a^2} \frac{n}{N_a} , \qquad \text{II–5.19}$$

where $N = V_1 + 2V_2$ = total concentration of free mobile defects, D_1/a^2 and D_2/a^2 are the jump frequencies of the mono- and divacancies respectively, 4 is the number of trapping sites per tetrahedron, n/N_a is the atomic fraction of tetrahedra, and Γ is a geometrical constant which involves the number of ways a defect can jump into the corner of a tetrahedron. The initial conditions are $n = 0$ and $N = N^0$ at $t = 0$. In order to express equation II–5.19 entirely in terms of N and n, de Jong and Koehler eliminate V_1 and V_2 through some approximations. They assume that V_1 and V_2 are in equilibrium, that V_2 is very small compared to V_1, and that under these conditions V_1 can be expressed as a function of N by the equation

$$V_1 = N(1 + 12Ne^{B_2/kT})^{-1} , \qquad \text{II–5.20}$$

where B_2 is the binding energy of a divacancy relative to two single isolated vacancies.

In order to formulate quantitatively the growth of the tetrahedron concentration (the sinks for the decay), it is assumed that the rate of tetrahedron formation is controlled by the rate of tetravacancy formation and, in turn, that the rate of tetravacancy formation is controlled by the collision of mono- and trivacancies. (The di-di encounter is neglected on the basis of arguments concerning divacancy lifetimes as deduced from their experiments.) It is also assumed that the trivacancy is in thermal equilibrium and that V_1 is still properly expressed by equation II–5.20. With these assumptions, the rate of growth of the tetrahedra is given by the equation

$$\frac{dn}{dt} = \frac{2}{3} N_a 12\nu_1 e^{-E_M{}^{(1)}/kT} p\left(\frac{N}{1 + pN}\right)^4 e^{B_3/kT}, \quad \text{II–5.21}$$

where B_3 is the binding energy of the trivacancy relative to the separated mono- and divacancies and $p = 12e^{B_2/kT}$. In order to solve this equation, de Jong and Koehler assume that at short times (near $t = 0$) one may replace N by N^0 in the denominator, and that $D_1/D_2 \ll pN^0 \ll 1$ for both equations II–5.19 and II–5.21, these latter assumptions again being justified by their experiments. With these approximations equations II–5.19 and II–5.21 become

$$dN/dt = - D_2 pN^2 4\Gamma n/N_a a^2, \quad \text{II–5.22}$$

$$dn/dt = \tfrac{2}{3}N 12\nu_1 e^{-E_M{}^{(1)}/kT} pe^{B_3/kT} N^4. \quad \text{II–5.23}$$

Division of II–5.23 by II–5.22 and integration gives

$$n = n_\infty \sqrt{1 - (N/N^0)^3}, \quad \text{II–5.24}$$

where

$$n_\infty = \frac{4\sqrt{2}\, N_a (N^0)^{1.5}}{\Gamma^{1/2} (1 + 12N^0 e^{B_2/kT})} \exp\left[\frac{-(E_M{}^{(1)} - E_M{}^{(2)} - B_3)}{2kT}\right].$$

Since n is now given as a function of N, equation II–5.22 may be integrated, although the result can be obtained only in series form (for this integration it is necessary to use the complete form, equation II–5.19, rather than the approximation II–5.22). De Jong and Koehler integrated separately for the regions $(N/N^0)^3 \cong 1$ and $(N/N^0)^3 \ll 1$, and found that N/N^0 may be expressed as a function of the reduced variable $t/t_{1/2}$ where $t_{1/2}$ is given by the expression

$$1/t_{1/2} = 3.23\Gamma\nu_2 e^{-(E_M^{(2)}-B_2)/kT} (n_\infty/N_a)N^0 . \qquad \text{II–5.25}$$

Thus, if the data are normalized with respect to N^0, n_∞, and $t_{1/2}$, then all the data should lie on a universal curve, i.e., the data should be normalizable via $t_{1/2}$ as a function of the quench temperature. It should be remembered that n_∞ is a function of the temperature and that, therefore, equation II–5.25 does not imply a simple Arrhenius behavior.

A typical calculated curve, on an arbitrary time scale, is shown in Fig. II–5.2. The shape of this curve is very sensitive to the number of absorption sites on the tetrahedra, although the S shape is preserved. Fig. II–5.2 also shows a calculated curve for the case of absorption of vacancies along the edges of the tetrahedra. Included for comparison is curve 1 of Fig. II–5.1, normalized to the scales of Fig. II–5.2, a typical variable sink decay curve from

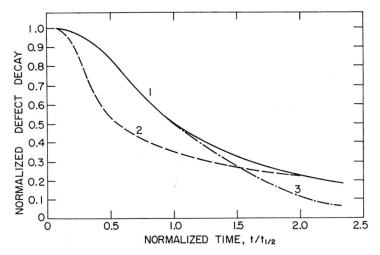

Fig. II–5.2 Comparison of the de Jong and Koehler[22] and the Kimura et al.[21] annealing theories. Curves 1 and 2: de Jong–Koehler mechanism with vacancy absorption at the corners and at the edges of the tetrahedra, respectively. Curve 3: variable sink decay of Kimura et al., curve 1 of Fig. II–5.1.

the Kimura et al. theory. The two theories clearly agree during the early stages (about one-half) of the decay and predict identical delays (S shape). The differences occur at long annealing times with the Kimura et al. curve falling off faster. It will be shown in V–7 that the de Jong-Koehler curve is in very good agreement with their experiments. However, it appears from Fig. II–5.2 that the Kimura et al. theory, if modified at long time, may also be brought into agreement with experiment. Therefore, the model of vacancy absorption at the corners of the tetrahedra may not be the unique explanation of the experimental results.

6. Annealing of Vacancies and Divacancies in Pure Metals

It has been shown in I–5 that the simplest vacancy cluster, the divacancy, is stable and is expected to be highly mobile. Divacancy formation is expected to be important when the single vacancy concentration is high enough to favor vacancy-vacancy encounters before annihilation at sinks. Under such conditions, and assuming random distribution of defects and a given concentration of un-fillable sinks, the general reaction scheme for the simultaneous annealing of vacancies and divacancies is[23,24]

$$V_1 + V_1 \underset{K_2}{\overset{K_1}{\rightleftharpoons}} V_2 , \qquad \text{II–6.1}$$

$$V_1 \overset{K_3}{\rightarrow} \text{sinks} , \qquad \text{II–6.2}$$

$$V_2 \overset{K_4}{\rightarrow} \text{sinks} , \qquad \text{II–6.3}$$

where V_1 and V_2 are the concentrations (atomic fractions) of single and divacancies respectively, and the K's are rate constants. The differential equations for these reactions are

$$dV_1/dt = K_2 V_2 - K_1 V_1{}^2 - K_3 V_1 , \qquad \text{II–6.4}$$

$$dV_2/dt = \tfrac{1}{2} K_1 V_1{}^2 - \tfrac{1}{2} K_2 V_2 - K_4 V_2 . \qquad \text{II–6.5}$$

The total vacancy concentration is $N = V_1 + 2V_2$ and, therefore,

$$dN/dt = dV_1/dt + 2dV_2/dt = -K_3 V_1 - 2K_4 V_2 . \quad \text{II--6.6}$$

These equations cannot be solved in closed form. Solutions were obtained, however, in various temperature regions by making suitable approximations, and the validity of the approximations was checked against analog computer solutions.[24]

The initial concentration of free mono- and divacancies was assumed to be the equilibrium concentration at the quench temperature and, therefore, was calculated from equations I–2.7 and I–2.12:

$$V_1^0 = \exp(-E_F/kT_q); \quad V_2^0 = 6\exp[-(2E_F - B)/kT_q],$$
$$\text{II--6.7}$$

where T_q is the quench temperature.

The K's are written as follows:

$$K_1 = 84\nu \exp(-E_M{}^{(1)}/kT), \qquad \text{II--6.8}$$

$$K_2 = 14\nu \exp[-(E_M{}^{(1)} + B)/kT], \qquad \text{II--6.9}$$

$$K_3 = \alpha\nu\lambda^2 \exp(-E_M{}^{(1)}/kT), \qquad \text{II--6.10}$$

$$K_4 = \alpha\nu\lambda^2 \exp(-E_M{}^{(2)}/kT), \qquad \text{II--6.11}$$

where 84 and 14 are the appropriate combinatory numbers for association and dissociation of divacancies, respectively, in a face-centered cubic lattice,* and the values assigned to the other constants are $\nu = 10^{13}$, $\lambda^2 = 10^{-15}$, and $\alpha = 10^{10}$. In these equations the various quantities are defined as follows:

E_F = formation energy of single vacancy.

B = binding energy of divacancy.

$E_M{}^{(1)}$ = migration energy of single vacancy (set equal to 0.8 eV).

$E_M{}^{(2)}$ = migration energy of divacancy.

---

* In the original paper an error in counting was made and factors of 42 and 7 were used instead of 84 and 14, respectively. Since the ratio of these numbers is the same, the error is of no consequence theoretically and of very little consequence numerically.

The solutions of equations II–6.4 and II–6.6 are sensitive to the values of the various rate constants, and therefore to the annealing temperature as well as to the initial defect concentration, which depends on the quench temperature. Several analytic approximations can be made, which are valid in different annealing temperature regions, for a given set of mobility energies. However, the region of validity of each approximation is sensitive to the nitial defect concentration and hence to the quench temperature. A systematic discussion may be based on the schematic diagram of Fig. II–6.1, where the variation of a set of K's is shown as a function of annealing temperature. The results are discussed below in terms of the five temperature regions labeled in Fig. II–6.1.

I. Calculations have indicated that the mobility energy of divacancies is less than that of single vacancies. Therefore, there is a temperature low enough that only the annealing of the initial concentration of divacancies will be observed, i.e., $K_1 = K_2 = K_3 = 0$.

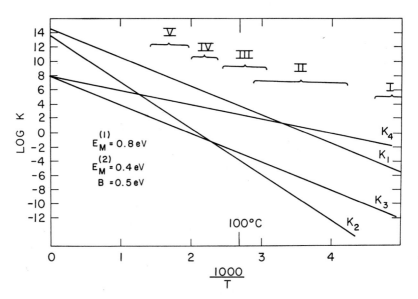

Fig. II–6.1 Schematic of the temperature dependence of a set of rate constants. The temperature regions I to V are discussed in the text. $E_M^{(1)} = 0.8$ eV; $E_M^{(2)} = 0.4$ eV; $B = 0.5$ eV. (From reference 24.)

This gives rise to simple exponential decay with rate constant K_4. For experimental observation a high divacancy concentration is preferable; however, equation II–6.7 shows that an increase of divacancy concentration results in an even higher single vacancy concentration, and interactions can occur which prevent the complete annealing of divacancies. The situation can be improved by increasing α, the trap concentration, so that the probability of a divacancy annealing is greater than the probability of formation of a relatively immobile trivacancy by collision with a single vacancy.

II. As the annealing temperature is increased, the combination of single vacancies to form divacancies is increased via the increased value of K_1 relative to K_4. The approximation for this region, as well as for region III, is derivable from a steady-state approximation for divacancies, namely

$$dV_2/dt = 0; \quad V_2 = K_1 V_1^2/(K_2 + 2K_4). \qquad \text{II–6.12}$$

Substitution into equation II–6.6 gives

$$dN/dt = dV_1/dt = - K_3 V_1 - (2K_4 K_1 V_1^2)/(K_2 + 2K_4). \quad \text{II–6.13}$$

In the low temperature part of region II, $K_1 < K_4$ and K_3 and K_2 are negligible. Under these circumstances V_2 is very small, $N = V_1$, and from equation II–6.13

$$dV_1/dt = - K_1 V_1^2. \qquad \text{II–6.14}$$

This quadratic approximation was confirmed by analog computer solutions. In this region, the decay constant K_1 is rate determining. With a single rate constant, all the standard methods can be used to determine a single activation energy, $E_M{}^{(1)}$.

III. As the temperature of annealing is increased, K_4 can become large enough to permit steady-state approximation on V_2, i.e., $dV_2/dt = 0$, but K_3 and K_2 are no longer negligible. Integration of equation II–6.13 then gives

$$\ln \left(\frac{2K_4 K_1}{K_2 + 2K_4} + \frac{K_3}{V_1} \right) = K_3 t + \ln \left(\frac{2K_4 K_1}{K_2 + 2K_4} + \frac{K_3}{V_1{}^0} \right),$$

$$\text{II–6.15}$$

where V_1^0 is the value of V_1 at $t = 0$. The resulting decay curve is quadratic plus linear. Use of equation II–6.15, as compared with computer solutions, gives excellent fit to V_1, very good fit to V_2 past a transient, and very good fit to N throughout since the contribution of V_2 is small. The pre-exponential factor in equation II–6.15 is temperature dependent and, therefore, the usual methods of activation energy determination are not valid.

A further approximation is of interest since it shows the relation of equation II–6.15 to the quadratic approximation. If K_2 is small compared to $2K_4$, equation II–6.15 simplifies to

$$\ln\left(K_1 + \frac{K_3}{V_1}\right) = K_3 t + \ln\left(K_1 + \frac{K_3}{V_1^0}\right). \qquad \text{II–6.16}$$

In this relation K_1 and K_3 have the same temperature dependence, and a simple Arrhenius plot will be valid. It is of interest to note that for small K_3 equations II–6.15 and II–6.16 reduce to the simple quadratic if expanded to first power in t. If the quench temperature is lowered to give a lower defect concentration, then $K_1 V_1^2$ is no longer large compared to $K_3 V_1$, and therefore the pure quadratic is restricted to a smaller temperature range and might disappear altogether. Correspondingly, case III will extend over a wider temperature range. This is illustrated in Fig. II–6.1, where the two regions are shown to overlap.

IV. If K_4 is small enough to lead to a small V_2, which decays very slowly, then apparent equilibrium is maintained between V_1 and V_2. This leads to the condition

$$V_2 = K_1 V_1^2 / K_2 = K V_1^2. \qquad \text{II–6.17}$$

This approximation leads to an integrable equation valid over a limited range of conditions and, although it agrees with the corresponding machine solutions, it appears too complicated to be useful for the analysis of experimental curves. However, as pointed out by de Jong and Koehler,[25] the differential form, equation II–6.6, may be used with the equilibrium approximation to derive an approximate value for $E_M{}^{(2)} - B$. An effective activation energy, E_{eff}, may be defined by the relation

$$d(\ln R)/d\beta = dR/Rd\beta = -E_{\text{eff}} , \qquad \text{II–6.18}$$

where

$$R = dN/dt = -K_3 V_1 - 2K_4 V_2 \qquad \text{II–6.6}$$

and

$$\beta = 1/kT .$$

Carrying out the differentiation gives

$$\frac{dR}{d\beta} = -V_1 \frac{dK_3}{d\beta} - K_3 \frac{dV_1}{d\beta} - 2V_2 \frac{dK_4}{d\beta} - 2K_4 \frac{dV_2}{d\beta} .$$

$$\text{II–6.19}$$

From the equilibrium approximation, equation II–6.17,

$$\frac{dV_2}{d\beta} = 2KV_1 \frac{dV_1}{d\beta} + V_1{}^2 \frac{dK}{d\beta}$$

and, since at equilibrium N is effectively a constant in $N = V_1 + 2V_2$,

$$dV_1/d\beta = -2dV_2/d\beta .$$

Furthermore

$$dK_3/d\beta = -E_M{}^{(1)} K_3 , \quad dK_4/d\beta = -E_M{}^{(2)} K_4 , \quad \text{and} \quad dK/d\beta = BK .$$

Inserting these derivatives into equation II–6.19, dividing by R, and replacing K by $V_2/V_1{}^2$ gives the expression for E_{eff} of equation II–6.18 as

$$E_{\text{eff}} = \frac{E_M{}^{(1)} + 2E_M{}^{(2)} \dfrac{K_4}{K_3} \dfrac{V_2}{V_1} - \dfrac{2BV_2/V_1}{1 + 4V_2/V_1}\left(\dfrac{K_4}{K_3} - 1\right)}{1 + 2\dfrac{K_4}{K_3} \dfrac{V_2}{V_1}} . \qquad \text{II–6.20}$$

If $V_2/V_1 \ll 1$ and, at the same time,

$$\frac{K_4}{K_3} \frac{V_2}{V_1} \gg 1 , \qquad \text{II–6.21}$$

then equation II–6.20 may be simplified to

$$E_{\text{eff}} \cong E_M{}^{(2)} - B . \qquad \text{II–6.22}$$

I

Clearly, it is assumed in approximation II–6.21 that B is sufficiently small to maintain the inequality for V_2/V_1 and that $E_M{}^{(1)}$ is sufficiently larger than $E_M{}^{(2)}$ to maintain the second inequality. Further, the condition for maintenance of the apparent equilibrium between V_2 and V_1 is that $K_4 \ll K_2$, which implies a small value of α (well-annealed specimen).

V. In the last region identified in Fig. II–6.1, a delay or inflection point can be shown to occur at early times of an annealing curve for appropriate combinations of the parameters. As already pointed out in I–4, the necessary condition for the occurrence of an inflection point in the decay curve is that d^2N/dt^2 be negative at $t = 0$. From equations II–6.4 and II–6.6 the second derivative of N is given by

$$d^2N/dt^2 = V_1{}^2(K_3 - K_4)K_1 + V_1(K_3)^2 + V_2(K_2K_4 - K_2K_3 + 2K_4{}^2),$$
$$\text{II–6.23}$$

which can clearly be negative for appropriate choices of the parameters. A typical analog computer solution of equations II–6.4 to II–6.6, exhibiting an inflection point in N, is shown in Fig. II–6.2. Corresponding to the inflection point in N, a maximum

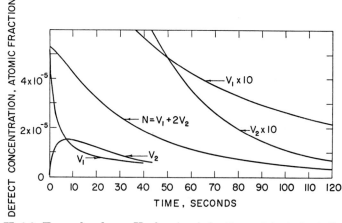

Fig. II–6.2 Example of case V, showing inflection point at short time in the decay of N and the corresponding maximum in V_2. $E_M{}^{(2)} = 0.7$ eV, $B = 0.35$ eV, $T_q = 900°C$, $T_a = 100°C$, $V_1{}^0 = 5.16 \times 10^{-5}$, $V_2 = 5.06 \times 10^{-7}$. (From reference 24.)

in V_2 is clearly observable. The conditions for the existence of an inflection point can be established on the basis of equation II–6.23. A sensible measure for the sharpness of the inflection is the value of V_2/V_1 at or near the inflection point. At the inflection point

$$d^2N/dt^2 = (V_1')^2 K_1(K_3 - K_4) + V_1' K_3^2 +$$
$$V_2'[K_2(K_4 - K_3) + 2K_4^2] = 0 , \qquad \text{II–6.24}$$

where V_1' and V_2' represent the values of V_1 and V_2 at the inflection point. Over the range of parameters investigated, the computer solutions showed that, for the curves with an inflection point, $V_1 K_3^2$ is negligible compared to the other two terms. It is also easily shown that, if $K_3 \geq K_4$, then d^2N/dt^2 is always positive and no inflection point results. Thus, one may write

$$\frac{V_2'}{(V_1')^2} = \frac{K_1(K_4 - K_3)}{2K_4^2 + K_2(K_4 - K_3)} \qquad \text{II–6.25}$$

and, since $K_3 < K_4$,

$$\frac{V_2'}{(V_1')^2} \simeq \frac{K_1}{2K_4 + K_2} . \qquad \text{II–6.26}$$

Equation II–6.26 is also the expression for the maximum in V_2, as can be seen by setting equation II–6.5 equal to zero. Thus, the maximum in V_2 and the inflection point occur very near each other with the inflection point always occurring at a somewhat earlier time.

On the basis of equation II–6.26 it can be said that the sharpness of the inflection will be increased by (a) decreasing K_4, i.e., increasing the activation energy for divacancy motion (but keeping $K_4 > K_3$), and (b) decreasing K_2, i.e., increasing the binding energy for divacancies.

The detailed calculations also showed that the percentage contribution of V_2 to the decay curve near the inflection point increases rapidly with increasing quenching temperature. This is understandable from equation II–6.26 if one considers the magnitude of V_2'/V_1' rather than of $V_2'/(V_1')^2$, i.e.,

$$V_2'/V_1' = V_1' K_1/(2K_4 + K_2) . \qquad \text{II–6.27}$$

V_1' increases rapidly with increasing quenching temperature because V_1^0 is much higher at the higher quench temperatures. The calculations also showed that the time to reach the maximum in V_2 decreases with increasing quench temperature and increasing annealing temperature.

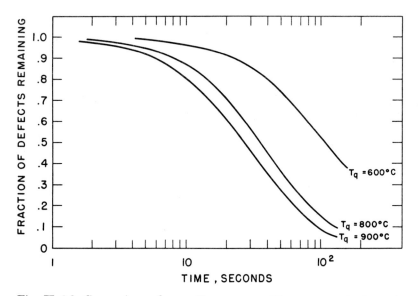

Fig. II–6.3 Comparison of annealing curves with same constants as in Fig. II–6.2, except for the quench temperatures, showing lack of normalization. $E_M^{(2)} = 0.7$ eV, $B = 0.35$ eV, $T_a = 100°C$. (From reference 24.)

T_q	V_1^0	V_2^0
600°C	1.74×10^{-6}	1.88×10^{-9}
800°C	2.06×10^{-5}	1.11×10^{-7}
900°C	5.16×10^{-5}	5.06×10^{-7}

In region V, no analytical approximation has been found, and no simple temperature dependence exists for either N, V_1, or V_2 for any portion of the annealing curve. Consequently, activation energies cannot be accurately determined. If at some future time a technique is developed for measuring V_1 and V_2 separately, then equation II–6.26 could be applied and the corresponding energies derived.

In practice, it would be desirable to compare and combine annealing curves for samples quenched from different temperatures, i.e., of different initial defect concentrations. However, the theoretical curves cannot be superimposed by plotting the fraction of defects remaining against time, except in region I, where the decay is exponential. Different normalization procedures are required for each analytic approximation and, because of the overlap of the various regions, even this procedure may be unsatisfactory. These difficulties are illustrated in Fig. II–6.3 for curves taken from region V. The curves do not superimpose, and in fact the curve of higher initial concentration decays an order of magnitude faster.

As indicated above, although activation energies are derivable from several analytic approximations of the complete decay scheme, none yields directly the migration energy for divacancies.

7. Annealing of Vacancies with Cluster Formation

In the vacancy-divacancy annealing mechanism discussed in the previous section, mono- and divacancies were migrating to sinks, but their possible encounters to form higher clusters were neglected. As the concentration of the defects increases, cluster formation becomes increasingly important, since it is known that trivacancies and higher clusters can be relatively stable (I–5). The process obviously becomes rather complicated, particularly if some dissociation of the clusters takes place, and only some preliminary calculations have been carried out.

Meshii, Mori and Kauffman[26] considered the reaction scheme

$$V_1 + V_1 \rightleftharpoons V_2 \,,$$
$$V_1 + V_2 \rightleftharpoons V_3 \,,$$
$$V_1 \rightarrow \text{sinks} \,,$$
$$V_2 \rightarrow \text{sinks} \,, \qquad\qquad \text{II–7.1}$$

at one annealing temperature and calculated the concentration of the various species as a function of time, with the aid of a computer. The results of this calculation are shown in Fig. II–7.1. It is to be noted that in the reaction scheme of equation II–7.1, decomposition of V_2 and V_3 is permitted to occur, and, therefore, the concentration of all the defects will go to zero at long time. A maximum is expected in the concentration of di- and trivacancies as a function of annealing time and is observed in Fig. II–7.1.

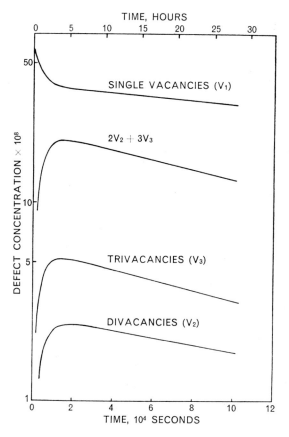

Fig. II–7.1 The calculated concentrations of mono-, di-, and trivacancies as a function of annealing time at 62.4°C, $E_M^{(1)} = 0.8$ eV, $E_M^{(2)} = 0.7$ eV, and $B = 0.3$ eV. (From reference 26.)

A preliminary investigation of the formation of higher clusters has also been made[27] on the basis of the following reaction scheme:

$$V_1 + V_1 \rightleftharpoons V_2 ,$$
$$V_1 \rightarrow \text{sinks} ,$$
$$V_2 \rightarrow \text{sinks} ,$$
$$V_1 + V_2 \rightarrow V_3 ,$$
$$\vdots \qquad \vdots$$
$$V_6 + V_2 \rightarrow V_8 ,$$
$$V_7 + V_1 \rightarrow V_8 . \qquad\qquad \text{II–7.2}$$

It should be noted that in this reaction scheme decomposition of clusters larger than V_2 was not permitted. A typical computer solution of the differential equations associated with the above reaction scheme is illustrated in Fig. II–7.2, which is a photograph of the machine output displayed on an oscilloscope. The variation as a function of time for each species is shown as well as the total

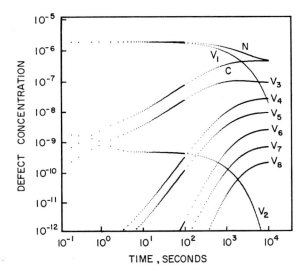

Fig. II–7.2 A typical computer solution for the clustering and annealing of vacancies. (From reference 27.)

vacancy concentration, N, and the concentration of vacancies in clusters, C, defined by

$$N = V_1 + 2V_2 + 3V_3 + \ldots 8V_8 \, ,$$
$$C = 3V_3 + \ldots 8V_8 \, .$$

The concentration of the various stable clusters after long annealing is shown in Fig. II–7.3, as a function of cluster size, from the data of Fig. II–7.2 (squares). For comparison, the results of similar calculations are also shown in which the clustering reaction was terminated at V_6. It is seen that the neglect of larger clusters does not seriously disturb the final distribution. It was also found that this distribution was insensitive to changes in annealing temperature, within the rather narrow temperature range investigated.

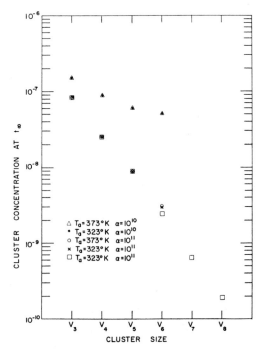

Fig. II–7.3 The concentration of the various stable clusters after long annealing time. (From reference 27.)

The detailed kinetics of the whole process is complex, and no simple analytic approximation was found for the major portion of the over-all vacancy decay. The last stage of annealing (about 5%) of N does obey, however, simple exponential decay and is governed by the migration of monovacancies to dislocations and to the clusters formed during the earlier stages.

8. Vacancy-Interstitial Annihilation with Interstitial Migration to Sinks

The kinetics of the recombination of vacancies and interstitials was discussed in II–3 with the assumption that all complicating side reactions could be neglected. In this and the succeeding two sections, some of the physically important side reactions will be considered. The most obvious complicating feature is the disappearance of some of the interstitials (the more mobile defect) at internal and external sinks (surfaces).

The simultaneous reactions of vacancy-interstitial annihilation and interstitial migration to sinks has been examined for two different conditions.[28] In the first, the irradiation is assumed to occur at a sufficiently low temperature to prevent the motion of the defects. After a given defect concentration has been produced, the sample is raised to a temperature high enough to allow the interstitials, but not the vacancies, to migrate. The kinetics of interstitial-vacancy annihilation with interstitial migration is then calculated. After the interstitials have disappeared, the sample is assumed to be irradiated again at low temperature and, since there are some residual vacancies present from the previous irradiations, the kinetics of the subsequent annealing is different. Each irradiation followed by annealing will be called a "cycle," and the accumulation of vacancies will be examined for several cycles, a case somewhat analagous to the accumulation of damage in a material subjected to on-and-off reactor operation. This over-all process will be referred to as "low temperature irradiation." The second situation of interest may be called "ambient temperature irradiation." In the analysis of this condition it is assumed that the irradiation is performed at a temperature at which the interstitials, but not the vacancies, can migrate as soon as they are created. This dynamic condition is similar to a series of infinitely short cycles of the first type of experiment. The process of vacancy accumulation is then compared for the two types of irradiations as a function of the integrated exposure.

The kinetic scheme for both conditions is

$$V + i \overset{K_1}{\to} \text{annihilation} , \qquad \text{II–8.1}$$

$$i \overset{K_2}{\to} \text{sinks} . \qquad \text{II–8.2}$$

For the condition of low temperature irradiation, in which a given defect concentration is present and the sample is then warmed to a temperature at which the interstitials are free to migrate, the differential equations corresponding to the above reactions are

$$dV/dt = - K_1 Vi , \qquad \text{II–8.3}$$

$$di/dt = - K_1 Vi - K_2 i . \qquad \text{II–8.4}$$

Division of equation II–8.4 by equation II–8.3 gives

$$di/dV = 1 + (K_2/K_1 V) , \qquad \text{II–8.5}$$

which is integrable and gives

$$i = (i_0 - V_0) + V + (K_2/K_1) \ln(V/V_0) . \qquad \text{II–8.6}$$

Substitution of i of equation II–8.6 into equation II–8.3 gives

$$dV/dt = - K_1 V [(i_0 - V_0) + V + (K_2/K_1) \ln(V/V_0)] . \qquad \text{II–8.7}$$

This equation is not integrable in terms of elementary functions but is easily solved graphically for V as a function of t. Some typical examples of V and i as a function of time are given in Fig. II–8.1, where V was obtained by graphical integration and i was calculated from equation II–8.6 with the constants

$$K_1 = 30\nu e^{-E_i/kT} , \qquad \text{II–8.8}$$

$$K_2 = \alpha\nu\lambda^2 e^{-E_i/kT} , \qquad \text{II–8.9}$$

where E_i is the migration energy of the interstitial, ν the vibrational frequency, λ the jump distance, and α the effective sink concentration (II–2). These calculations were done at 50°K, and the following values were assigned to the various constants: $E_i = 0.1$ eV, $\nu = 10^{13}$, $\lambda^2 = 10^{-15}$, and $\alpha = 10^{10}$. The combinatory number of equation II–8.8 was evaluated on the assumption that the interstitial is in the "split" configuration (I–4).

Figure II–8.1 shows the decay of V and i for three different irradiations and, therefore, three different initial concentrations. It has been assumed that the irradiation occurred at a sufficiently low temperature for all the defects to be completely frozen in and that, when the sample is warmed to 50°K, the interstitials become mobile but the vacancies do not. The following features of these curves are to be noted: (a) i decays much faster than V and approaches zero as t approaches infinity, while V approaches a constant value, V_∞. (b) The decay of i and V as a function of t obeys no simple law.

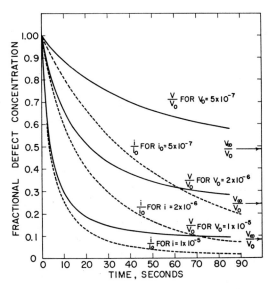

Fig. II–8.1 The decay of vacancies and interstitials for various initial concentrations of defects (with equal initial concentrations of vacancies and interstitials). $E_i = 0.1$ eV, $T = 50°$K. The final vacancy concentrations V_∞/V_0 are also indicated. (From reference 28.)

It can be seen from equation II–8.7 that the temperature dependence of the rate of annealing is controlled by K_1, and hence by the migration energy of the interstitial, because the ratio K_2/K_1 is independent of the temperature (see equations II–8.8 and II–8.9). Thus the curves of Fig. II–8.1 can be calculated for any other temperature via equations II–8.8 and II–8.9. It should be noted that the ratio K_2/K_1 controls the departure from the simple bimolecular recombination of vacancies and interstitials developed in II–3. This departure increases with increasing sink concentration since K_2/K_1 is directly proportional to α.

The terminal value, V_∞, of any given anneal is given by equation II–8.6 by setting i equal to zero. Therefore, V_∞ is independent of the temperature but does depend on the initial concentrations and on the sink concentration via the ratio K_2/K_1. The number of interstitials that have been removed from the system at sinks is, of course, equal to V_∞.

In practice a solid is often irradiated and annealed several times. Let such a cycle consist of a given irradiation at low temperature (no annealing during irradiation) followed by complete annealing of interstitials at some higher temperature. From equation II–8.6 one can calculate V_∞, i.e., the fraction of vacancies remaining in the sample, after each cycle and add this to the concentration of vacancies introduced by the next irradiation cycle, to correct the initial condition at the beginning of each periodic anneal. Clearly vacancies will accumulate in the sample, since a fraction of the interstitials anneal at sinks instead of undergoing recombination. The fraction of vacancies remaining in the sample after a given number of cycles, i.e., the accumulation of vacancies, depends very sensitively on the radiation dosage of each cycle and is large for a short irradiation interval (small V_0), although this fractional increase is not to be confused with total vacancy increase. This is to be expected physically, since low concentrations of defects favor interstitial migration to sinks and hence vacancy accumulation. Thus, each successive cycle contributes less residual vacancies to the accumulated total because more of the interstitials combine with the accumulating vacancies. Vacancy

accumulation also implies that the rate of annihilation in each
cycle increases with the number of cycles. This is easily seen from
equation II–8.7 as a simple concentration effect.

One of the purposes of an ambient temperature irradiation is to
study the change of concentration of defects during the irradiation
at a temperature at which the interstitials are mobile. Equations
II–8.3 and II–8.4 must be modified by adding a constant, K,
which is the constant rate of defect production by the radiation.
The corresponding differential equations are

$$dV/dt = K - K_1 Vi, \qquad \text{II–8.10}$$

$$di/dt = K - K_1 Vi - K_2 i. \qquad \text{II–8.11}$$

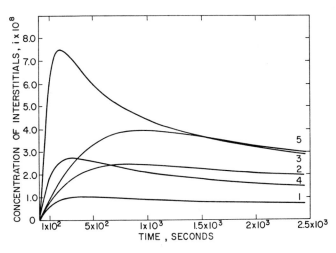

Fig. II–8.2 Concentration of interstitials vs. irradiation time. (Run 6:
interstitial concentration is too small to be observable on this scale.) (From
reference 28.)

Curve	Sink concentration	Defect production/sec	Temperature, °K
1	10^{10}	10^{-10}	50
2	10^{10}	10^{-10}	48
3	10^{10}	10^{-9}	50
4	10^{10}	3×10^{-10}	50
5	10^{9}	10^{-10}	50
6	10^{11}	10^{-10}	50

These equations cannot be solved analytically. Approximations can be made, however, and the validity can be investigated by obtaining the complete numerical solution on a computer. Some typical examples are shown in Figs. II–8.2 and II–8.3 with the parameters used given in the captions. It is seen that all the i curves exhibit a maximum. The magnitude of the maximum and its dependence on the various parameters can be obtained by setting $di/dt = 0$ in equation II–8.11. This gives

$$i_{max} = K/(K_2 + K_1 V) . \qquad \text{II–8.12}$$

Since V is a variable, equation II–8.12 can be used only as an approximation in discussing the influence of the various parameters. It is expected that the magnitude of i_{max} increases with increasing defect production rate and decreases with increasing sink concentration and interstitial mobility. The computer curves verify these characteristics, and also show that the time to reach the maximum in i increases with decreasing defect production rate, sink concentration, and mobility.

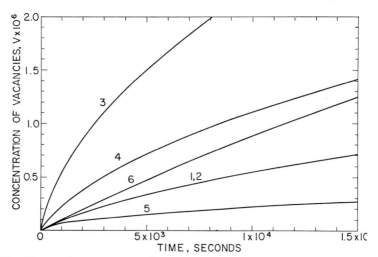

Fig. II–8.3 Concentration of vacancies vs. irradiation time. Curves numbered as in Fig. II–8.2. (From reference 28.)

Equation II–8.12 is also the condition for a steady-state approximation on i. Comparison with the computer solutions showed that equation II–8.12 is quite accurately obeyed past the maximum in i. Therefore, equation II–8.12 can be substituted into equation II–8.10 and integrated to give the growth of V with time (a relation also derived by Barnes[29]) as

$$V^2 + 2(K_2/K_1)V = 2(K_2/K_1)Kt . \qquad \text{II–8.13}$$

This relation was also checked against the computer solutions and found to be accurately obeyed past the value of V that corresponds to the maximum in i. Typical V vs. time curves are shown in Fig. II–8.3. The limiting conditions on V can be determined from equations II–8.10 and II–8.11. When no defects anneal, i.e., $K_1 = 0$ in equation II–8.10, there is an upper bound to the growth rate of V given by the value of K. There is also a lower bound on the growth rate for any given value of K and at any given temperature. This is obtained by setting $K_2 = 0$ in equation II–8.11 and hence $i = V$. Integration of equation II–8.11 with $i = V$ gives the equation for the minimum growth of V as a function of time as

$$\frac{K + V\sqrt{KK_1}}{K - V\sqrt{KK_1}} = e^{2t\sqrt{KK_1}} . \qquad \text{II–8.14}$$

In equation II–8.13, V is not a function of temperature, since K and K_2/K_1 are independent of temperature, but V does depend on the dose and the sink concentration. (Equation II–8.13 is valid only past the maximum in i, and the time to reach the maximum, as previously stated, does depend on temperature as well as on K.) It should be noted, however, that in equation II–8.13, K only appears as Kt on the right-hand side and, therefore, all curves for V past i_{max} can be normalized if plotted against integrated exposure (for neutrons $K = nv$ and $Kt = nvt$). It is of interest to compare the accumulation of vacancies by continuous irradiation at temperature T (equations II–8.10 and II–8.11) with the accumulation arising from periodic irradiation at low temperature followed by annealing at T. On the basis of the above discussion this comparison can be made (past the initial transient) independently of K, and of temperature, if V at any time is plotted against integrated exposure, nvt. Figure II–8.4 illustrates this comparison. The curve labeled "continuous irradiation" is representative of runs 1, 2, 3 and 4 of Fig. II–8.3, since all have the same sink concentration. The curves labeled 1, 2, 3, 4, and 5 are those calculated via equation II–8.7 with the number of cycles expressed as nvt. Figure II–8.4 shows clearly that the vacancy accumulation is decreased when the mechanism of accumulation involves periodic irradiation and annealing and the annealing consists of the two simple reactions given by equations II–8.1 and II–8.2. The accumulation is smallest for the largest irradiation dosage because the annihilation reaction is favored by a high concentration of defects.

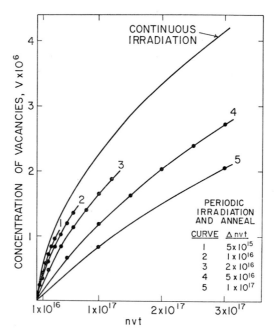

Fig. II–8.4 Comparison of vacancy accumulation by continuous irradiation with vacancy accumulation by periodic low temperature irradiation and annealing. (From reference 28.)

9. Vacancy-Interstitial Annihilation with Interstitial Trapping at Impurities

In this section the importance of impurities in the kinetics of interstitial-vacancy annihilation is discussed. As already indicated (I–6), interstitials may be trapped at impurities to form an immobile complex and thereby alter the kinetics of annihilation.[30] The physical model to be investigated here is the following one.[31] Equal concentrations of vacancies and interstitials have been produced by irradiation. The sample contains a certain concentration of impurities which can trap interstitials with a significant binding energy to form a non-mobile complex. The defects and the impurities are assumed to be randomly distributed in the solid. As before, the interstitials are assumed to be much more mobile than the vacancies. It is also assumed that interstitial migration to sinks may be neglected and, therefore, the vacancies and interstitials can decay only by vacancy-interstitial annihilation. This approximation is favored by a low value of α (sink concentration) and by a relatively high concentration of vacancies and interstitials. The above physical picture is described by the simple kinetic scheme

$$V_1 + i \xrightarrow{K_1} \text{annihilation} , \qquad \text{II–9.1}$$

$$i + I \underset{K_3}{\overset{K_2}{\rightleftharpoons}} C , \qquad \text{II–9.2}$$

where C is the atomic fraction of interstitial-impurity complexes and the other symbols have their usual meaning. In this kinetic scheme

$$N = V_1 + i + C = 2V_1 , \qquad \text{II–9.3}$$

$$V_1 = i + C , \qquad \text{II–9.4}$$

and

$$K_1 = K_2$$

since both K_1 and K_2 are determined by the diffusion coefficient for the interstitial atom to a substitutional stationary trap. The

K

differential equations that describe the above kinetic scheme are

$$dV_1/dt = - K_1 V_1 i \,, \qquad\qquad \text{II-9.5}$$

$$di/dt = - K_1 i(i + I_0) + K_3 C \,, \qquad\qquad \text{II-9.6}$$

$$dC/dt = K_1 i(I_0 - C) - K_3 C \,. \qquad\qquad \text{II-9.7}$$

These equations may be solved by the substitution $u = C/i$, which gives an immediately integrable expression for u. The result is

$$u = \frac{\dfrac{K_1}{K_3} I_0 (C_0 + i_0) e^{\alpha t} + \left(C_0 - \dfrac{K_1}{K_3} I_0 i_0 \right)}{(C_0 + i_0) e^{\alpha t} - \left(C_0 - \dfrac{K_1}{K_3} I_0 i_0 \right)} \qquad\qquad \text{II-9.8}$$

with

$$\alpha = K_1 I_0 + K_3 \,.$$

Substitution of C/u for i in II-9.5 gives

$$u\, dV_1/dt = - K_1 V_1 C \,, \qquad\qquad \text{II-9.9}$$

and addition of II-9.9 to II-9.5 and elimination of $(C + i)$ via II-9.4 yields

$$\frac{dV_1}{K_1 V_1{}^2} = \frac{-dt}{1 + u(t)} \,, \qquad\qquad \text{II-9.10}$$

where $u(t)$ is given by equation II-9.8. Upon integration and some algebraic manipulation, the final results for V_1, i, and C are

$$V_1 = \frac{\left(\dfrac{K_1}{K_3} I_0 + 1 \right)(C_0 + i_0)\alpha}{K_1 \alpha (C_0 + i_0)t + K_1 \left(C_0 - \dfrac{K_1}{K_3} I_0 i_0 \right)(e^{-\alpha t} - 1) + \left(\dfrac{K_1}{K_3} I_0 + 1 \right)\alpha} \,,$$

$$\text{II-9.11}$$

$$i = \frac{\alpha(C_0 + i_0) - \alpha \left(C_0 - \dfrac{K_1}{K_3} I_0 i_0 \right) e^{-\alpha t}}{K_1 \alpha (C_0 + i_0)t + K_1 \left(C_0 - \dfrac{K_1}{K_3} I_0 i_0 \right)(e^{-\alpha t} - 1) + \left(\dfrac{K_1}{K_3} I_0 + 1 \right)\alpha} \,,$$

$$\text{II-9.12}$$

$$C = \frac{\alpha(C_0 + i_0)\dfrac{K_1}{K_3} I_0 + \alpha\left(C_0 - \dfrac{K_1}{K_3} I_0 i_0\right)e^{-\alpha t}}{K_1\alpha(C_0 + i_0)t + K_1\left(C_0 - \dfrac{K_1}{K_3} I_0 i_0\right)(e^{-\alpha t} - 1) + \left(\dfrac{K_1}{K_3} I_0 + 1\right)\alpha} \cdot$$

$$\text{II–9.13}$$

From the kinetic scheme, equations II–9.1 and II–9.2, one expects the following behavior. At low temperature, where the dissociation of the complex is negligible, the concentration of free interstitials approaches zero, since a certain fraction of them will be trapped while the rest will be annihilated by recombination with vacancies. At the same time the vacancies and complexes will approach a limiting concentration. This situation corresponds to $K_3 = 0$ in equations II–9.11 to II–9.13, which, with initial complex concentration zero, $C_0 = 0$, reduce to

$$V_1 = \frac{I_0 i_0}{(I_0 + i_0) - i_0 e^{-K_1 I_0 t}}, \quad V_1 \to \frac{I_0 i_0}{I_0 + i_0} \text{ as } t \to \infty \; ; \quad \text{II–9.14}$$

$$i = \frac{I_0 i_0}{(I_0 + i_0)e^{K_1 I_0 t} - i_0}, \quad i \to 0 \text{ as } t \to \infty \; ; \qquad \text{II–9.15}$$

$$C = \frac{I_0 i_0 (1 - e^{-K_1 I_0 t})}{(I_0 + i_0) - i_0 e^{-K_1 I_0 t}}, \quad C \to \frac{I_0 i_0}{I_0 + i_0} \text{ as } t \to \infty . \quad \text{II 9.16}$$

These equations show clearly the approach to saturation by means of exponential functions. It is to be noted, however, that none of the relations represents a simple exponential decay or growth.

Whenever the temperature is high enough for K_3 to be important, the annealing process starts off with annihilation of vacancies and interstitials and the simultaneous formation of complexes, with C going through a maximum. This transient is followed by the decay of the defects, which is controlled essentially by the decomposition of the complexes. At times long enough for the transients to be negligible a simple kinetic law is obtained. As the exponentials

approach zero, equations II–9.11 to II–9.13 become the integrated
expressions for simple quadratic decay:

$$\frac{1}{V_1} = \left(\frac{K_3 K_1}{K_1 I_0 + K_3}\right)t + \left[\frac{K_1{}^2 I_0}{(K_1 I_0 + K_3)^2} + \frac{1}{i_0}\right], \qquad \text{II–9.17}$$

$$\frac{1}{i} = K_1 t + \left[\frac{K_1{}^2 I_0}{K_3(K_1 I_0 + K_3)} + \frac{K_1 I_0 + K_3}{K_3 i_0}\right], \qquad \text{II–9.18}$$

$$\frac{1}{C} = \left(\frac{K_3}{I_0}\right)t + \left[\frac{K_1}{K_1 I_0 + K_3} + \frac{K_1 I_0 + K_3}{K_1 I_0 i_0}\right]. \qquad \text{II–9.19}$$

The total defect concentration,

$$N = i + C + V_1 ,$$

will not generally decay strictly quadratically. This will happen
only if i is negligible in comparison with V_1 and C, and if K_3
$< K_1 I_0$. Under these circumstances

$$C = V_1 = \left[\left(\frac{1}{I_0} + \frac{1}{i_0}\right) + \frac{K_3}{I_0} t\right]^{-1}$$

and, therefore,

$$\frac{1}{N} = \frac{1}{2}\frac{K_3}{I_0} t + \frac{1}{2}\left(\frac{1}{I_0} + \frac{1}{i_0}\right). \qquad \text{II–9.20}$$

However, equation II–9.20 is a good approximation in practice
even when i is not negligible.

The asymptotic solutions, equations II–9.17 to II–9.19, can
also be obtained by a steady-state approximation on i. If, after
the transient, steady-state approximation is assumed for i in
equation II–9.6 then

$$K_3 C = K_1 i(i + I_0)$$

which, for $i \ll I_0$, gives

$$i = \frac{K_3}{K_1}\frac{C}{I_0} . \qquad \text{II–9.21}$$

This relation between i and C permits integration of dN/dt
$= -2K_1 V_1 i$ (the sum of equations II–9.5 to II–9.7) in the following manner:

$$dN/dt = 2dC/dt + 2di/dt = -2K_1 i(i + C) . \qquad \text{II–9.22}$$

Substitution for i and di/dt from equation II–9.21 gives

$$\frac{dC}{dt}\left(1 + \frac{K_3}{K_1 I_0}\right) = -\left(1 + \frac{K_3}{K_1 I_0}\right)\frac{K_3}{I_0} C^2 , \qquad \text{II–9.23}$$

which immediately integrates to

$$\frac{1}{C} = -\frac{K_3}{I_0} t + \frac{1}{C_0} , \qquad \text{II–9.24}$$

which is the same as equation II–9.19. It is to be noted that if di/dt is taken to be zero in the differential equation II–9.22, one still obtains a quadratic form but with the incorrect coefficient.

It is of interest to present some curves calculated from equations II–9.11 to II–9.13. The constants K_1 and K_3 are given by

$$K_1 = 30\nu e^{-E_i/kT} ,$$

$$K_3 = 5\nu e^{-(E_i+B)/kT} ,$$

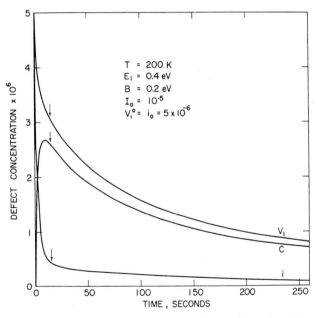

Fig. II–9.1 Plot of equations II–9.11 to II–9.13 for selected parameters. Arrows indicate beginning of quadratic decay. (From reference 31.)

where $\nu = 10^{13}$, E_i = activation energy for interstitial migration, and B = binding energy of interstitial to impurity. The combinatory numbers were evaluated on the assumption that the interstitial is in the "split" configuration (I–4).

A typical example of an isothermal anneal is shown in Fig. II–9.1. The transients are clearly shown, and for decay past the arrows the quadratic approximations of equations II–9.17 to II–9.19 are valid. The total defect concentration, N (not shown

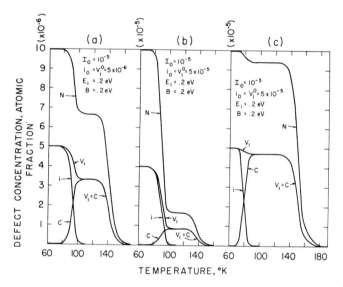

Fig. II–9.2 Ten-second, ten-degree isochronal curves calculated with equations II–9.11 to II–9.13. (a) and (b): Comparison at two different initial concentrations. (b) and (c): Comparison at two different impurity levels. (From reference 31.)

on the graph), also decays very closely as a quadratic beyond the arrows. An important result of this calculation is that quadratic kinetics is shown to be obeyed at long times even though the reaction is controlled by the decomposition of complexes rather than by direct vacancy-interstitial annihilation. Some isochronal annealing curves (annealing for equal time intervals at a series of

successively higher temperatures) are shown in Fig. II–9.2, calculated with $E_i = 0.2$ eV and $B = 0.2$ eV in 10°C and 10-second
steps. These values for the energies were chosen to illustrate the
clear separation of the low and high temperature processes when
E_i and $(E_i + B)$ differ appreciably. Comparison of curves (a) with
curves (b) shows the influence of initial concentration in the decay
curves for the same impurity concentration. Curves (b) and (c)
show the comparison of decay for the same initial concentration
of defects at two different levels of impurity content.

10. Vacancy-Interstitial Annihilation with Di-interstitial Formation

In the preceding section vacancy-interstitial annihilation with
interstitial-impurity trapping was discussed. In this section the
annihilation process without impurities but with di-interstitial
formation[32] is examined. In the impurity case a complete analytic
solution was obtained, but an analytic solution has not been found
when di-interstitial formation occurs. The kinetics will be described, therefore, on the basis of selected analog computer calculations and some approximations. As before, the solid is assumed to
contain equal numbers of vacancies and interstitials randomly
distributed. Also, the study is restricted to the condition that the
vacancies and interstitials can decay only by vacancy-interstitial
annihilation. The interstitials are again assumed to be much more
mobile than the vacancies. The above physical picture is described
by the simple kinetic scheme:

$$V_1 + i \overset{K_1}{\rightarrow} \text{ annihilation ,} \qquad \text{II–10.1}$$

$$i + i \underset{K_3}{\overset{K_2}{\rightleftharpoons}} i_2 , \qquad \text{II–10.2}$$

where i_2 is the atomic fraction of di-interstitials. This reaction
scheme is described by the differential equations

$$dV_1/dt = - K_1 V_1 i , \qquad \text{II–10.3}$$

$$di/dt = - K_1 V_1 i - K_2 i^2 + K_3 i_2 , \qquad \text{II–10.4}$$

$$di_2/dt = \tfrac{1}{2} K_2 i^2 - \tfrac{1}{2} K_3 i_2 , \qquad\qquad \text{II–10.5}$$

$$dN/dt = - 2K_1 V_1 i , \qquad\qquad \text{II–10.6}$$

with $N = V_1 + i + 2i_2$; $V_1 = i + 2i_2$; $V_1{}^0 = i_0$.

Valid approximations can be made at very high ($i_2 \cong 0$) and at very low ($K_3 \cong 0$) temperatures, as will be shown later. No suitable approximations have been found in any region where none of the constants and none of the variables is negligible. This complex region was explored by analog computer calculations.

The rate constants are given by the relations

$$K_1 = 30\nu e^{-E_i/kT} ,$$

$$K_2 = 84\nu e^{-E_i/kT} ,$$

$$K_3 = 14\nu e^{-(E_i+B)/kT} , \qquad\qquad \text{II–10.7}$$

where B is the binding energy of two interstitials.

Some assumptions are involved in selecting the numerical constants, i.e., the combinatory factors. The interstitial is taken to be in the "split" configuration (I–4). Recent calculations by Vineyard for the f.c.c. lattice indicate that the most stable configuration of the di-interstitial is that in which the two split interstitials are parallel to each other.[33] The number of independent orientations of this parallel arrangement is 6, and therefore $K_2/K_3 = 6$. The coefficient for K_1 is the same as in the impurity case discussed in the previous section, since the number of ways an interstitial can arrive at a vacancy is the same as for combination with a substitutional impurity.

A typical analog computer solution is shown in Fig. II–10.1. It is evident that vacancy-interstitial annihilation and di-interstitial formation are of about equal importance. Although V_1 and i_2 decay in a very similar way, steady-state approximation on i (a procedure which gave the correct long-time solution in the case of interstitial-impurity trapping) does not lead to a valid long-time solution even when i is much smaller than in the case illustrated in Fig. II–10.1. Other possible approximations, for example V_1/i_2 = constant, were also found to be invalid. (The major difference in the basic equations from those given in II–9 is the i^2 term, which is probably what prevents the use of these approximations.)

At sufficiently high temperature, or for small values of B, the decomposition reaction of i_2 is fast enough to render its concentration small, particularly past an initial transient. Thus, in this temperature region $i_2 \cong 0$. Under these conditions the annihilation reaction dominates giving quadratic decay for V_1 and i governed by rate constant K_1. The computer solutions showed this to be a valid approximation even though a small i_2 transient is present.

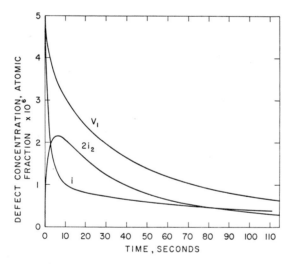

Fig. II–10.1 Analog computer solutions for the general case. $V_1^0 = i_0$ = 5 × 10⁻⁶, $T = 200°K$, $E_i = 0.4$ eV, $B = 0.2$ eV. (From reference 32.)

At sufficiently low temperature, or for large values of B, the decomposition reaction for i_2 is extremely slow and one may let $K_3 = 0$. Thus, the interstitials decay to zero, a fraction forming i_2 and the remainder annihilating an equal number of V_1's. V_1 and i_2, therefore, will approach a constant.

If $K_3 = 0$, then division of equation II–10.4 by equation II–10.3 gives

$$\frac{di}{dV_1} = 1 + \frac{K_2}{K_1} \frac{i}{V_1} \, .$$

II–10.8

Equation II–10.8, and by substitution equation II–10.3, can be integrated when K_2/K_1 is an integer or a simple fraction. For the choice of rate constants used in this calculation, $K_2/K_1 \cong 3$. A closed solution can be obtained in this case as

$$\frac{1}{V_1^0} - \frac{1}{V_1} + \frac{\sqrt{3}}{2V_1^0} \left[\ln \frac{-(\sqrt{3}V_1/V_1^0) - 1}{(\sqrt{3}V_1/V_1^0) - 1} - \ln \frac{-\sqrt{3} - 1}{\sqrt{3} - 1} \right]$$

$$= \frac{1}{2} K_1 t \, ,$$

$$i = \tfrac{3}{2} V_1 [(V_1/V_1^0)^2 - \tfrac{1}{3}] \, .$$

II–10.9

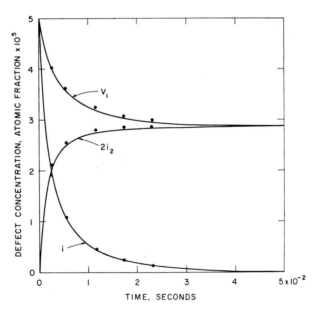

Fig. II–10.2 Analog computer solutions illustrating di-interstitial formation for small value of K_3/K_1. $V_1^0 = i_0 = 5 \times 10^{-5}$, $T = 250°K$, $E_i = 0.4$ eV, $B = 0.3$ eV. The dots represent calculated values from equation II–10.9. (From reference 32.)

It is seen that at infinite time $V_1/V_1{}^0 = 1/\sqrt{3}$. Calculations from equation II–10.9 for defect concentration as a function of annealing times yield the points indicated by dots in Fig. II–10.2. The results are obviously in good agreement with the analog computer solution shown on the same graph for comparison.

The choice of $K_2/K_1 = 3$ is somewhat arbitrary. Vineyard's calculation[33] has shown that there are several configurations of i_2 of differing but close binding energies (see Fig. I–5.4). It is therefore possible that the i_2 configuration chosen here is not the correct one, and, furthermore, several configurations may occur simultaneously. For this reason, equations II–10.8 and II–10.3 have been integrated in the original paper for other K_2/K_1 ratios.[32] It should be noted that the rate constant K_3 does not appear in either the high or the low temperature approximation. Thus, there is no simple method for determining the binding energy of the di-interstitial on the basis of this analysis.

11. Vacancy-Interstitial Annihilation with Several Interactions

Corbett, Smith and Walker[16] have obtained some computer solutions for the kinetics of vacancy-interstitial annihilation when interstitials are allowed to form di- and tri-interstitials. They allow no back reactions to occur, i.e., di- and tri-interstitials are assumed to be stable, and they assume that only the isolated interstitial is mobile. Since their calculations are meant to apply to the low temperature annealing stages of irradiated metals, the above assumptions are expected to be reasonably valid. With these restrictions, by a simple extension of the scheme of equations II–10.1 to II–10.6, the kinetic equations are

$$dV_1/dt = -\,K_1iV_1\,, \qquad\qquad \text{II–11.1}$$

$$di/dt = -\,K_1iV_1 - K_2i^2 - K_4ii_2\,, \qquad \text{II–11.2}$$

$$di_2/dt = \tfrac{1}{2}K_2i^2 - K_4ii_2\,, \qquad\qquad \text{II–11.3}$$

$$di_3/dt = K_4ii_2\,, \qquad\qquad\qquad \text{II–11.4}$$

where the K's are proportional to the jump frequency of an interstitial. Computer solutions for V_1 as a function of time were
obtained for three cases as shown in Fig. II–11.1, where the three
curves are identified for the particular choice of the rate constants
used. Although the curves are presented as normalized with respect

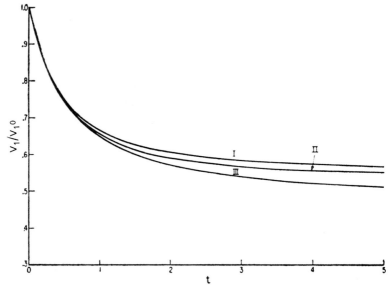

Fig. II–11.1 Computer solutions of equations II–11.1 to II–11.4 for several
choices of rate constants. I: $K_4 = K_2 = 2K_1$; II: $K_4 = \frac{1}{2}K_2 = K_1$;
III: $K_4 = 0$; $K_1 = \frac{1}{2}K_2$. (From reference 16.)

to V_1^0, they are valid for only one initial concentration (not
specified in the original paper). Curve III represents di-interstitial
formation only and is therefore similar to the V_1 vs. time curve of
Fig. II–10.2 discussed in II–10. Curves I and II illustrate the
influence of tri-interstitial formation. As in the calculation in
II–10, V approaches a finite value at $t = \infty$. Also as in II–10,
escape of the interstitial is not permitted, i.e., the treatment is
applicable only at a relatively low sink concentration.

It is also of interest to examine these equations under some
special conditions which may arise in selected experiments.

Corbett et al. have discussed equations II–11.1 to II–11.3 under the conditions that a certain concentration, C_t, of unsaturable traps is present, which will add a term to equation II–11.2, and that $K_4 = 0$, which allows neglect of the third term in equation II–11.2. They further assume that $K_2 = 2K_1$. Under these conditions the modified equations are

$$dV_1/dt = - K_1 iV , \qquad \text{II–11.5}$$

$$di/dt = - K_1 iV - 2K_1 i^2 - K_1 C_t i , \qquad \text{II–11.6}$$

and their first integral (V as a function of i) is easily obtained. Division of equation II–11.6 by II–11.5 and integration gives

$$\frac{V}{V_0} = \frac{2 + \dfrac{2i + C_t}{V}}{2 + \dfrac{2i_0 + C_t}{V}} . \qquad \text{II–11.7}$$

V_∞, the saturation value of V, is obtained by allowing i to approach zero (as time approaches infinity). Thus,

$$\left(\frac{V_\infty}{V_0}\right)^2 = \frac{2V_\infty + C_t}{2V_0 + 2i_0 + C_t} , \qquad \text{II–11.8}$$

which defines V_∞ for any values of V_0, i_0, and C_t. If ΔV is defined as $\Delta V = V_0 - i_0$, then equation II–11.8 may be put in the form

$$\left(\frac{V_\infty}{i_0}\right)^2 \left[\frac{2 + \Delta V/i_0 + C_t/2i_0}{(1 + \Delta V/i_0)^2}\right] - \frac{V_\infty}{i_0} = \frac{C_t}{2i_0} . \qquad \text{II–11.9}$$

This form is convenient for treating cases in which an extra concentration of vacancies is present coming, for example, from an irradiation following a prior irradiation and anneal (one of the cycles discussed in section II–8).

References

1. H. S. Carslaw and J. C. Jaeger, *Conduction of Heat in Solids*, Oxford University Press, 1947.
2. P. M. Morse and H. Feshbach, *Methods of Mathematical Physics*, McGraw-Hill, New York, 1954.

3. G. J. Dienes and G. H. Vineyard, *Radiation Effects in Solids*, Chapter 5, Interscience, New York, 1957.
4. A. H. Cottrell and B. A. Bilby, *Proc. Phys. Soc. (London)* **A62**, 49 (1949).
4a. G. Sines, R. K. Kikuchi and W. Grupen, *J. Phys. Soc. Japan* **18**, Suppl. III (*Intern. Conf. on Crystal Lattice Defects*) 30 (1963).
5. A. Blandin and J. Friedel, *Acta. Met.* **8**, 384 (1960).
6. P. Penning, *Philips Res. Repts.* **14**, 337 (1959).
7. G. H. Vineyard, *J. Math. Phys.* **4**, 1191 (1963).
8. M. v. Smoluchowski, *Ann. Physik* **48**, 1103 (1915); *Z. Physik. Chem. (Leipzig)* **92**, 129 (1917).
9. F. C. Collins and G. E. Kimball, *J. Coll. Sci.* **4**, 425 (1949).
10. M. Reiss, C. S. Fuller and F. J. Morin, *Bell System Tech. J.* **35**, 535 (1956).
11. R. C. Fletcher and W. L. Brown, *Phys. Rev.* **92**, 585 (1953).
12. T. R. Waite, *Phys. Rev.* **107**, 463 (1957).
13. B. Ya. Yurkov, *Soviet Phys. – Solid State (English Transl.)* **3**, 2591 (1962).
14. V. V. Antonov-Romanovsky, *Phys. Rev.* **125**, 1 (1962).
15. R. Stockmeyer, Thesis, Technische Hochschule, Aachen, 1960.
16. J. W. Corbett, R. B. Smith and R. M. Walker, *Phys. Rev.* **114**, 1460 (1959).
17. J. R. Streetman, in *Radiation Effects Symposium, May, 1957*, Vol. 2, ANP Doc. No. NARF-57-19T.
18. A. C. Damask and G. J. Dienes, *Phys. Rev.* **120**, 99 (1960).
19. A. Sosin, *Phys. Rev.* **122**, 1112 (1961).
20. D. Kuhlmann-Wilsdorf, *Phil. Mag.* **3**, 125 (1958).
21. H. Kimura, R. Maddin and D. Kuhlmann-Wilsdorf, *Acta. Met.* **7**, 145 (1959).
22. M. de Jong and J. S. Koehler, *Phys. Rev.* **129**, 49 (1963).
23. J. S. Koehler, F. Seitz and J. E. Bauerle, *Phys. Rev.* **107**, 1499 (1957).
24. G. J. Dienes and A. C. Damask, *Discussions Faraday Soc.* No. **31**, 29 (1961).
25. M. de Jong and J. S. Koehler, *Phys. Rev.* **129**, 40 (1963); see also G. Schottky, *Z. Physik* **160**, 16 (1960).
26. M. Meshii, E. Mori and J. W. Kauffman, *Phys. Rev.* **125**, 1239 (1962).
27. A. C. Damask and G. J. Dienes, *Bull. Am. Phys. Soc.* **8**, 216 (1963).
28. G. J. Dienes and A. C. Damask, *Phys. Rev.* **128**, 2542 (1962).
29. R. S. Barnes, *Phil. Mag.* **6**, 1487 (1961).
30. R. R. Hasiguti, *J. Phys. Soc. Japan* **15**, 1807 (1960).
31. A. C. Damask and G. J. Dienes, *Phys. Rev.* **125**, 444 (1962). A similar treatment for semiconductors has been given by A. V. Spitsyn and L. S. Smirnov, *Soviet Phys.–Solid State (English Transl.)* **4**, 2529 (1963).
32. G. J. Dienes and A. C. Damask, *Phys. Rev.* **125**, 447 (1962).
33. G. H. Vineyard, *J. Phys. Soc. Japan* **18**, Suppl. III (*Intern. Conf. on Crystal Lattice Defects*) 144 (1963).

CHAPTER THREE

METHODS OF ANALYSIS OF ANNEALING CURVES

1. Introduction

Experimental data can be used to determine the kinetics of the annealing process. In general this will involve the identification of various annealing steps and the determination of the characteristic rate constants and the corresponding activation energies. It is clear from the discussions of Chapter II that this may sometimes be a formidable problem. General methods of analysis of isothermal and isochronal annealing data exist for rather simple cases only. Whenever possible, experiments should be designed to separate the various kinetic steps of an annealing process. If a single activated process can be isolated, then the methods discussed in the present chapter become applicable.

For a single activated process the activation energy is determinable under rather general assumptions. If the single activated process is describable by a chemical rate equation, then the order of the reaction may also be determined by several procedures. These general methods are described in this chapter. In addition, some of the complications which have been treated mathematically will be discussed, such as a distribution of activation energies and the influence of a variable activation energy on the order of the reaction.

2. Determination of Activation Energy

If the annealing of a defect occurs by a single activated process with a constant activation energy, then the rate of change of the

145

concentration of the defect is describable by the simple equation

$$dn/dt = - F(n)K \equiv - F(n)K_0 e^{-E/kT}, \qquad III-2.1$$

where n is the fractional concentration of the defect; $F(n)$ is any continuous function of n; and K is the characteristic rate constant, which can be separated into a pre-exponential constant, K_0, and an exponential involving the activation energy of the process, E. There are two basic assumptions implicit in this equation, namely, (a) the Boltzmann factor, $\exp(-E/kT)$, can be expressed as a multiplicative factor, and (b) the activation energy, E, is independent of n. Under these rather unrestrictive assumptions several methods can be used to determine the activation energy, E.

a) Method of cross-cut[1]

Suppose that isothermal annealing curves have been determined experimentally at several temperatures on a set of identical samples, i.e., samples containing the same initial concentration of

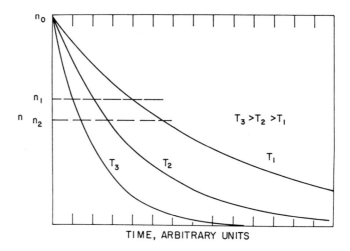

Fig. III–2.1 Schematic sketch of cross-cut procedure for determining the activation energy from isothermal annealing curves.

defects, n_0, as illustrated in Fig. III–2.1. Such data can be analyzed as follows. Equation III–2.1 is formally integrable to give

$$-\int_{n_0}^{n_1} \frac{dn}{F(n)} = K_0 t e^{-E/kT} . \qquad \text{III–2.2}$$

If a line parallel to the time axis is drawn in Fig. III–2.1 (dashed line) at a given value of n, say n_1, then the left-hand side of equation III–2.2 is a constant. Different times and temperatures needed to reach the line n_1 are therefore related by the equation

$$t e^{-E/kT} = \text{constant} \equiv C . \qquad \text{III–2.3}$$

Thus two times, t_1 and t_2, required to reach a constant value of n at temperatures T_1 and T_2, respectively, are related by

$$\ln \frac{t_1}{t_2} = \frac{E}{k}\left(\frac{1}{T_1} - \frac{1}{T_2}\right). \qquad \text{III–2.4}$$

When the cut crosses several curves, the times are related to the temperatures by

$$\ln(t_i) = \ln C + E/kT_i , \qquad \text{III–2.5}$$

i.e., the logarithm of t_i is linear in $1/T_i$ with E/k as the slope of the curve. If a cut is taken at another point, n_2, only the constant C is altered in equation III–2.5 and the lines described by this equation should be parallel. This characteristic is a check on the assumption that a single process with a constant activation energy is operative.

b) Ratio of slopes[2]

A closely related method involves the sudden alteration of the annealing temperature during the annealing of one specimen, as illustrated in Fig. III–2.2. At point A corresponding to $n = n^*$, let the temperature be changed from T_1 to T_2 and let the slope of the n vs. t curve be constructed at A on both sides of the discontinuity. If R_1 and R_2 are the slopes corresponding to the temperatures T_1 and T_2, then, from equation III–2.1,

$$R_1 = - F(n^*)K_0 e^{-E/kT_1} ,$$
$$R_2 = - F(n^*)K_0 e^{-E/kT_2} , \qquad \text{III–2.6}$$

L

and, therefore, the activation energy is immediately calculable from the relation

$$\ln \frac{R_1}{R_2} = -\frac{E}{k}\left(\frac{1}{T_1} - \frac{1}{T_2}\right).$$
III–2.7

Just as in the method of cross-cuts, a single activation energy should result for temperature changes at different n^* values when

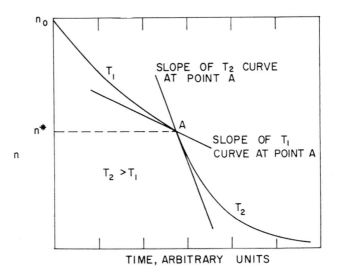

Fig. III–2.2 Schematic sketch illustrating the ratio of slopes method of activation energy determination.

a process with a single activation energy is operative. In practice it is somewhat difficult to construct an accurate slope, and more than one experiment is usually performed.

c) Constant rate of heating[1,3]

In many experiments a sample containing defects is gradually warmed at a constant rate, and a physical property, p, related to the number of defects, is observed during the annealing. Since K

in equation III–2.1 depends exponentially on the temperature, dp/dt is very small during the low temperature stages and then grows rather suddenly, and within a rather small temperature

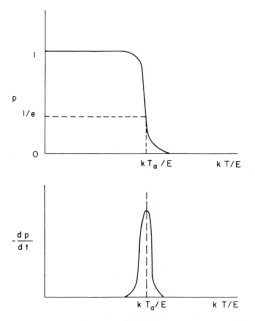

Fig. III–2.3 Schematic sketch of a typical constant rate of heating annealing experiment. The lower curve is proportional to the differential of the upper one.

range in the vicinity of a characteristic annealing temperature, T_a, virtually all the defects responsible for a given annealing stage disappear and dp/dt decreases to zero, as illustrated in Fig. III–2.3. When such an experiment is carried out in discrete steps, i.e., the sample is held for a given time at each annealing temperature, the technique is called isochronal annealing. In this section the continuous process is discussed. The results will be applicable to an isochronal anneal if the temperatures are rather closely spaced. A more detailed analysis of the isochronal anneal is given in the next section.

Suppose the temperature is brought up from absolute zero at a constant rate, so that $T = \alpha t$, where t is the time from the start of the experiment and α is the heating rate. With this relation between time and temperature, the independent variable in equation III–2.1 can be changed from time to temperature to give, in terms of the defect concentration, n,

$$\frac{dn}{F(n)} = -\frac{K_0}{\alpha} e^{-E/kT} dT \cdot \qquad \text{III–2.8}$$

The solution of this equation can be expressed with the aid of the exponential integral

$$Ei(-x) = \int_{-\infty}^{-x} \frac{e^x}{x} dx \cdot \qquad \text{III–2.9}$$

If n_0 is the value of n at $t = 0$, then

$$\int_{n_0}^{n} \frac{dn}{F(n)} = -\frac{K_0 E}{k\alpha} \left[\frac{Tk}{E} e^{-E/kT} + Ei\left(-\frac{E}{kT}\right) \right]. \qquad \text{III–2.10}$$

K_0 is an effective frequency (see II–2) and is very large compared to 1. This means that, for any reasonable time scale, the major portion of the annealing will take place at temperatures much lower than E/k. Thus, in equation III–2.10 one can set

$$E/kT \gg 1 \, ,$$

and use the following approximation to the exponential integral:[6]

$$Ei(-x) \cong e^{-x} (1/x^2 - 1/x) \, , \qquad \text{III–2.11}$$

which is valid for $x \gg 1$. Equation III–2.10 then becomes

$$\int_{n_0}^{n} \frac{dn}{F(n)} = -\frac{K_0 E}{k\alpha} e^{-E/kT} \left(\frac{kT}{E}\right)^2 . \qquad \text{III–2.12}$$

Formally the integral on the left may be taken to give

$$\int_{n_0}^{n} \frac{dn}{F(n)} = h(n) = -\frac{K_0 E}{k\alpha} \left(\frac{kT}{E}\right)^2 e^{-E/kT} . \qquad \text{III–2.13}$$

Let α_1 and α_2 characterize two annealing experiments at these two different heating rates. Then, at identical values of n, $h(n)$ is a constant for these two experiments; since the right-hand side of equation III–2.13 is now equal to a constant, one obtains

$$\ln \left(\frac{\alpha_2 T_1{}^2}{\alpha_1 T_2{}^2} \right) = \frac{E}{k} \left(\frac{1}{T_1} - \frac{1}{T_2} \right) \qquad \text{III–2.14}$$

where T_1 and T_2 are the temperatures at which identical values of n are achieved at heating rates α_1 and α_2, respectively. From this equation E is easily evaluated.

d) Combination of isochronal and isothermal anneal[4]

Let a specimen be annealed isochronally, i.e., at a series of successively higher temperatures, for equal time intervals (the temperature intervals need not necessarily be equal). Let T_i denote the temperature (constant during each pulse) during the ith pulse, n_i the value of n at the end of the ith pulse, and t_i the total elapsed time at the end of the ith pulse. Define Θ as

$$\Theta = te^{-E/kT} . \qquad \text{III–2.15}$$

since the time intervals are equal,

$$\Delta t_i \equiv t_i - t_{i-1} = \text{constant} \equiv C . \qquad \text{III–2.16}$$

From the isochronal annealing curve illustrated in Fig. III–2.4 one can write

$$\Theta_i = t_i e^{-E/kT_i} \qquad \text{at } n = n_i ,$$

$$\Theta_{i-1} = t_{i-1} e^{-E/kT_i} \quad \text{at } n = n_{i-1} ,$$

at the end and the beginning of the ith pulse, respectively. Thus,

$$\Delta\Theta_i = \Delta t_i e^{-E/kT_i}$$

or

$$\ln\Delta\Theta_i = C' - E/kT_i , \qquad \text{III–2.17}$$

where

$$C' = \ln\Delta t_i .$$

Consider now an isothermal curve obtained as a function of the isothermal annealing time τ at a constant temperature T_a as illustrated in Fig. III–2.5. Since according to the basic relation

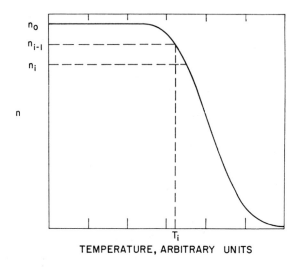

Fig. III–2.4 Combination of isochronal and isothermal anneal. Analysis of the isochronal curve.

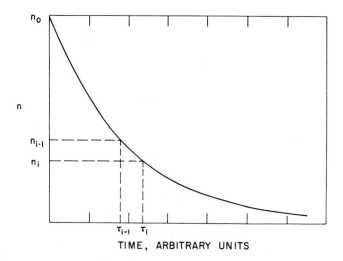

Fig. III–2.5 Combination of isochronal and isothermal anneal. Analysis of the isothermal curve.

(equations III–2.1 and III–2.2) n is a function of Θ only, $\Delta\tau_i$ determined between n_{i-1} and n_i is given by

$$\Delta\tau_i = \Delta\Theta_i e^{E/kT_a} . \qquad \text{III–2.18}$$

By using the data from both types of annealing curves one can eliminate $\Delta\Theta_i$ from equations III–2.17 and III–2.18 to give

$$\ln\Delta\tau_i = C' + C'' - E/kT_i , \qquad \text{III–2.19}$$

and since $C'' = E/kT_a$, therefore

$$\ln\left(\frac{\Delta\tau_i}{\Delta t_i}\right) = \frac{E}{k}\left(\frac{1}{T_a} - \frac{1}{T_i}\right). \qquad \text{III–2.20}$$

According to equation III–2.19 a plot of $\ln\Delta\tau_i$ is linear in $1/T_i$ for a single activated process. The slope of this line is $-E/k$.

In this as well as in the preceding methods, two activated processes governed by two distinct activation energies will yield a varying activation energy with changing n in the regions where the processes overlap, and a constant activation energy with changing n in the region where a single activation process dominates.

3. Chemical Rate Equation

Single activated processes are often governed by a chemical rate equation,

$$dn/dt = - Kn^\gamma \equiv - K_0 n^\gamma e^{-E/kT} , \qquad \text{III–3.1}$$

where γ is the order of the reaction. As shown in Chapter II, random diffusion to a fixed number of sinks corresponds to a first-order reaction, $\gamma = 1$, while random annihilation of equal concentration of vacancies and interstitials is described by a second-order equation, $\gamma = 2$. A knowledge of γ is therefore important in the interpretation of any annealing process. All the methods of activation energy determination described in the previous section are clearly applicable since $F(n)$ is simply replaced by n^γ in equation III–2.1. Some of the methods of determining γ are briefly described in this section.

Equation III–3.1 is easily integrated for $\gamma = 1$ or any other $\gamma \neq 1$. The integrated forms are

$$n/n_0 = e^{-Kt} \qquad \text{for } \gamma = 1 \;,$$

and

$$\frac{1}{n_0{}^{\gamma-1}} - \frac{1}{n^{\gamma-1}} = (1 - \gamma)\,Kt \quad \text{for } \gamma = 1 \;. \qquad \text{III–3.2}$$

From these integrated forms it is apparent that γ cannot be found except by trial and error.

In general it is advantageous to use the differential form, equation III–3.1, for determining γ. By taking logarithms of both sides one finds

$$\ln(-dn/dt) = \ln K + \gamma \ln n \;, \qquad \text{III–3.3}$$

so that the appropriate log-log plot gives the rate constant, K, and the order of the reaction, γ. A check of consistency can be made by determining K from each of several plots of equation III–3.3 for annealing at different temperatures and then calculating the activation energy, E. This value of E must be the same as that obtained by the cross-cut method or by any other method that does not depend on an assumption of the specific kinetic form.

The order of the reaction can be determined from an annealing curve obtained at a constant rate of heating provided the activation energy, E, is known. In the previous section this activation energy was shown to be determinable from two different rates of heating. The differential form of the constant rate of heating curve is given by a modification of III–2.8,

$$-\frac{dn}{dT} = \frac{K_0}{\alpha}\,n^{\gamma}\,e^{-E/kT} \;; \qquad \text{III–3.4}$$

by taking the logarithm,

$$\frac{E}{kT} + \ln\left(-\frac{dn}{dT}\right) = \ln\frac{K_0}{\alpha} + \gamma \ln n \;, \qquad \text{III–3.5}$$

if E and T are known, the left-hand side can be plotted against $\ln n$ with the slope given by γ.

4. Examples of Complications

a) *Variable activation energy*

A single activated rate process may be disturbed by the presence of the annealing defects themselves, i.e., the disturbance is a function of the defect concentration. As an example, the strains arising from the presence of defects in a crystal can alter the activation energy for the migration of the defects. A simple case of this, when the activation energy is proportional to the number of defects, can be treated mathematically.[5] In this case the activation energy, E, can be expressed as

$$E = E_0 - \alpha n$$

where E_0 is the activation energy in the absence of all but one defect, n is the number of defects present, and α is a proportionality constant. The chemical rate equation for the disappearance of n is then

$$dn/dt = - K_0 n^\gamma e^{-E_0/kT} e^{\alpha n/kT} . \qquad \text{III–4.1}$$

Integrating formally gives

$$\int_{n_0}^{n} \frac{e^{-\alpha n/kT}}{n^\gamma} \, dn = - K_0 t e^{-E_0/kT} . \qquad \text{III–4.2}$$

At a fixed value of n one may write

$$t = K' e^{E_0/kT} e^{-\alpha n/kT} , \qquad \text{III–4.3}$$

where K' is a constant for any given value of γ. Thus, a plot of $\ln t$ vs. $1/T$ obtained at a fixed n is linear, just as in the simple case of constant activation energy, but the effective activation energy, $E_0 - \alpha n$, depends on the value of n, i.e., the activation energy determined by, for example, the method of cross-cuts varies systematically with n. Such a variable activation energy can give an apparent order of reaction which is different from the correct γ. This is shown in Fig. III–4.1, in which curves are shown for $\gamma = 2$ and $\gamma = 3$ with a constant and a variable activation energy. Equation III–4.2 can be integrated in terms of the exponential integral[6] for any integer value of γ, and the corresponding curves of Fig. III–4.1 were obtained by numerical computation. It is seen that a variable activation energy which increases with decreasing n has the effect of lengthening the time scale for any given isothermal annealing curve. A rather small variation of E with n leads to a very large change in the time

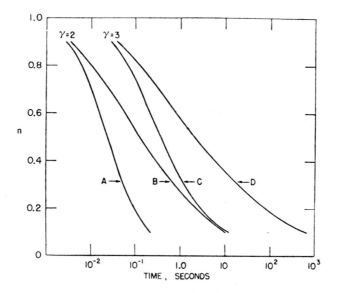

Fig. III–4.1 Comparison of constant and variable activation energy for the decay of n (at 250°C). A and C: $E_0/k = 12{,}500°K$, $\alpha/k = 0$. B and D: $E_0/k = 15{,}000°K$, $\alpha/k = 25{,}000°K$. (From reference 5.)

scale. Fig. III–4.1 also shows that an increase in the order of reaction (from $\gamma = 2$ to $\gamma = 3$ in the figure) has an effect qualitatively similar to that of an E increasing with decreasing n. Computations showed that an annealing curve characterized by a given γ and a variable E can often be fitted by a constant E but a higher and not necessarily integer value of γ.

b) *Unequal initial concentrations of reactants*

Deviations from the simple form of the chemical rate equation, III–3.1, also occur when the reactants are present in unequal initial concentrations. A bimolecular reaction, for example, does not obey a quadratic decay law, i.e., $\gamma = 2$ in equation III–3.1, unless the concentrations of the reactants are equal.

A simple example of the situation is the trapping or annihilation of one defect by another, which may be symbolized as

$$n_1 + n_2 \xrightarrow{K} \text{product} , \qquad \text{III–4.4}$$

where n_1 and n_2 are the atomic fractions of the two defects, K is the rate constant, and the back reaction is assumed to be negligible. If x is the amount reacted, then the differential equation for this process is

$$dx/dt = K(n_1{}^0 - x)(n_2{}^0 - x) , \qquad \text{III–4.5}$$

where $n_1{}^0$ and $n_2{}^0$ are the initial concentrations of the reactants, and at $t = 0$, $x = 0$. This equation is easily integrated, and the result may be expressed in the following form (for $n_1{}^0 = n_2{}^0$ one must start, however, with equation III–3.1):

$$Kt = \frac{1}{n_2{}^0 - n_1{}^0} \ln \left\{ \frac{(n_2{}^0/n_1{}^0) - 1 + (n_1/n_1{}^0)}{(n_2{}^0/n_1{}^0)(n_1/n_1{}^0)} \right\} . \quad \text{III–4.6}$$

A set of normalized decay curves with $K = 1$ are shown in Fig. III–4.2 for a series of initial concentration ratios.[7] If these curves are analyzed for order of reaction on the basis of the simple rate equations III–3.1 and III–3.2, the resulting apparent order of reaction is as shown by the right-hand curve of Fig. III–4.2. This is just the procedure one would use with experimental decay data of $n_1/n_1{}^0$ vs. time. If it were not known from independent information that the reaction under consideration was bimolecular with unequal concentrations, the derived order of reaction would not be interpretable. It should be noted that the apparent order of reaction for $n_1/n_1{}^0$ approaches 1 as $n_2{}^0/n_1{}^0$ becomes large (a well-known concentration effect). Similarly, the apparent order of reaction for $n_2/n_2{}^0$ approaches 1 as γ for $n_1/n_1{}^0$ becomes large (at $n_2{}^0/n_1{}^0 \ll 1$).

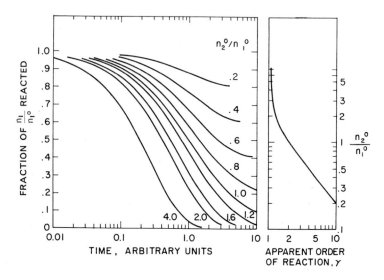

Fig. III–4.2 Bimolecular decay for unequal initial concentration of reactants. (From reference 7.)

c) Distribution of activation energies

If a number of different defects are present and each anneals independently of the others with its own activation energy, then a compound annealing process will be found by the observation of changes in one or a few physical properties. A similar situation arises if one kind of defect, for example the interstitial, is trapped at a variety of sites with a corresponding variety of activation energies for removal. If one studies the change in a physical property characteristic of an interstitial and proportional to its concentration, then for the case of traps with well separated energies separate annealing steps will be observed. If, however, there are a large number of closely spaced trapping energies, a superposition of the individual annealing steps occurs and the result will be a gradual change in the physical property over a large temperature range. In this case the annealing process is best analyzed in terms of a distribution in activation energy with an attempt to describe both the distribution function and the average activation energy. In general, this analysis is exceedingly difficult although some simple cases have been treated and are described in this section.[8,9]

Processes distributed in activation energy are generally treated on the basis of the chemical rate equation, equation III–3.1. A description of the over-all process can be given most simply if it is also assumed that there is a measurable physical property, p, proportional to the concentration of defects, n, although the case of p proportional to a power of n has also been treated. When $p = fn$, where f is a proportionality constant, the basic differential equation III–3.1 can be written as

$$-dp/dt = fK_0(p/f)^\gamma e^{-E/kT} , \qquad\qquad \text{III–4.7}$$

where $\gamma \geqslant 1$. In the case of isothermal annealing this equation can be integrated, analogously to equation III–3.2, to give

$$p = p_0 [1 - (1 - \gamma)Bte^{-E/kT}]^{1/(1-\gamma)} , \qquad\qquad \text{III–4.8}$$

where p_0 is the value of the p at $t = 0$ and

$$B = K_0(f/p_0)^{1-\gamma} .$$

If there is a distribution of activation energies, p and p_0 are functions of E and, by the superposition principle, the measured value of the physical property, P, is given by the integral

$$P(t) = \int_0^\infty p_0(E)\Theta_\gamma(E,t)dE \qquad\qquad \text{III–4.9}$$

where

$$\Theta_\gamma = [1 - (1 - \gamma)Bte^{-E/kT}]^{1/(1-\gamma)}, \qquad\qquad \text{III–4.10}$$

and is called the characteristic isothermal annealing function. It should be kept in mind that Θ_γ is a function of γ and T, and therefore $P(t)$ is also an implicit function of these variables.

If the activation energy distribution is broad, i.e., p_0 is a slowly varying function of E compared to the exponential variation of Θ with E, then the annealing process is dominated by the exponential term (if the distribution of E is narrow the process may be approximated by a process with a constant activation energy). Equation III–4.10 can be solved for E to give

$$E = kT\{\ln\left[(1 - \gamma)B\right] + \ln t - \ln\left[1 - \Theta^{(1-\gamma)}\right]\} . \quad \text{III–4.11}$$

If p_0, and therefore B, is assumed to be constant then as the isothermal annealing progresses the Θ vs. E curve is displaced along E with no change in shape. This curve has an inflection point which may be determined by setting the second derivative of equation III–4.10 equal to zero. The characteristic activation energy, E_0, corresponding to this inflection point is independent of the order of the reaction, γ, and is given by

$$E_0 = kT \ln(Bt) . \quad \text{III–4.12}$$

If the Θ vs. E curve is approximated by a step function passing through E_0, then equation III–4.9 becomes

$$P(t) \cong \int_{E_0}^{\infty} p_0(E)dE \quad \text{III–4.13}$$

and

$$dP/dt \cong - p_0(E_0)\,(dE_0/dt) . \quad \text{III–4.14}$$

Substitution of dE_0/dt from equation III–4.12 gives

$$p_0(E_0) \cong - (t/kT)\,(dP/dt) . \quad \text{III–4.15}$$

The right-hand side is calculable from an experimentally determined P vs. t curve and gives the approximate shape of the initial activation energy spectrum $p_0(E_0)$ but does not fix its location on the activation energy axis because B is not known. Any given isothermal anneal reveals only a portion of the activation energy spectrum. From several isothermal curves obtained at different temperatures, different portions of $p_0(E_0)$ can be derived and fitted together to locate them on the energy axis with the requirement that B is a constant. Detailed methods of accomplishing this analysis from isothermal as well as from isochronal annealing curves are given by Primak.[9]

Some specific distribution functions have also been treated in the literature in connection with a variety of relaxation problems.[10,11] In metals and alloys, for example, the log normal distribution (Gaussian distribution in the logarithm of the relaxation times) has been found to be particularly useful for magnetic and anelastic relaxation, and detailed methods of analysis have been worked out.[12]

References

1. For further details see W. E. Parkins, G. J. Dienes and F. W. Brown, *J. Appl. Phys.* **22**, 1012 (1951).
2. For further details see R. A. Dugdale, *Phil. Mag.* **43**, 912 (1952); A. W. Overhauser, *Phys. Rev.* **90**, 393 (1953).
3. For further details see G. J. Dienes and G. H. Vineyard, *Radiation Effects in Solids*, Chapter 5, Interscience, New York, 1957.
4. C. J. Meechan and J. A. Brinkman, *Phys. Rev.* **103**, 1193 (1956).
5. G. J. Dienes, *Phys. Rev.* **91**, 1283 (1953).
6. E. Jahnke and F. Emde, *Tables of Functions*, Stechert and Co., New York, 1938.
7. F. E. Fujita and A. C. Damask, *Acta Met.* (in press).
8. V. Vand, *Proc. Phys. Soc. (London)* **A55**, 222 (1943).
9. W. Primak, *Phys. Rev.* **100**, 1677 (1955); **101**, 1268 (1952); **103**, 1681 (1956).
10. For a general discussion see B. Gross, *Mathematical Structure of the Theories of Viscoelasticity*, Hermann and Co., Paris, 1953.
11. J. R. MacDonald, *J. Chem. Phys.* **36**, 345 (1962).
12. A. S. Nowick and B. S. Berry, *IBM J. Res. Div.* **5**, 297, 312 (1961); *Acta Met.* **10**, 312 (1962).

CHAPTER FOUR

PHYSICAL PROPERTIES AND POINT DEFECTS

1. Introduction

The basic properties of defects as revealed by theory have been outlined in previous chapters. The next essential step is to devise experimental methods for observing and studying point defects. This can be done in two distinct ways: (1) by direct observation, and (2) by measuring a change in some bulk physical property of the solid that is sensitive to the presence of the defects.

Most of the currently available information is based on the second method, that is, indirect measurement. Many physical properties are sensitive in varying degrees to the presence of point defects, and in fact much of the impetus for research in the field stems from a need to know the relation between physical properties and imperfections in a crystal, since many physical properties are known to be structure sensitive. Conversely, a structure sensitive physical property can be used to investigate the nature, concentration, mobility, and interaction of defects. For example, point defects and the distorted regions around them scatter electrons and neutrons and thus manifest themselves in changes in electrical resistivity and neutron transmission. They also cause changes in density and in lattice parameter and, because of their energy of formation, they raise the heat content of the crystal, i.e., store energy in the solid. Point defects interact with dislocations and thereby cause striking changes in the mechanical properties of a solid. The basic theoretical features of the physical property changes associated with point defects are outlined in this chapter. Comparison with experiment is discussed in Chapter V.

The above indirect method of investigation has a very serious limitation. Point defects occur on an atomic scale, and usually an accurate theory is not available for connecting a given physical property to the detailed atomic arrangement. Direct observation of defects is clearly necessary and desirable but is, because of the atomic dimensions of the defects, difficult to achieve. Excellent techniques have been worked out in the last decade or so for observing relatively large imperfections in crystals such as dislocations, clusters of defects, fission fragment tracks, etc.[1] Transmission electron microscopy of thin films is a very powerful and versatile technique in this category, since it offers high resolution, down to about 10 Å. The individual defects obviously cannot be made visible by this technique, but rather small clusters of defects can be studied.[2-4] Transmission electron microscopy of two superposed thin films can, under certain conditions, give rise to Moiré patterns which are sensitive to the distortions around defects.[1] However, even this slightly more sensitive variation of standard transmission electron microscopy has not been able to reveal the presence of a single point defect. Similarly, chemical and physical etching techniques[1] reveal clearly the presence of dislocation lines, small voids, and disturbed regions but cannot achieve discrimination at the atomic level. One recently developed instrument, the field-ion emission microscope,[5] has a resolution of 2 to 3 Å and is therefore capable of showing individual atoms. However, the instrument can see atoms or defects only on the surface of a crystal. This technique is discussed in the next section.

2. Direct Observation by Field-Ion Microscopy

The field-ion microscope, invented by Müller,[6] is basically a small hemispherically shaped metal tip located in an evacuated chamber which contains a trace of gas, usually helium, and a fluorescent screen a few centimeters away from the specimen tip. This specimen tip is positively charged relative to the screen to a high potential (5000 to 15000 volts). The positively charged metal ions on the surface of the tip are partly exposed because the free electron gas is pulled slightly into the metal by the high field. The image of these ions is carried to the screen by the helium atoms. When one of the helium atoms approaches a surface ion, it becomes a positive helium ion by giving up an electron to the metal. The high potential then accelerates the helium ion, which then produces an image at the point where it strikes the screen. A pattern of bright spots will be seen on the screen, each produced by the helium ions which originate from one ionization center on the surface. These ionization centers will clearly be the most exposed atoms on the surface, such as those on crystal faces of high index and at steps at the edges of crystal planes. Displaced atoms such as interstitials will also serve as strong ionization centers and thereby show up in the form of bright spots. Conversely, lattice vacancies show up as dark spots.

At a sufficiently high voltage, field evaporation occurs, i.e., atoms of the metal itself are pulled off the surface. Field evaporation is high at the edges of steps in crystal planes because the local field in these regions is higher than the average. Layers of atoms can be removed in a controlled manner by evaporating atom chains along the lattice steps where the local field is at its maximum. Thus, defects in the crystal can be revealed by systematic removal of the outer layers.

Müller has shown by this technique that quenched-in vacancies in platinum are indeed visible and that their concentration in the bulk crystal can be determined by the above peeling procedure.[7] Fig. IV–2.1 is an example of a vacancy rendered visible in quenched platinum. In part (a) of the figure an individual vacancy is visible on the (102) plane. In part (b) four atomic layers have been removed by field evaporation at 20°K; the (102) plane is now perfect and there is a new vacancy present on the adjacent (203) plane. In a typical experiment platinum was quenched from 1800°K, and 5 individual vacancies were found within 71 consecutive (102) layers. The total number of atoms in these planes was 8500, giving a vacancy concentration of 5.9×10^{-4} by direct counting, in reasonable agreement with other measurements (see Chapter V).

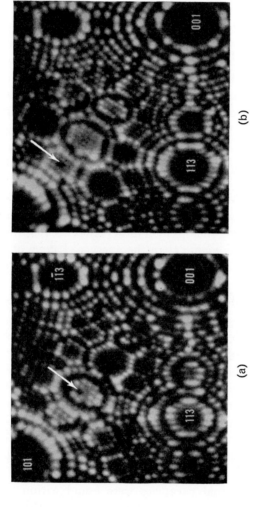

Fig. IV–2.1 (a) Individual vacancy on (102) plane of a platinum crystal. (b) Same crystal after removal of four atomic layers by field evaporation at 20°K. The (102) plane is now perfect. There is a new vacancy in the adjacent (203) plane. (From reference 7.)

Irradiation-produced defects can also be seen by this technique. In some recent work Brandon and Wald[8] irradiated a tungsten tip with 5-MeV α particles. This was done within the microscope so that pictures of the same surface could be examined before and after irradiation. Fig. IV–2.2 shows the tungsten tip (a) before and (b) after the α-particle impact. The atoms that are missing in (b) because they have been knocked out of the surface are marked by dots in (a). Two displaced, or interstitial, atoms are marked in (b).

This powerful technique is unfortunately limited at present to the very strongly bonded refractory metals because only those metals can be studied whose low temperature evaporation field lies above the ionization field of the gas used for ionizing the surface. It should also be borne in mind that the high fields produce high mechanical stresses which the specimen must withstand. Since all observations are of specimens under high stress, distortions around defects cannot be deduced in a reliable way.

3. Neutron Transmission

Neutrons of sufficiently long wavelength are scattered isotropically by isolated point defects.[9] This scattering can be measured in materials of low neutron capture cross section when crystalline effects (Bragg scattering) are absent. Under these circumstances the incident neutrons can be represented by a plane wave, and the neutrons scattered by m defects are described by the radially symmetric scattering wave,

$$\psi = \sum_{j=1}^{m} a_k e^{i(\mathbf{s} \cdot \mathbf{r}_j)} , \qquad \text{IV–3.1}$$

where a_k is the neutron "scattering length" for an atom of the crystal and is positive for interstitials and negative for vacancies, $\mathbf{r}_j$ is the vector distance to the jth atom from an arbitrary origin, and $|\mathbf{s}| = (4\pi \sin \Theta)/\lambda$ (Θ = scattering angle, λ = neutron wavelength).

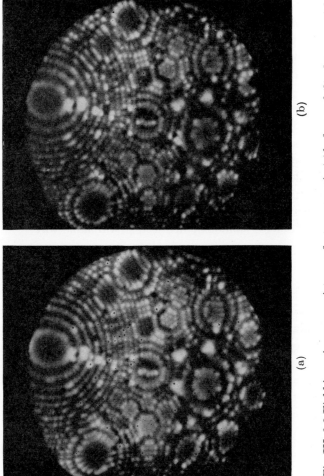

(b)

(a)

Fig. IV–2.2 Field ion microscope pictures of a tungsten tip (a) before and (b) after α-particle bombardment. The atoms marked in (a) are missing in (b) because they have been knocked out by the bombardment. Two interstitial atoms are marked in (b). (From reference 8.)

The differential cross section $\sigma(\Theta)$, which corresponds to intensity in a diffraction pattern, is given by the square of equation IV–3.1,

$$\sigma(\Theta) = \psi\psi^* = \sum_{j,j'}^{m} a_k{}^2 e^{i s \cdot (r_j - r_{j'})} ,\qquad\qquad \text{IV–3.2}$$

where the primes distinguish between scatterers of the same kind. This expression is correct if it is assumed that the defects are randomly arranged and at a sufficient distance from one another that they do not interact while scattering. Upon performing the sum in equation IV–3.2, only when $j = j'$ is there a non-zero result, so that

$$\sigma(\Theta) = \text{ma}^2 .\qquad\qquad \text{IV–3.3}$$

Since a is squared, both vacancies $(-a)$ and interstitial $(+a)$ will scatter similarly. In optical scattering, this is known as Babinet's principle. The cross section per atom is

$$\sigma_d = 4\pi\text{ma}^2/\text{N} = 4\pi\text{a}^2\text{n} ,\qquad\qquad \text{IV–3.4}$$

where n is the atomic fraction of scatterers in the material, and σ_d is the cross section for scattering by defects alone. $4\pi a^2$ is the scattering cross section, σ_b, for the atoms of the crystal, accurately known from other nuclear experiments. Thus, if the scattering from the defects is measurable, an absolute method is at hand for determining their concentration.

It is not practical to measure directly the scattered neutron intensity. Instead, the attenuation of a long-wavelength neutron beam during its passage through the material is measured in a transmission experiment. There are other sources of attenuation which have to be taken into account and whose cross sections should be small compared to that for defect scattering.

In the absence of defects and beyond the last Bragg cutoff $(\lambda > 2d_{max})$, the transmitted intensity, I_s, is given by

$$I_s = I_0 \exp\left[-NX(\sigma_a + \sigma_i + \sigma_{dis})\right] ,\qquad\qquad \text{IV–3.5}$$

where $I_0 =$ incident intensity, $N =$ number of nuclei per cm^3, $X =$ path length traversed through the sample, $\sigma_a =$ cross section for absorption, $\sigma_i =$ cross section for inelastic scattering, and

σ_{dis} = cross section for disorder scattering other than by defects (isotopic, spin, etc.).

For n atomic fraction of defects the transmitted intensity, I_d, is

$$I_d = I_0 \exp\left[-NX(\sigma_a + \sigma_i + \sigma_{\text{dis}} + \sigma_b n)\right] . \qquad \text{IV–3.6}$$

A direct comparison of a crystal containing n defects to a control crystal gives

$$I_d/I_s = \exp\left[-NX\sigma_b n\right] , \qquad \text{IV–3.7}$$

from which n is immediately calculable.

The distortion around the defects has been neglected in this derivation as was the possible clustering of the defects. Both these effects can alter the cross section, σ_d, as well as render it wavelength dependent. In open lattices the distortion correction appears to be rather small.[10] In close-packed metallic crystals, however, the distortions may play a rather important role as indicated by Martin's[11] calculations. The contribution of clusters to the cross section and to the wavelength dependence can also be estimated.[12] These two effects appear to be of about equal importance and it may be rather difficult to separate them since the calculations at present are rather approximate. The neutron transmission technique has been used successfully for measuring defect concentration in graphite,[9] aluminum oxide,[12] quartz,[13] and beryllium oxide.[14] In beryllium oxide, even though it is a close-packed crystal, clustering appears to be far more important than distortion around the defects in imparting wavelength dependence to the scattering. The technique has not yet been used on metals, although it should be applicable to a few metals of low neutron capture cross section such as Be, Mg, Al, Si.

4. Lattice Parameter and Dilatation

If a defect is formed in a perfect crystal, the density of the crystal is changed because the number of lattice sites is altered. When a vacancy is formed, an atom is taken from the interior to the surface of the crystal, and the volume of the crystal is thereby increased by one atomic volume with a corresponding decrease in the density. An analogous argument shows that the opposite happens for an interstitial. These simple arguments give the correct change in density if there is no atomic relaxation around the defect. Under these circumstances the atomic distances are not altered and therefore the lattice parameter of the crystal is not changed.

It was shown in Chapter I that relaxation around defects does occur. The region of relaxation can be considered a point source of pressure within the crystal resulting in a distortion of the entire crystal out to the surface. Eshelby[15] has carried out a general analysis of this problem, treating the crystal as a homogeneous isotropic elastic continuum. He showed that a center of pressure, such as that arising from a point defect, gives a change in lattice parameter which corresponds exactly to the volume expansion produced by the relaxation around the defect. Thus, if V_x is the volume change produced by the strains of one defect, then the change in lattice parameter is given by

$$\frac{\Delta a}{a} = \frac{1}{3} \frac{V_x}{V_0} n , \qquad \text{IV-4.1}$$

where n is the atomic fraction of defects, and V_0 is the atomic volume of the perfect crystal. The volume per atom of the crystal, V, is given by

$$V = V_0 (1 \pm n) + V_x n , \qquad \text{IV-4.2}$$

where the plus sign applies to vacancies and the minus sign to interstitials. The change in volume, ΔV, is given by

$$\Delta V = \pm V_0 n + V_x n = \pm V_0 n + 3 V_0 \Delta a / a , \qquad \text{IV-4.3}$$

and, since for small strains

$$\Delta V / V_0 = 3 \Delta L / L ,$$

one finds that

$$n = \pm 3 \left(\frac{\Delta L}{L} - \frac{\Delta a}{a} \right) . \qquad \text{IV-4.4}$$

Thus a method is available for the measurement of the concentration of defects by a comparison of x-ray parameter change with dilatation measured either by a change in hydrostatic volume or by linear macroscopic expansion. It should be noted that the derivation of equation IV–4.4 depends only on the validity of equation IV–4.1 and not on any knowledge of V_x itself.

V_x itself has been calculated by Eshelby for an isotropic medium on the basis of linear elasticity theory. The displacement, δ, of an atom at a distance r from a center of pressure is radial and of magnitude

$$\delta = c/r^2 \qquad\qquad \text{IV–4.5}$$

where c is a constant characterizing the strength of the center of pressure. This equation is valid only at distances greater than several atomic distances away from the center of the imperfection. Eshelby has shown that if equation IV–4.5 is valid then V_x is given by the expression

$$V_x = 12\pi \frac{(1 - \sigma)}{(1 + \sigma)} cn\,, \qquad\qquad \text{IV–4.6}$$

where σ is Poisson's ratio. The actual value of c depends, of course, on the distortions in the immediate neighborhood of the defect and also on just how and at what point an elastic solution is matched to the local distortions and is therefore difficult to calculate exactly.[16–19]

5. Stored Energy

When defects are present in a crystal at a concentration higher than that corresponding to the thermodynamic equilibrium number, the heat content (enthalpy) is increased by an amount referred to as the stored energy. The stored energy is the number of defects times the enthalpy of formation for each defect. (The enthalpy of formation is frequently used interchangeably with the energy of formation because they are equal at zero pressure). The stored energy can be measured by a variety of methods. The measurement must be made by measuring the heat released when a crystal, containing defects in excess of the thermodynamic concentration at a given temperature, is annealed at the same temperature to a state in which it contains only the thermodynamic equilibrium concentration of defects. Any intermediate observation may be affected by clustering, trapping, or other association of defects, all of which alter the heat content of the crystal. The best type of measurement, therefore, is one which ensures that all defects in excess of thermodynamic equilibrium are completely gone, as, for example, in burning or solution experiments. Since in many experiments, such as radiation damage or cold work, more than one species of point defect is present, it is often desirable to obtain intermediate annealing stages of stored energy and to attempt to relate them to the disappearance of individual defects. The intermediate stages of energy release obtained in this manner cannot be precisely related to the number of defects times the formation energy because no experimental reference state exists to which the stored energy can be corrected. Thus, although characteristic annealing curves of stored energy of several defects are informative, the energies of formation thus obtained are not completely reliable.

6. Electrical Resistivity

The electrical resistivity of pure metals is increased by the introduction of impurities and defects into the lattice.[20] The change in resistance is mainly due to an increase in the residual resistivity of the metal, although some changes in the thermal component of the resistivity have been observed.[21] The residual resistivity is very sensitive to the presence of imperfections because any disturbance of the ideally periodic lattice results in scattering of the conduction electrons and hence an increase in the electrical resistance. At low defect concentrations one expects the increase in the residual resistivity to be proportional to the concentration of defects, since the interference among the various defects can be neglected. The change in the residual resistivity is therefore an appropriate and convenient measure of the defect concentration in metals. The change in the thermal component of the resistance depends upon the change in the vibrational spectrum in the solid caused by the presence of the defect. Since the defect contribution to the thermal component is poorly known (although known to be small) and is difficult to estimate theoretically, measurements are usually made at a sufficiently low temperature to avoid the problem.

The contribution of point defects to residual resistivity depends on the type of defect and on the kind of metal. The effectiveness of point defects in raising the resistivity has been estimated for some metals by several authors. The general method and the results are reviewed in this section.

The extra residual resistivity due to point defects is, following Mott and Jones,[22] given by

$$\Delta\rho_\infty = \frac{mvnA}{n_e e^2} \; ; \quad A = \int(1 - \cos\Theta)\, I(\Theta)\, d\omega \, , \qquad \text{IV–6.1}$$

where m is the electronic mass, v the velocity of the electrons at the top of the Fermi distribution, n_e the number of free electrons per atom, e the electronic charge, n the atomic fraction of defects, A the effective scattering area, and $I(\Theta)$ the intensity of the scattered wave in direction Θ. The theoretical determination of the resistivity involves the calculation of A, which can be determined from scattering theory[23] with the result that for free electron scattering

$$A = \frac{4\pi}{k^2} \sum_l (l + 1) \sin^2 (\alpha_l - \alpha_{l+1}) \, , \qquad \text{IV–6.2}$$

where k is the wave number at the Fermi level and is given by $k = 2mv/\hbar$, and α_l is the phase shift of order l evaluated from the asymptotic solution of the wave equation. A variety of scattering potentials may be used for the defects but, as shown by Friedel,[24] the phase shifts of the plane wave representing the wave function of the electron and the charge, Z, required to screen the potential of the defect are related by the equation

$$Z = \frac{2}{\pi} \sum_l (2l + 1)\, \alpha_l \, . \qquad \text{IV–6.3}$$

Phase shifts calculated for any particular potential must therefore obey the Friedel sum rule.

Except for Abeles,[25] who used a square barrier potential, most calculations have been made with a screened Coulomb potential adjusted to the Friedel sum rule. In Dexter's[26] early calculation the potential was not checked by the Friedel sum rule. The parameters of the screened potential were selected by various authors in slightly different ways. In addition, Dexter[26] and Jongenburger[27] allowed atoms around the vacancy to relax and showed that only a small correction resulted from this atomic relaxation. Roth[28] chose a slightly different potential and formulated the problem in terms of Bloch functions instead of free electron functions. Table IV–6.1 shows that in the noble metals all the calculations for vacancy contribution to the resistivity agree within about a factor of 3.

Reale[29] has used the above theoretical procedure for multivalent metals in which the free electron model is, in general, not applicable, by simply introducing the effective mass of the electrons obtained from specific heat data.

Atomic relaxation is known to be far more extensive around an interstitial compared to a vacancy, and plays a correspondingly more important role in the contribution to residual resistivity. Various authors have treated the relaxation problem in different ways, and, as shown in Table IV–6.1, arrived at contributions to residual resistivity that differ rather widely. The disagreement comes mainly from the treatment of the relaxation, since general agreement is obtained for the scattering of the interstitial ion alone. All interstitial calculations have been made for the body-centered configuration, not the split one.

The resistivity of clusters of vacancies has been calculated by similar methods.[30–32] The results are usually expressed in terms of the resistivity increment per vacancy in the cluster. Within the accuracy of the calculations the divacancy contribution has not been shown to differ from that of two isolated vacancies. As the size of the cluster is increased, the contribution per vacancy decreases slowly but steadily as shown in Fig. IV–6.1 (see page 177).

TABLE IV–6.1

The Residual Resistivity of Vacancies and Interstitials in
Several Metals

Metal	Resistivity, $\mu\Omega$–cm/atom %	Reference
Vacancy		
Copper	0.4	Dexter[26]
,,	1.3	Jongenburger[27]
,,	1.3	Abeles[25]
,,	1.5	Blatt[33]
,,	1.5	Overhauser and Gorman[34]
,,	1.7	Seeger[35]
,,	0.6	Roth[28]
Silver	0.4	Dexter[26]
,,	1.5	Jongenburger[27]
,,	1.5	Abeles[25]
Gold	0.4	Dexter[26]
,,	1.5	Jongenburger[27]
,,	1.5	Abeles[25]
Nickel	4.0	Seeger[35]
Aluminum	3.4	Reale[29]
Beryllium	0.7	,,
Magnesium	2.8	,,
Zinc	1.4	,,
Tin	3.3	,,
Lead	5.9	,,
Interstitial		
Copper	0.6	Dexter[26]
,,	5.0	Jongenburger[27]
,,	1.3	Blatt[33]
,,	10.5	Overhauser and Gorman[34]
Silver	0.6	Dexter[26]
Gold	0.6	,,

Keller[36] recently carried out a calculation to estimate the change in resistivity that can be expected when a vacancy moves from an isolated position in a lattice to a position of nearest neighbor to a substitutional impurity. If ρ_{pair} is the resistivity of the vacancy and impurity in nearest-neighbor positions, and ρ_{imp} and ρ_{vac} are the resistivities of the isolated impurity and

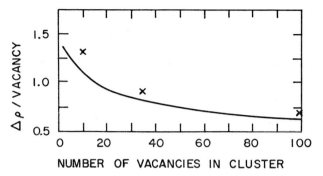

Fig. IV–6.1 Change of resistivity per vacancy, in units of $\mu\Omega$–cm per atomic fraction, as a function of cluster size. Solid line: calculation of Asdente and Friedel.[31] Crosses: calculation of Dexter.[30]

vacancy, respectively, then the result for silver impurities in gold is

$$\rho_{\text{pair}} = \rho_{\text{vac}} + \rho_{\text{imp}} - 0.1 \; \rho_{\text{vac}} \; (\rho_{\text{vac}} \; \rho_{\text{imp}})^{1/2} \, ,$$

and for zinc in gold it is

$$\rho_{\text{pair}} = \rho_{\text{vac}} + \rho_{\text{imp}} + 0.1 \; (\rho_{\text{vac}} \; \rho_{\text{imp}})^{1/2} \, .$$

Since this calculation was done with use of the Born approximation and without use of lattice relaxation effects or the Friedel sum rule, the results are only approximate.

7. Mechanical Properties

The mechanical properties of metals are influenced in varying degrees by the presence of point defects.[37–39] A variety of measurements have been used to study these effects, which range all the way from changes in the elastic moduli to changes in brittleness, i.e., from the smallest possible measurable strain to mechanical failure. This wide range of conditions can be illustrated, as in Fig. IV–7.1, by a schematic stress-strain curve. At small strains the elastic moduli and small amplitude internal friction are the characteristic mechanical properties. As the strain is increased the specimen often exhibits a yield point followed by a hardening region and eventual fracture. In this section the theories of the relations between the above mechanical properties and point defects are discussed. It should be noted that many of the ideas involved in these treatments were originally developed for interpreting the influence of impurity atoms, solutes, and precipitation nuclei on the mechanical properties. Many of the results were found to be quite directly adaptable to the explanation of the effects of point defects on the mechanical properties.

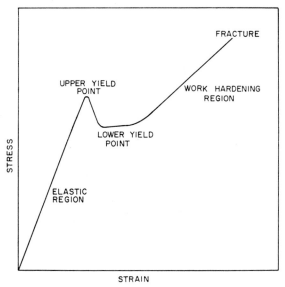

Fig. IV–7.1 Schematic stress-strain curve for a typical metal, illustrating important mechanical phenomena.

a) Elastic modulus

The presence of point defects can alter the elastic moduli in two distinct ways, namely, the direct effect of the change in the number of interatomic bonds associated with the defect and the indirect effect of the defect on the motion of dislocations.

The direct effect[40–42] of vacancies and interstitials has been estimated for simple close-packed metals. In these crystals the elastic constants are determined primarily by the essentially exponential repulsive interactions of the closed ion shells. The creation of a vacancy results in the destruction of some normal interactions, i.e., the breaking of metallic bonds. This loss of interaction energy decreases the moduli by a bulk effect, that is, the fractional decrease in modulus is approximately equal to the fractional concentration of vacancies. When interstitials are introduced into the crystal, extra interactions are introduced at a distance shorter than nearest neighbor. These strong interactions lead to an increase in the modulus of the order of 5 to 10% per one percent interstitials,[40] an effect much larger than that due to vacancies. Relaxation of nearest neighbors was included in this calculation.

The reversible motion of dislocations under an applied stress contributes a reversible plastic strain component to the total strain. As has been indicated in I–13, defects can interact with dislocations and thereby pin them. When dislocation pinning occurs, the dislocations contribute a reduced reversible plastic strain component because their motion is restricted. Consequently, the elastic moduli are increased by the pinning of dislocations. The currently accepted presentation of the theory of the above effect is that of Granato and Lücke,[43] based on the earlier works of Friedel,[44] Koehler,[45] and Thompson and Holmes.[46] In this model it is assumed that a pure single crystal contains a network of dislocations. Segments of dislocations of length L_n connect the immobile node points of the network. These segments are pinned along their length by a random distribution of point defects or impurities. The distance between the pinning points is designated by the characteristic length L_c. Under a relatively small stress the dislocation segments bow out in a reversible way. The contribution of this motion to the effective modulus can be calculated by balancing the applied stress by the line tension of the dislocation. The calculation was performed by using the differential equation for the motion of a string, and the Poisson distribution was taken for the loop length between pinning points. The resulting modulus change is given by the relation

$$\Delta G/G = K\Lambda L^2 , \qquad\qquad \text{IV–7.1}$$

N

where Λ is the dislocation density, L is the average loop length, and K is a constant. This formula is applicable to static experiments and to dynamic experiments in which the experimental frequency is much below the resonant frequency of the dislocation loop.

b) Internal friction

Internal friction is the capacity of a vibrating solid to convert its mechanical energy of vibration into heat. The most common manifestation of internal friction is the loss of vibration amplitude, or the damping of a freely vibrating body. A metal crystal contains many sources of internal friction. Two mechanisms are of particular importance for studying point defects, namely, the oscillatory motion of dislocation segments between pinning points and the actual motion of a point defect in such a direction as to relieve an applied stress.

Under an alternating stress the dislocation segments between two pinning points execute a damped oscillation similar to that of a vibrating string. At low frequencies the damping is small because the dislocation segments move almost in phase with the applied stress. At very high frequencies the damping is also small because the segments are unable to follow the applied stress. Damping is very high at some intermediate frequency in the neighborhood of the resonant frequency. Thus, if the internal friction is observed as a function of frequency, a maximum occurs at the resonant frequency. The same basic differential equation that led to the modulus change of equation IV–7.1 can be solved for the damped oscillatory response. Damping is usually expressed as the decrement Δ, defined as the fractional decrease in vibrational energy per cycle, i.e.,

$$\Delta = \Delta W/W , \qquad\qquad IV–7.2$$

where W is the total vibrational energy of the specimen. Granato and Lücke[43] have obtained theoretical curves for the internal friction as a function of frequency for several loop length distributions. The resonant frequency for the vibration of dislocation

loop segments in metals occurs at such a high frequency that it is
not readily accessible for measurement (the order of hundreds of
megacycles per second). A most useful analytical approximation
was obtained, however, for frequencies well below the maximum
in the form

$$\Delta = K' \Lambda L^4 \omega^2 \,, \qquad\qquad\qquad \text{IV--7.3}$$

where ω is the frequency of the vibration and K' is a constant.

It is clear from the preceding discussion that the internal friction arises from the motion of the dislocations in such a direction
as to relieve the applied external stress. This is the general response of a system to an applied stress, a direct application of the
principle of Le Chatelier. Any point defect that produces an internal strain different from the symmetry of the crystal can give rise
to internal friction. A single vacancy obviously cannot cause
internal friction since it always has the symmetry of the crystal
and there are no preferential positions to which it could move to
relieve an applied stress. Defects which can cause internal friction
because of their anisotropic strain field are, for example, the
divacancy, the split interstitial, and interstitial impurity atoms in
body-centered cubic crystals.

The mechanical behavior of solids exhibiting internal friction
that is amplitude independent (at very small vibration amplitudes)
can be described by the equations of a standard linear solid.[47,48]
The standard linear solid is characterized by a linear relation
between the stress, strain, and their first time derivatives, that is,

$$\sigma + \tau_\epsilon \dot{\sigma} = M_R \left(\epsilon + \tau_\sigma \dot{\epsilon} \right) , \qquad\qquad \text{IV--7.4}$$

where τ_ϵ is the time of relaxation of stress at constant strain, τ
is the time of relaxation of strain at constant stress, and M_R is
the relaxed elastic modulus. For periodic stress and strain of
angular frequency ω, the tangent of the phase angle δ, i.e., the
angle by which strain lags behind stress, is given by

$$\tan \delta = \frac{M_U - M_R}{M} \frac{\omega\tau}{1 + (\omega\tau)^2} \,, \qquad\qquad \text{IV--7.5}$$

where the average time of relaxation is $\tau = (\tau_\sigma \tau_\epsilon)^{1/2}$; the average modulus is $M = (M_R M_U)^{1/2}$; and M_U, the unrelaxed modulus, is the modulus at infinite frequency. For small δ,

$$\tan \delta \; = \frac{1}{2\pi} \frac{\Delta W}{W} = \frac{\Delta}{2\pi} \, ,$$

where Δ is the measure of internal friction given in equation IV–7.2.[47] Tan δ is a maximum when $\omega\tau = 1$ with the peak value equal to $\frac{1}{2}\Delta_M$, where

$$\Delta_M = \frac{M_U - M_R}{M} \, , \qquad\qquad \text{IV–7.6}$$

and is called the relaxation strength. It can also be shown[47] that the two relaxation times, τ_σ and τ_ϵ, are related by the equation $\tau_\sigma/\tau_\epsilon = M_U/M_R$. In the cases under consideration here the relaxation strength Δ_M is small and, therefore, M_U and M_R differ by a few percent only. Consequently, $\tau_\sigma \cong \tau_\epsilon \cong \tau$, i.e., very closely the same relaxation time is measured in different mechanical experiments, such as internal friction and mechanical aftereffect.

The simplest example of a successful application of this theory to point defects is the migration of interstitial carbon in iron under an applied stress.[49] Consider a crystal of α-iron (body-centered cubic) which contains a low concentration of interstitial carbon atoms in solution. The interstitial positions, namely the centers of the faces or edges, have tetragonal symmetry. In a stress-free crystal the interstitial atoms are distributed isotropically, but in the presence of stress the equilibrium distribution is no longer isotropic. For example, a tensile stress along the (100) axis will induce a preferential distribution in which each interstitial atom has a greater probability of being in an interstitial position whose tetragonal axis is along the (100) axis than along either of the other two [100] directions. The continual striving of the metal to maintain an equilibrium distribution will give rise to time dependent mechanical responses. A detailed analysis[49] shows that the relaxation strength Δ_M is proportional to the concentration of carbon atoms in interstitial positions and that its magnitude can be estimated from the strain produced by the interstitial atoms. It has also been shown[50,51] that the τ value of equation IV–7.5

is proportional to the mean time of stay of a carbon atom in its interstitial position and is therefore also proportional to the reciprocal of the diffusion coefficient of carbon in iron. Thus, τ is governed by the activation energy for interstitial migration and can be used to measure this quantity experimentally. This treatment is clearly applicable to any point defect which produces an anisotropic strain.

In the above discussion the interstitial atoms were assumed to be distributed at random in the absence of an applied stress. Upon the application of a stress they moved into a preferential or ordered array. This idea of stress-induced ordering can be extended to systems, such as substitutional solid solutions, in which a state of order exists even in the absence of stress.[52,53] Application of stress in this case will alter the state of order. The time required to achieve the new equilibrium state is proportional to the number of vacancies present and to the mean rate of vacancy jumping, of course, with the assumption that the mechanism of atom migration in the substitutional solid is by means of vacancies. Since the internal friction in this case is proportional to the number of vacancies present, it can be used to measure the lifetime of an excess number of vacancies and thereby their migration energy.*

c) Hardening

As already indicated (I–13), there is a strong interaction between point defects and dislocations. The presence of point defects can therefore alter the motion of dislocations and thereby cause changes in yield stress and hardening of the crystal. Two types of

---

* Another manifestation of the reorientation of anisotropic defects is a change in magnetic susceptibility.[54,55] The measurements are made under low field conditions so that the susceptibility can be determined by the ease of motion of the Bloch walls. Because of the stabilization of the Bloch walls that accompanies defect alignment, the wall mobility and hence the susceptibility is decreased. This is often described as disaccommodation of permeability, and the general phenomenon is referred to as magnetic aftereffect. Thus magnetic aftereffect measurements are selectively sensitive to the presence of anisotropic defects and offer also the possibility of determining the symmetry axis of the defect.[56,57]

defect distributions play important roles in impeding the motion of dislocations, namely, (a) defects aggregated on the dislocations, and (b) defects dispersed in the lattice. In order for case (a) to arise, the defects must have been mobile at some time after their creation to migrate to the dislocations.

The segregation of point defects or solute atoms around the dislocation can be characterized by two types of distributions.[58] The first is a Maxwellian distribution

$$n = n_0 \exp(U/kT) , \qquad\qquad \text{IV–7.7}$$

where n_0 is the over-all defect concentration and n is the concentration in a region around the dislocation with binding energy U. This formula is valid for small values of n and breaks down when there is appreciable interaction among the defects themselves. As the temperature is lowered n increases rapidly, and below a critical temperature the defects will form a condensed line along the dislocation at the position of maximum binding. The critical temperature, T_c, is related to the maximum binding energy, U_{max}, and to the defect concentration by the equation

$$T_c = \frac{U_{max}}{k \ln (1/n_0)} . \qquad\qquad \text{IV–7.8}$$

Rough theoretical estimates have been made of the stress needed to pull a dislocation away from the defect atmosphere in each of these two regions. Above T_c, in the region of the dilute atmosphere, the critical stress for breakaway is given by the expression

$$\sigma_c = 17 A n_0 N/a , \qquad\qquad \text{IV–7.9}$$

where N is the number of atoms per unit volume; a is the atomic spacing; and A is the constant in the defect dislocation interaction energy, $U = A \sin \alpha/R$, and depends on the elastic properties of the material, on the strain around the defect, and on the strength of the dislocation. Below T_c, where condensation has occurred, the critical shear stress is given by

$$\sigma_c = A/a^2 R_0^2 , \qquad\qquad \text{IV–7.10}$$

where R_0 is the distance to the atom which lies immediately below the half-plane of the dislocation.

The above theoretical ideas were originally devised to account for the development of a yield point and the increase in critical shear stress when impurity atoms are segregated at dislocations. To produce plastic flow in such cases the applied force must exceed the anchoring force calculated above. Since it generally takes a smaller force to keep a dislocation in motion than to detach it from its impurity atmosphere, a yield point, with a typical yield drop, is sometimes observable.

Some difficulties arise in applying these ideas directly to single point defects because, as indicated in I–13, it is not clear in just what configuration the point defects enter the core of a dislocation. One theory[59,60] suggests that the point defects are actually annihilated at the dislocation producing jogs, and it is the jog itself that interferes with the gliding motion of a dislocation. Another suggestion[61] is that vacancies gather at the center of a dislocation and are not annihilated but form voids with radii of about 10^{-7} to 10^{-6} cm on the dislocation line. The dislocation is anchored by a string of such voids along the dislocation line.

Defects dispersed in the lattice can also interfere with the motion of dislocations. These dispersed defects may be present as isolated point defects or small clusters. In the first case the dislocations are held up in a manner akin to the theory of alloy hardening,[62] that is, the stress fields of the defects impede the motion of dislocations. The stable clusters of defects constitute obstacles in the slip planes which the dislocations can pass only with difficulty. The action of these clusters is similar to that of small precipitate particles, which has also been treated theoretically.[63] The most recent development in the theory of obstacle hardening is that given by Seeger,[64] who developed it specifically for clusters of defects to explain radiation hardening effects. In this theory, each obstacle is assumed to be a potential energy barrier for dislocations, having a width $2X_0$ and a height U_0. Under an applied stress, σ, the effective height of the barrier is lowered, and at sufficiently high stresses is reduced to zero. The rate of plastic deformation is proportional to the rate at which a dislocation gathers enough energy to surmount the barrier, and this depends exponentially on the barrier height divided by the temperature. The stress required to maintain any particular rate of deformation at a particular temperature can be found from this rate expression, once the dependence of barrier height on stress has been found. The resulting stress varies essentially logarithmically with the rate of deformation, and thus effectively defines a critical stress for any nominal rate of deformation. Seeger assumes a particular barrier profile and works out the case in which the stress is just large enough to reduce the effective barrier height to zero. Assuming also that, because a pinned dislocation line bows out under stress, the distance between obstacles is effectively reduced by stress, he finds that the critical shear stress, σ_c, depends on temperature in the following way:

$$\sigma_c = (A - BT^{2/3})^{3/2} , \qquad \text{IV–7.11}$$

where A and B are given by

$$A = \left(\frac{N_z}{Gb}\right)^{1/3} \frac{U_0}{4X_0b} , \qquad \text{IV–7.12}$$

$$B = A\left[\frac{k}{U_0}\ln\left(\frac{lb\nu}{N_z\dot{\epsilon}}\right)\right]^{2/3} . \qquad \text{IV–7.13}$$

Here N_z is the number of obstacles per unit area of the glide plane, l is the total length of dislocations per unit volume, G is the shear modulus, k is Boltzmann's constant, ν is the effective vibrational frequency of a dislocation as it tries to surmount an obstacle, $\dot{\epsilon}$ is the strain rate, and b is the magnitude of the Burgers' vector.

For polycrystalline metals there is a useful empirical relation[65,66] between the lower yield stress, σ_y, and the grain diameter, $2d$, of the form

$$\sigma_y = \sigma_i + K_y d^{-1/2} , \qquad \text{IV–7.14}$$

σ_y being the stress at which plastic deformation propagates as a Luders band. Some success has been achieved in interpreting equation IV–7.14 on the basis of a dislocation model for this propagation in which piled up dislocations at the boundaries of yielded grains trigger the operation of dislocation sources in adjacent unyielded grains.[67] In this model σ_i is a lattice friction stress which opposes the movement of dislocations on their glide planes, and K_y is a measure of the stress required to free a dislocation from its atmosphere of impurity atoms. Because of the strong interaction between point defects and dislocations it is expected that both σ_i and K_y will be affected by the presence of point defects. These two characteristic quantities can also be used to arrive at a criterion for the transition from ductile to brittle fracture, a phenomenon of particular importance in the body-centered cubic metals. It has been shown[67] that the equation

$$(\sigma_i d^{1/2} + K_y)K_y = \beta M \gamma \qquad \text{IV–7.15}$$

is satisfied at the transition temperature. In this equation β is a constant near unity, M is the rigidity modulus, and γ is the effective surface energy for fracture. This relation has recently been modified[68] on the basis of the idea that for brittle fracture the upper yield stress should be greater than the crack propagation stress. In this case the following relation is satisfied at the brittle-ductile transition temperature:

$$\sigma_i + K_y d^{-1/2} + \Delta\sigma = (E\gamma/2\pi d)^{1/2}\,, \qquad \text{IV–7.16}$$

where $\Delta\sigma$ is the magnitude of the yield drop and E is Young's modulus. Thus it may be expected that the temperature of the brittle-ductile transition can be significantly altered by the presence of both clustered and dispersed point defects.

It has been suggested that hardening produced by fatigue deformation is different from work hardening and may be more akin to radiation hardening, which would indicate that point defects may play an important role in the fatigue process.[38] It has been observed, for example, that the energy stored in fatigue-hardened copper is released below the recrystallization temperature,[69] and that fatigue hardening may be partly annealed at temperatures at which there is no annealing of work hardening.[70] It has also been shown that, as in the case of irradiated metals, the critical shear stress of copper upon fatigue hardening becomes a sensitive function of the temperature.[71] It has also been suggested, mainly on the basis of precipitation and softening effects produced by fatigue deformation, that cyclic plastic deformation may be a very effective method of point defect production.[71,72]

References

1. See, for example, *Direct Observations of Imperfections in Crystals*, J. B. Newkirk and J. H. Wernick, Editors, Interscience, New York, 1962.
2. P. B. Hirsch, J. Silcox, R. E. Smallman and K. H. Westmacott, *Phil. Mag.* **3**, 897 (1958).
3. H. G. F. Wilsdorf, *Phys. Rev. Letters* **3**, 172 (1959).
4. I. G. Greenfield and H. G. F. Wilsdorf, *J. Phys. Soc. Japan* **18**, Suppl. III (*Intern. Conf. on Crystal Lattice Defects*) 20 (1963).
5. E. W. Müller, in *Advances in Electronics and Electron Physics*, L. Marton, Editor, Vol. XIII, pp. 83–177, Academic Press, New York, 1960.
6. E. W. Müller, *Z. Physik* **131**, 136 (1951).
7. E. W. Müller, reference 1, p. 85.
8. D. G. Brandon and M. Wald, *Phil. Mag.* **6**, 1035 (1961).
9. J. J. Antal, R. J. Weiss and G. J. Dienes, *Phys. Rev.* **99**, 1081 (1955); see also *Proceedings of the Conferences on Carbon*, University of Buffalo, 1956, pp. 137–41.
10. G. J. Dienes and G. H. Vineyard, *Radiation Effects in Solids*, pp. 72–3, Interscience, New York, 1957.
11. D. G. Martin, *Phil. Mag.* **5**, 1235 (1960).
12. J. J. Antal and A. N. Goland, *Phys. Rev.* **112**, 103 (1958).
13. E. W. J. Mitchell and P. T. Wedepogl, *Phil. Mag.* **3**, 1280 (1958).
14. T. M. Sabine, A. W. Pryor and B. S. Hickman, *Nature* **191**, 1385 (1961); *Phil. Mag.* **6**, 190 (1962).
15. J. D. Eshelby, in *Solid State Physics*, F. Seitz and D. Turnbull, Editors, Vol. 3, pp. 79–107 (particularly Section 8), Academic Press, New York, 1956.
16. C. W. Tucker and J. B. Sampson, *Acta. Met.* **2**, 433 (1954).
17. H. B. Huntington, *Acta. Met.* **2**, 554 (1954).
18. R. W. Balluffi and R. O. Simmons, *J. Appl. Phys.* **31**, 2284 (1960).
19. R. O. Simmons and R. W. Balluffi, *Phys. Rev.* **117**, 52 (1960).
20. For general reviews see: G. J. Dienes and G. H. Vineyard, *Radiation Effects in Solids*, Chapter 3, Interscience, New York, 1957; F. J. Blatt, in *Solid State Physics*, F. Seitz and D. Turnbull, Editors, Vol. IV, pp. 200–357, Academic Press, New York, 1957; T. Broom and R. K. Ham, in *Vacancies and Other Point Defects in Metals and Alloys*, pp. 41–79, Institute of Metals, London, 1958; W. M. Lomer, in *Progress in Metal Physics*, Vol. 8, pp. 255–321, Pergamon, London, 1959; J. Friedel, in *Low Temperature Physics*, C. De Witt et al., Editors, pp. 551–638, Gordon and Breach, New York, 1962.
21. D. Brown and G. W. Rodeback, *Acta. Met.* **1**, 649 (1953).

22. N. F. Mott and H. Jones, *Theory of the Properties of Metals and Alloys*, pp. 263–89, Dover Publications, New York, 1958.
23. See, for example, N. F. Mott and H. S. W. Massey, *The Theory of Atomic Collisions*, Chapter II, Oxford University Press, Oxford, 1959.
24. J. Friedel, *Phil. Mag.* **43**, 153 (1952).
25. F. Abeles, *Compt. Rend.* **237**, 796 (1953).
26. D. L. Dexter, *Phys. Rev.* **87**, 768 (1952).
27. P. Jongenburger, *Phys. Rev.* **90**, 710 (1953); *Appl. Sci. Res.* **B3**, 237 (1953); *Nature* **175**, 545 (1955).
28. L. Roth, Thesis, Harvard University, 1956.
29. C. Reale, *Physics Letters* **2**, 268 (1962).
30. D. L. Dexter, *Phys. Rev.* **103**, 107 (1956).
31. M. Asdente and J. Friedel, *J. Phys. Chem. Solids* **11**, 115 (1959).
32. A. Seeger and H. Bross, *J. Phys. Chem. Solids* **6**, 324 (1958).
33. F. J. Blatt, *Phys. Rev.* **99**, 1708 (1955); **100**, 666 (1955).
34. A. W. Overhauser and R. L. Gorman, *Phys. Rev.* **102**, 676 (1956).
35. A. Seeger, *Z. Physik* **144**, 637 (1956).
36. J. M. Keller, *J. Phys. Chem. Solids* (in press); see also C. P. Flynn, *J. Phys. Radium* **23**, 654 (1962).
37. A. H. Cottrell, *Dislocations and Plastic Flow in Crystals*, Oxford University Press, Oxford, 1953.
38. A. H. Cottrell in *Vacancies and Other Point Defects in Metals and Alloys*, pp. 1–40, Institute of Metals, London, 1958.
39. J. Friedel, *Les Dislocations*, Gauthier-Villars, Paris, 1956.
40. G. J. Dienes, *Phys. Rev.* **86**, 228 (1952).
41. F. R. N. Nabarro, *Phys. Rev.* **87**, 665 (1952).
42. G. J. Dienes, *Phys. Rev.* **87**, 666 (1952).
43. A. Granato and K. Lücke, *J. Appl. Phys.* **27**, 583 (1956).
44. J. Friedel, *Phil. Mag.* **44**, 444 (1953).
45. J. S. Koehler, in *Imperfections in Nearly Perfect Crystals*, W. Shockley et al., Editors, pp. 197–219, Wiley, New York, 1952.
46. D. O. Thompson and D. K. Holmes, *J. Appl. Phys.* **27**, 713 (1956).
47. C. Zener, *Elasticity and Anelasticity of Metals*, Chapter V, University of Chicago Press, 1948.
48. A. S. Nowick, in *Progress in Metal Physics*, Vol. 4, pp. 1–71, Pergamon, New York, 1961.
49. J. L. Snoek, *Physica* **6**, 591 (1939).
50. C. A. Wert, *Phys. Rev.* **79**, 601 (1950).
51. C. A. Wert and C. Zener, *Phys. Rev.* **76**, 1169 (1949).
52. C. Zener, *Phys. Rev.* **71**, 34 (1947).
53. A. D. LeClaire and W. M. Lomer, *Acta. Met.* **2**, 731 (1954).
54. J. L. Snoek, *Physica* **6**, 161 (1939); **8**, 711 (1939).
55. L. Néel, *J. Phys. Radium* **12**, 339 (1951); **13**, 249 (1952).
56. A. Seeger, P. Schiller and H. Krönmuller, *Phil. Mag.* **5**, 853 (1960); *Z. Naturforsch.* **15A**, 740 (1960).
57. M. V. Klein and H. Krönmuller, *J. Appl. Phys.* **33**, 2191 (1962).
58. A. H. Cottrell, in *Progress in Metal Physics*, Vol. 4, pp. 205–65, Pergamon, New York, 1953; *Dislocations and Plastic Flow in Crystals*, Chapter 4, Oxford University Press, Oxford, 1953.
59. C. H. Li, J. Washburn and E. R. Parker, *Trans. AIME* **197**, 1223 (1953).
60. R. Maddin and A. H. Cottrell, *Phil. Mag.* **46**, 735 (1955).

61. J. Friedel, *Les Dislocations*, Chapter XV, Gauthier-Villars, Paris, 1956.
62. N. F. Mott and F. R. N. Nabarro, in *Report of a Conference on the Strength of Solids*, p. 1, The Physical Society, London, 1948; see also N. F. Mott, in *Imperfections in Nearly Perfect Crystals*, W. Shockley et al., Editors, pp. 173–91, Wiley, New York, 1952.
63. J. C. Fisher, E. W. Hart and R. H. Pry, *Acta. Met.* **1**, 336 (1953).
64. A. Seeger, in *Proc. 2nd UN Intern. Conf. on Peaceful Uses of Atomic Energy*, Vol. 6, p. 250, UN, Geneva, 1958.
65. N. J. Petch, *J. Iron and Steel Inst.* **174**, 25 (1953).
66. L. Codd and N. J. Petch, *Phil. Mag.* **5**, 30 (1960).
67. A. H. Cottrell, *Trans. AIME* **212**, 192 (1958).
68. A. A. Johnson, *Phil. Mag.* **7**, 177 (1962).
69. L. M. Clarebrough, M. E. Hargreaves, A. K. Head and G. W. West, *Trans. AIME* **203**, 99 (1955).
70. R. D. McCammon and H. M. Rosenberg, *Phil. Mag.* **1**, 964 (1956).
71. T. Broom and R. K. Ham, *Proc. Roy. Soc. London* **242A**, 166 (1957).
72. For a review see, A discussion on work-hardening and fatigue in metals, *Proc. Roy. Soc. London* **242A**, 145–227 (1957).

CHAPTER FIVE

SOME BASIC EXPERIMENTS

1. Introduction

The major theoretical developments concerning defects in metals have been outlined in the previous chapters. A large number of experiments were performed concurrently with the development of the theory and reported in the literature. The experimental techniques, like the theoretical ones, have become increasingly more sophisticated with better realization of the need to control important parameters such as purity of materials, dislocation content, quenching speeds, temperature of metal during introduction of defects by radiation or cold work, etc. Furthermore, some experimental methods yield much more clearly interpretable results than others. Because of the difficulties in proper control of conditions, and because of the inherent difficulty of untangling the complicated interplay among defects when several are present, there is still considerable controversy in several areas of the field. The purpose of this chapter is to describe and discuss selected basic experiments which illustrate the best currently available experimental methods and the most clearly interpretable results. Therefore, a detailed review of all the literature will not be given, but the reader is referred to references 1 to 5 for the most recent reviews of available data in several areas.

2. Equilibrium Experiments

In Chapter I the basic formula for the concentration of defects in equilibrium at any given temperature T was shown to be

$$n = e^{S/k} e^{-E_F/kT} , \qquad \text{I–3.10}$$

where n is the atomic fraction of defects, and S and E_F are the entropy and energy of formation, respectively. For an experimental test of this relation, as well as for a quantitative determination of the characteristic constants S and E_F, it is necessary to measure the equilibrium concentration of defects as a function of temperature.

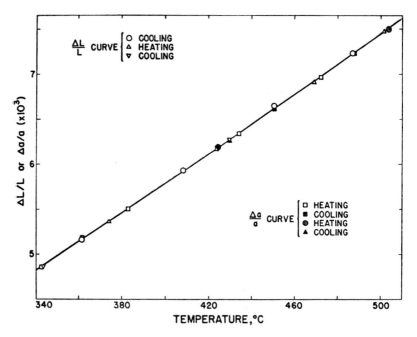

Fig. V–2.1 Measured length expansion, $\Delta L/L$, and lattice parameter expansion, $\Delta a/a$, versus temperature for gold in the 340° to 510°C interval. The x-ray and length expansions agree within experimental error. (From reference 6.)

As shown in Chapter IV, several methods can be used for determining the presence of lattice defects, but probably the most direct method involves the simultaneous measurement of the changes in lattice parameter (a) and in dilation, or the direct measurement of the change in length (L) of a thin specimen.

These changes are related to the defect concentration by the equation

$$n = \pm\, 3 \left(\frac{\Delta L}{L} - \frac{\Delta a}{a} \right).\qquad\qquad \text{IV–4.4}$$

In a typical recent experiment on gold, Simmons and Balluffi[6] shown in Figs. V–2.1 and V–2.2. Fig. V–2.1 shows that at low measured simultaneously $\Delta L/L$ and $\Delta a/a$ in the temperature interval 15° to 1057°C during both heating and cooling. The specimen was a bar about $1 \times 1 \times 50$ cm. $\Delta a/a$ was measured by x-ray lattice parameter techniques from one grain of the bar, and $\Delta L/L$ was measured by microscopic determination of the spacing between two fiduciary marks made on the bar. The results are temperature, where a very small concentration of defects is

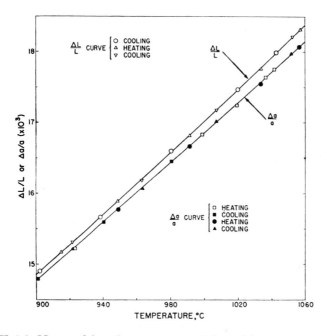

Fig. V–2.2 Measured length expansion, $\Delta L/L$, and lattice parameter expansion, $\Delta a/a$, versus temperature for gold in the 900° to 1060°C interval. $\Delta L/L$ is larger than $\Delta a/a$ in the high temperature region corresponding to the thermal generation of lattice vacancies. (From reference 6.)

present, the two expansions $\Delta a/a$ and $\Delta L/L$ are the same, and Fig. V–2.2 shows that at high temperatures these quantities diverge. This divergence is related via equation IV–4.4 to the number of defects present. The data obeyed a linear plot of ln$n$ vs. $1/T$, as required by equation I–3.1, and, therefore, E_F was determined from the slope of this curve and S from the extrapolated value of ln$n$ at $1/T = 0$. Since the right-hand side of equation IV–4.4 was positive at all temperatures, the defect present must be of the vacancy type. The experimentally determined values of the energy parameters are $E_F = 0.94 \pm 0.09$ eV, and $S/k = 1 \pm 0.1$. It is concluded that these values are for the energy of formation and entropy of the single vacancy because the contribution of divacancies is small if they have a binding energy less than 0.4 eV. A binding energy < 0.4 eV is consistent with the theoretical estimate given in I–5 and also with a binding energy value deduced from annealing experiments to be discussed later. The 0.9-eV value for the formation energy and an S/k value of 1 for the entropy are in reasonable agreement with the theoretical estimates discussed in I–4.

Other metals have been studied with this technique and the values obtained are shown in Table V–2.1. The theoretical values from I–4 are also listed.

The results for lead are indicated as maximum values because a difference in $\Delta L/L$ and $\Delta a/a$ was not observed, and the indicated results are the number of vacancies and their corresponding energy of formation which might be present but not detectable within the accuracy of the experiment. In this experiment on lead, as well as in the experiment on aluminum by Feder and Nowick,[10] the measurements of $\Delta L/L$ and $\Delta a/a$ were made on the same specimen but not together in the same furnace. As stated, no deviations were found for lead, and data sufficient to obtain a $1/T$ plot for aluminum were not obtained. These data are therefore considered less reliable. In the Simmons and Balluffi[9] experiment on aluminum, the single vacancy concentration is high enough to create an uncertainty about the role of divacancies, particularly since their binding energy has been neither estimated nor measured.

TABLE V-2.1

Monovacancy Parameters Derived from
Equilibrium Experiments

Experimental technique	Metal	E_F, exptl. (eV)	E_F, theoret. (eV)	S/k	n at melting point (atomic fraction)	Reference
Length and x-ray	Au	0.94 ± 0.09	0.6, 0.77	1	7.2×10^{-4}	6
	Ag	1.09 ± 0.1	0.6, 0.92	~ 1.5	1.7×10^{-4}	7
	Cu	1.17 ± 0.11	1.1, 0.9, 0.81	~ 1.5	1.9×10^{-4}	8
	Al	0.75 ± 0.07		2.4	9×10^{-4}	9
	Al	(0.77)			3×10^{-4}	10
	Pb	< 0.53			$< 1.5 \times 10^{-4}$	10
Resistivity	Li	0.4	0.55			12
	Na	0.4, 0.2	0.53			12, 13
	K	0.4	0.36			12
Specific heat	K	0.4	0.36			11, 12

As pointed out before, the interpretation of the deviation of $\Delta L/L$ and $\Delta a/a$ at high temperatures is simple and clear. Deviations of other physical properties from the expected behavior of a perfect crystal have also been observed in equilibrium experiments, for example, excess specific heat[11] and extra resistivity[12,13] at high temperatures. These deviations have been attributed to the presence of point defects and used to measure their concentration. An example of such a deviation in a specific heat curve for potassium is shown in Fig. V-2.3, and in an electrical resistivity curve for sodium is shown in Fig. V-2.4. Results from experiments of this type have been combined to obtain an estimate of the energy of formation of defects, very probably vacancies, in some of the alkali metals. These results, also shown in Table V-2.1, are seen to be in reasonable agreement with theoretical estimates, but are considered to be far less reliable than the thermal expansion

o

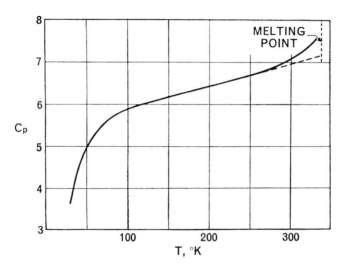

Fig. V–2.3 The specific heat of pure potassium as a function of temperature. The dashed line is the extrapolation for the perfect crystal. (From reference 12.)

results, since the magnitude of the deviation is obtained by subtracting an extrapolated curve for the perfect crystal and the extrapolation is uncertain because of poor theoretical knowledge of the anharmonic effects that play an important role at high temperatures.[14] Similar resistivity experiments on the noble metals have led to values for the energy of formation that are generally considered to be unacceptably low.[15,16] A recent experiment on gold by Misek and Polak[17] gave a value of 0.80 eV, in approximate, although not good, agreement with values obtained by other techniques.

Borelius,[18] in a more refined analysis of the total energy content of a metal, has attempted to separate out the structural energy contribution ascribable to thermal lattice defects. The vacancy formation energies determined by this technique are in good agreement with other measurements for gold and silver, but in rather poor agreement for copper and aluminum. Åström,[19] on the basis of calorimetric measurements on silver, has reported the

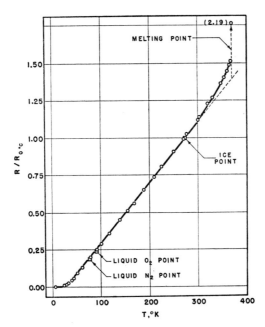

Fig. V–2.4 The electrical resistance of sodium from 0°K to the melting point. The dashed line is the extrapolation for the perfect crystal. (From reference 12.)

presence of another thermally generated defect, so far unidentified, with an energy of formation of about 0.2 eV. Borelius' analysis shows that this second type of defect is probably present also in gold, copper, and aluminum.

3. Quench Experiments

By an appropriate quench from high temperature the equilibrium concentration of vacancies that exists at high temperature in a specimen may be "frozen in" and thereby preserved. Any physical property that depends sensitively and proportionally on the concentration of defects may be used to measure the quenched-in vacancy concentration. From the variation of the relative concentration with quench temperature the enthalpy of formation is directly derivable. The most convenient physical measurements are those of resistivity, length, and stored energy. Typical examples of such experiments are described in this section.

a) Resistivity and stored energy studies

The Bauerle-Koehler[20] study of quenched-in vacancies in gold is an example of a series of careful experiments in which the various important parameters discussed in I–10 were kept under good control. Gold was chosen for these experiments because it does not oxidize in air or react with water, and because the vacancies migrate slowly at room temperature. Thus, water, which is the most suitable quenching medium (high termal capacity, conductivity, and heat of vaporization), could be used in these experiments. High purity gold wires of 0.016 in. diameter were used, which could be quenched at speeds of about 4×10^4 C°/sec by sudden immersion in water. The specimens were thin enough to prevent the quenching stresses from exceeding the yield point and thus to avoid the generation of dislocations and dislocation-produced vacancies, and thick enough to avoid cold-working of the specimen during subsequent handling. A series of quenches from different temperatures were carried out, and the increase in resistivity of the quenched specimens relative to an annealed wire was measured at liquid nitrogen temperature.

As shown in Fig. V–3.1, the quenched-in resistivity, $\Delta\rho$, depends exponentially on the reciprocal of the quench temperature, T_q, and is therefore described by the equation

$$\Delta\rho = Ae^{-E_F/kT_q} . \qquad\qquad \text{V–3.1}$$

This is just the relation to be expected if $\Delta\rho$ is proportional to the concentration of vacancies. Comparison of equation V–3.1 with equation I–3.1 shows that A is equal to the product of the proportionality constant relating $\Delta\rho$ to n, and the entropy factor, $e^{S/k}$. From Fig. V–3.1, $E_F = 0.98 \pm 0.03$ eV and $A = (4.9 \pm 1.0) \times 10^{-4}$ Ω-cm. The energy of formation is in good agreement with that determined by the Simmons and Balluffi equilibrium experiments discussed in the previous section. From the equilibrium experiment the value of S/k is known and is equal to 1.0 in gold. Assuming that the energies of formation determined in these two different experiments are equal, the ratio of equation V–3.1 to equation I–3.1 gives 1.8×10^{-6} Ω-cm as the resistivity change for 1% vacancy concentration in gold. It is to be noted that this value is in reasonable agreement with the theoretical estimates of section IV–6. Bauerle and Koehler also measured $\Delta\rho$ and the change in

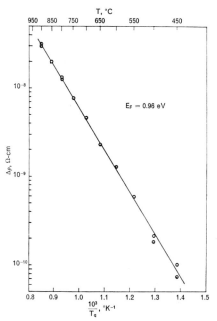

Fig. V–3.1 Semilogarithmic plot of quenched-in resistivity versus reciprocal of the absolute quench temperature for gold. (From reference 20.)

length, $\Delta L/L$, during annealing following these quenches. The annealing experiments will be discussed in detail in a later section, but it is pertinent here that $\Delta\rho$ and $\Delta L/L$ were found to decay identically over the complete range of annealing. Thus $\Delta\rho$ and $\Delta L/L$ are proportional to each other, and the proportionality constant is 1.0×10^{-3} Ω-cm, or 3.3×10^{-4} Ω-cm in terms of $\Delta V/V$.

DeSorbo[21] measured the energy stored in a thin foil (0.015 in.)

of gold quenched at a rate of about 1×10^4 °C/sec from a series
of temperatures in the range 820° to 920°C. He used an adiabatic
calorimeter and measured the temperature rise while the quenched
sample was being annealed. He obtained the total energy by
integrating the heat release curve extrapolated to both zero and
infinite times. Most of the energy released is thought to come from
the complete annihilation of single vacancies. However, some
fraction of the vacancies may end up in clusters or collapsed dislocation rings and therefore may not be completely annihilated.
Because of this, as discussed in IV–5, the experiment may not
have been carried to a proper thermodynamic end point. This
error may not be large, and DeSorbo's experiment, within his
stated accuracy of 10 to 15%, is in good agreement with other
types of quenching experiments. DeSorbo finds that the amount
of stored energy, ΔE, depends exponentially on the reciprocal of
the quench temperature with an energy of formation for vacancies
of 0.97 $\pm$ 0.1 eV and a pre-exponential factor of 2 eV per atom.
From these two quantities the vacancy concentration is directly
given by the ratio $\Delta E / E_F$ as

$$V = 2e^{-0.97/kT} . \qquad\qquad \text{V–3.2}$$

This result is in excellent agreement with the resistivity studies
discussed above and with the equilibrium measurements discussed
in the previous section. Combined with the results of Bauerle and
Koehler's resistivity experiments, this gives a value of (1.8 ± 0.6)
$\times 10^{-6}$ Ω-cm for the resistivity of one atomic percent vacancies.
From the fractional change of volume as measured by Bauerle and
Koehler, the increase in volume per vacancy is found to be 0.57
times the atomic volume, in reasonable agreement with the
theoretical estimates of section I–9.

b) Effects of quenching parameters

It has been pointed out in section I–10 that quenching results
are sensitive to the quench rate used because a quench must be
fast enough to freeze in a high percentage of the vacancies but
not so fast as to introduce appreciable quenching stresses.

The first parameter, sufficient rate of quench, was studied in detail by Mori, Meshii and Kauffman[22] over a range of quenching rates and temperatures. The quenching rate was controlled by varying the speed of motion of the specimen through the quenching medium and the temperature of the medium. Their results are illustrated in Fig. V–3.2, where the quenched-in resistivity is plotted against quenching rate for a series of quench temperatures.

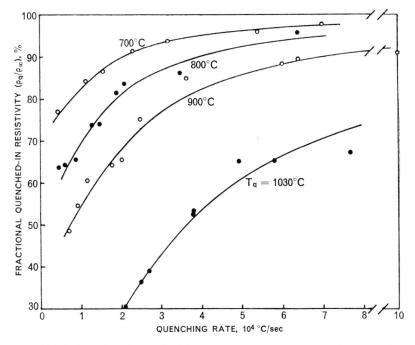

Fig. V–3.2 Fractional quenched-in resistivities versus quenching rates for several quenching temperatures. The extrapolated quenched-in resistivity at infinite quenching rate is taken as 100%. (From reference 22.)

When the quenching rate is high the dependence on this rate is minimized and a large fraction of the vacancies remain in the specimen. An approximate relation was obtained between the concentration of the quenched-in vacancies and the rate of quenching on the basis of a simple model. (The more exact computer treatment by Lomer is given in section I–10.) A first-order decay process was assumed to be dominant during the quench, and the change in the equilibrium concentration, considered in Lomer's more complicated analysis, was neglected. Thus, the vacancies were assumed to decay according to the relation, analogous to equation II–2.1,

$$dV/dt = - KVe^{-E_M/kT} .$$

V–3.3

The quenching rate, R, was assumed to be constant so that

$$T = T_q - Rt .$$

V–3.4

Substitution for t in equation V–3.3 and integration gives

$$\ln (V/V_\infty) = I/R ,$$

V–3.5

where

$$I = K \int_{T_q}^{T} e^{-E_M/kT} \, dT .$$

At any given temperature, therefore, $\ln V$ is expected to vary linearly with $1/R$. The experimental results of Fig. V–3.2 were found to obey this relation quite accurately, as shown in Fig. V–3.3. The data, therefore, can be extrapolated to infinite quenching rate to correct for the vacancy loss during the quench. The extrapolated line (labeled ∞) taken from the intercepts of Fig. V–3.3 is shown in Fig. V–3.4 for comparison with the experimental data. The characteristic departures due to inadequate quenches are clearly seen. Such lowering of the apparent slope of the curve usually leads to a low value of E_F. From the extrapolated data the parameters of equation V–3.1 were obtained as $E_F = 0.97$ eV and $A = 5 \times 10^{-4}$ Ω-cm, confirming the results of Bauerle and Koehler. Mori et al. also observed the correspondence between $\Delta\rho$ and $\Delta V/V$ during annealing and found the proportionality constant to be $(3.6 \pm 0.3) \times 10^{-4}$ Ω-cm, in agreement with the Bauerle-Koehler experiments.

Takamura[23] studied the second important parameter, namely the effect of quenching stresses, by varying the size of the specimen. He determined the relative vacancy concentration by measuring the contraction of quenched gold rods of various diameters during annealing at room temperature. If complete annealing is obtained, then the contraction is equal to the fractional increase in length, $\Delta L/L$, produced by the quench. $\Delta L/L$, in turn, is directly proportional to the vacancy concentration quenched in the specimen if, as Takamura concludes, the effect

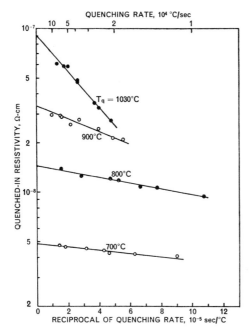

Fig. V–3.3 Logarithm of quenched-in resistivity versus reciprocal of quenching rate. (From reference 22.)

of relaxation of piled-up dislocations, which could contribute to a change in length, is small. For any specimen of a given size, $\Delta L/L$ was found to vary exponentially with $1/T_q$. The energy of formation and the pre-exponential factor were found to be functions of the specimen diameter. The energy of formation was found experimentally to depend on the radius of the specimen, r, as

$$E_F = E_F{}^0 - br^2 , \qquad\qquad \text{V–3.6}$$

and the pre-exponential factor, A, as

$$A = A_0 e^{-ar^2}. \qquad\qquad \text{V–3.7}$$

All the experimental results could be described by the following equation for the vacancy concentration:

$$V = \frac{A_0}{\alpha} \exp\left[-ar^2 - \frac{E_F{}^0 - br^2}{kT_q} \right], \qquad\qquad \text{V–3.8}$$

where α is the fractional volume of formation of a vacancy. If the data are extrapolated to $r = 0$ according to equation V–3.8, then the energy of formation, $E_F{}^0$, is 0.98 eV, in agreement with the resistivity and stored energy measurements. In these experiments the vacancy concentration increased with increasing specimen radius, whereas it is expected to decrease because of the slower cooling rate of large diameter rods. Clearly, therefore, extra

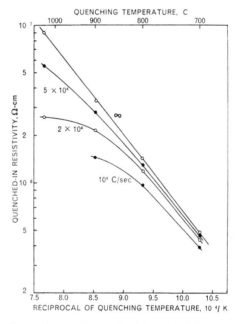

Fig. V–3.4   Logarithm of quenched-in resistivity versus reciprocal of quenching temperature for the indicated quenching rates. (From reference 22.)

vacancies were produced by quenching stresses during the quench, indicating that the criterion given in section I–10 for maximum quenching rate without plastic deformation was exceeded. The pre-exponential factor decreases with increasing radius and is therefore primarily influenced by the quench rate rather than the plastic deformation. The concentration of thermal vacancies, V_{th}, in a specimen of radius r is given by the expression

$$V_{th} = \frac{A_0}{\alpha} \exp\left[-ar^2 - \frac{E_F{}^0}{kT_q}\right].$$ V–3.9

The difference between this quantity and the total number of vacancies observed, equation V–3.8, is the concentration of vacancies produced by plastic deformation. The concentration of thermal vacancies calculated from equation V–3.9, the total vacancy concentration determined experimentally, and the

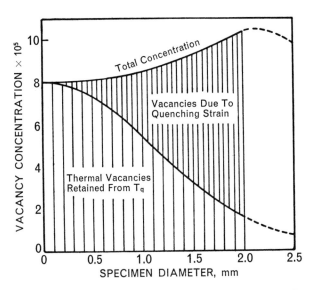

Fig. V–3.5 Graphical representation of the relation between the vacancy concentration and specimen size for a quench temperature of 800°C. The total vacancy concentration is the sum of the thermal vacancies retained during quenching and those formed by the quenching strains. (From reference 23.)

vacancy concentration produced by the quenching stresses are shown in Fig. V–3.5 as a function of specimen diameter for a quench temperature of 800°C.

The parameters that must be kept under control in a quenching experiment have been emphasized in this discussion. Further information can be obtained by the purposeful variation of other parameters, such as the external pressure. This is a thermodynamic variable which is contained in the basic equation for defect concentration as a function of temperature. The basic equation derived in section I–3 may be written, for the atomic fraction of vacancies in equilibrium at any temperature T, as

$$V = e^{S/k}\, e^{-H_F/kT}\,. \qquad\qquad \text{V–3.10}$$

In the discussions up to now, the enthalpy of formation, H_F, and the energy of formation, E_F, have been used interchangeably because they differ only by a PV_F term (where V_F is the volume change associated with the formation of a vacancy) which is negligible at atmospheric pressure. In high pressure experiments, however, the PV_F term is important, and such experiments provide a direct determination of V_F. At high pressure equation V–3.10 becomes

$$V = e^{S/k}\, e^{-(E_F+PV_F)/kT}\,. \qquad\qquad \text{V–3.11}$$

Huebener and Homan[24] carried out quenching experiments under high pressure on gold wires with a quenching temperature of 680°C, an average quench rate of 2×10^4°C/sec, and a pressure range from 400 to 11,000 atmospheres. They measured the resistivity associated with the quenched-in defects in a manner similar to that of Bauerle and Koehler. As shown in Fig. V–3.6, they found the logarithm of the quenched-in resistivity to decrease linearly with increasing applied pressure. The slope of this curve can be related to the formation volume, V_F, as follows. The logarithmic derivative of equation V–3.11 with respect to the pressure is

$$\frac{\partial \ln V}{\partial P} = -\frac{1}{kT}\left(T\,\frac{\partial S}{\partial P} - \frac{\partial E_F}{\partial P} + P\,\frac{\partial V_F}{\partial P} + V_F\right). \qquad \text{V–3.12}$$

The variation of entropy and energy of formation with pressure is expected to be small and, therefore, the first two terms on the right-hand side of equation V–3.12 can be neglected. The experimental curve of Fig. V–3.6 shows that, within the pressure range studied, the slope of the curve is a constant and hence the logarithmic derivative is independent of the pressure. Thus the $P\partial V_F/\partial P$ term is small compared to V_F and the slope is equal to $-V_F/kT$.

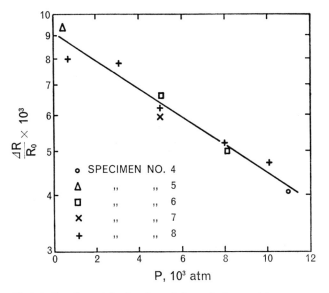

Fig. V–3.6 Semilogarithmic plot of the relative resistance quenched in at 680°C versus the gas pressure during quenching. R_0 is the annealed resistance at liquid nitrogen temperature. (From reference 24.)

From these experiments Huebener and Homan found that for gold $V_F = (9.16 \pm 0.68) \times 10^{-24}$ cm^3 = 0.53 $\pm$ 0.04 atomic volume. The same value, 0.53 $\pm$ 0.07 atomic volume, was found by Grimes et al.[25] in a similar experiment. As previously mentioned in this section, DeSorbo has calculated V_F to be 0.57 atomic volume by combining the results of his stored energy measurements with those of the Bauerle-Koehler experiments. There is good agreement between this indirectly derived value and that measured directly by Huebener and Homan, and these experimental values are in reasonable agreement with the theoretical estimates given in section I–9.

The change in volume associated with the migration of the quenched-in vacancy in gold has also been measured recently by

TABLE V–3.1

Monovacancy Formation Energies from
Quench Experiments

Metal	E_F (eV)	Physical property measured	Reference
Gold	0.98 ± 0.03	resistivity	20
	0.97	,,	22
	0.98 ± 0.1	,,	28
	0.95 ± 0.1	,,	29
	0.79	,,	30
	0.98	length change	23
	0.97 ± 0.1	stored energy	21
	0.98	resistivity	24
Silver	1.10 ± 0.04	resistivity	31
	1.10	,,	32
	1.06	,,	33
	1.04 ± 0.1	,,	34
	1.0	thermal electromotive force	35
Platinum	1.4 ± 0.1	resistivity	36
	1.3 ± 0.1	,,	37, 38
	1.18	,,	30
	1.4	thermal electromotive force	35
Copper	1.0	resistivity	39
Aluminum	0.76 ± 0.04	resistivity	40
	0.79 ± 0.04	,,	41
	0.76 ± 0.03	,,	42
	0.76	,	43
Tin	0.51 ± 0.05	resistivity	44
Magnesium	0.89 ± 0.06	resistivity	44a

a high pressure experiment. Emrick[26] studied the effect of hydro-static pressure up to 10,000 kg/cm² on the annealing rate of vacancies quenched into gold from 700°C. By a theoretical treat-ment analogous to that expressed by equation V–3.12, a value of 0.15 times the atomic volume was derived for the migration volume, V_m. The migration volume is, therefore, considerably smaller than the formation volume, V_F. The over-all activation volume in a self-diffusion experiment is the sum of these two volumes. The predicted value for gold is therefore about 0.68 atomic volume, but this quantity has not yet been measured. From diffusion experiments on other systems, it appears that half an atomic volume is a typical value for the self-diffusion activa-tion volume.[27] The implication is that in many systems the migra-tion volume may be considerably smaller than the formation volume. The most recent calculation for copper indicates that, also theoretically, $V_m < V_F$ (section I–9).

The energy of vacancy formation has been determined in several metals by the techniques discussed in this section. A summary of the results is given in Table V–3.1. The data show clearly that, as the techniques have become more sophisticated, excellent agreement has been achieved among experiments done by various techniques as well as among experiments carried out by different investigators in different laboratories. Comparison of Table V–3.1 with experimental equilibrium values, Table V–2.1, and with the theoretical estimates, Table I–4.1, shows reasonable agreement.

4. Irradiation Experiments

Only vacancies and vacancy complexes are produced in quench experiments because the energy of formation of the interstitial, the other basic point defect, is high. According to the estimates given in Chapter I, the energy of formation of an interstitial is about three times that of a vacancy and, therefore, the number of interstitials present at any temperature is undetectably small. High energy radiation, however, produces interstitials and vacan-cies simultaneously. Thus quench and irradiation experiments are complementary to each other, since in the former vacancies alone can be studied and the knowledge gained can be used in the latter to deduce the properties of the interstitials. As discussed in I–12, bombardment with massive particles will produce complex clusters of defects in addition to the simple vacancy-interstitial pairs. These complications can be avoided by using electron irradiation, which will produce only vacancies and interstitials. It should be kept in mind, however, that the resulting vacancy-interstitial distribution is nonhomogeneous because an interstitial and its own vacancy are generally created close to each other. This nonrandom distribution can be particularly important in the interpretation of annealing experiments. In this section some electron irradiation experiments will be discussed that have been useful in measuring some of the important parameters involved in the production of defects by radiation.

The threshold energy, E_d, for the displacement of an atom from its lattice site is a fundamental parameter in the production of defects by radiation. This quantity has been determined for several metals by measuring at low temperature the increase in resistivity per incident bombarding electron as a function of the average electron energy. Typical data from Lucasson and Walker[45,46] are shown in Fig. V–4.1, where the average bombarding energy has been corrected for increase in path length and straggling. The concentration of defects is given by $C = n\sigma_d$ where n is the number of incident particles per cm² and σ_d is the displacement cross section. C is also equal to the ratio $\Delta\rho/\Delta\rho_F$, where $\Delta\rho_F$ is the resistivity change per unit defect concentration. Thus the measured quantity $\Delta\rho/n$ is given by $\Delta\rho/n = \Delta\rho_F\sigma_d(E)$, since σ_d is a function of the bombarding energy. For comparison with theory it is convenient to eliminate $\Delta\rho_F$ by normalizing at the arbitrary energy of 1.35 MeV (the highest value in Fig. V–4.1), that is, by plotting $\sigma_d(E)/\sigma_d(1.35 \text{ MeV})$ vs. the average electron energy. The variation of $\sigma_d(E)$ with energy is controlled by two major factors. The first, the distribution of atom recoil energies, can be calculated from scattering theory and is given fully by Seitz and Koehler.[47] The second is the displacement probability function, which gives the probability of an atom with a given recoil energy being displaced. This function starts from zero at some minimum threshold energy and rises to unity at some higher recoil energy. Various displacement probability functions

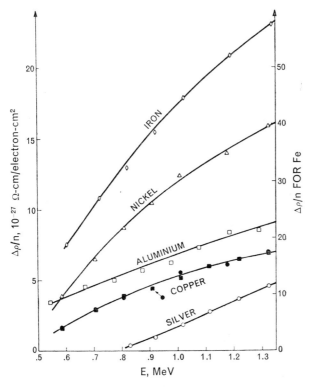

Fig. V–4.1 Resistivity changes per electron/cm² in various metals as a function of the average bombarding energy. Corrections have been made for increase in path length and electron straggling. (From reference 45.)

have been studied, but these will not be described here, since Lucasson and Walker found their data to be in rather good agreement with a simple step function, i.e., a sharp threshold. However, since their experiments were done on polycrystalline samples, the threshold they measured is an average threshold and not the true

P

onset threshold energy, which may be lower. In Fig. V–4.2 are shown two theoretical cross section vs. energy curves calculated on the basis of the above ideas, together with the experimental points normalized from the data of Fig. V–4.1 for silver. Agreement with theory is good when the threshold energy for silver is taken as 28 eV.

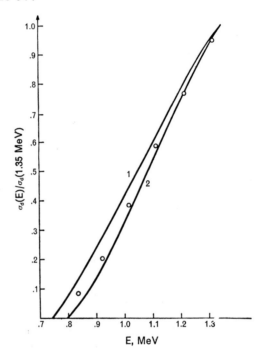

Fig. V–4.2 Normalized displacement cross section versus energy for silver. Curve 1: $E_d = 26$ eV, $\Delta E_d = 0$. Curve 2: $E_d = 28$ eV, $\Delta E_d = 0$. The circles are experimental points normalized from those in Fig. V–4.1. (From reference 45.)

Determination of E_d by the above procedure also determines the theoretical cross section vs. energy curve for the metal under investigation, i.e., the normalized cross section as a function of the average electron energy is known. Therefore, since $\sigma(1.35)$ is known from theory, the absolute value of the cross section, $\sigma_d(E)$, is known for any given energy. By direct comparison with the experimental $\Delta\rho/n$ vs. energy data, the value of $\Delta\rho_F$, the resistivity per vacancy-interstitial pair, can be determined. The values of the threshold energy, E_d, and the resistivity per atomic percent of vacancy-interstitial pairs, $\Delta\rho_F$, are given in Table V–4.1 for various metals, grouped according to their crystal structure.

TABLE V–4.1

Effective Threshold Energy and Vacancy-Interstitial Pair
Resistivity for Various Metals

Structure	Metal	E_d (eV)	$\Delta\rho_F$ ($\mu\Omega$-cm/atom %)	Reference
f.c.c.	Ag	28	1.4	46
	Cu	22	1.3	46
	Cu	19–20	2–3	48
	Ni	24	3.2	46
	Al	32	3.4	46
	Au	>40		46
	Au	35		50
b.c.c.	Fe	24	12.5	46
	Mo	37	4.5	46
	W	>35		46
hex.	Ti	29	42	46

In comparison with the theoretical values discussed in section I–12 and the experimental values of the resistivity for vacancies discussed in this chapter, the $\Delta\rho_F$ values for the noble metals obtained by Lucasson and Walker appear to be too low. Sosin[48,49] has carried out a more detailed study of copper and has shown that the step function approximation is rather poor at low energies. Using a modified theoretical approach he obtained the values for copper given in Table V–4.1. Although his value for the threshold energy is only about 10% lower than that of Lucasson and

Walker, his value for $\Delta\rho_F$ is about twice as large, in better agreement with theory and other types of experiments. It appears from these experiments that the threshold values are relatively insensitive to the details of the theory but the resistivity values are highly sensitive.

The stored energy associated with a vacancy-interstitial pair has been measured by Meechan and Sosin[51] in copper after electron irradiation at liquid helium temperature. They determined the release of stored energy in the temperature range from 20° to 60°K by carrying out a differential temperature measurement between an irradiated specimen and an unirradiated standard. By comparing their stored energy results with other resistivity measurements of electron irradiated copper they obtained a stored energy to resistivity ratio of 5.4 ± 0.8 cal/g/$\mu\Omega$-cm. In their paper they assumed the value of the resistivity of a vacancy-interstitial pair to be 3.6 $\mu\Omega$-cm. Using this value, and assuming that the stored energy release comes from the annihilation of vacancies with interstitials, they found 5.4 ± 0.8 eV for the stored energy of a vacancy-interstitial pair. Use of the later value of about 2.5 $\mu\Omega$-cm per atomic percent vacancy-interstitial pairs, suggested by Sosin (Table V–4.1), gives the stored energy as 3.7 eV. This number is in reasonable agreement with the theoretical estimates for the energy of formation of a vacancy and interstitial discussed in Chapter I. All the above data indicate that the theoretically calculated and experimentally observed displacement production rates for electrons are in agreement within about a factor of two, with the theory giving the higher value.

No such close agreement is observed when heavy particle irradiation is used. Low temperature reactor irradiations have been carried out on a number of metals[52-54] and the resulting neutron damage studied. The $\Delta\rho$ vs. exposure curves were found to be linear for small doses and from these experimental damage rates the number of displaced atoms can be estimated by assuming $\Delta\rho_F$ values such as those given in Table V–4.1. In Table V–4.2 the experimentally determined damage rates have been converted

flux distribution is difficult, but the best estimate[55] for the above experiments changes the discrepancy to a factor of 8 instead of 20. There are other factors which can influence this ratio. Recent reactor experiments have shown that high energy events are less efficient than low energy ones in producing damage.[162] Clustering of defects, particularly vacancies, is expected, since they are formed in a highly nonrandom way (I–12). Koehler and Seitz[56] indicate that as much as 80% of the defects may be in clusters whose resistivity per defect, according to the discussion of IV–6, is lower than that of isolated defects. The cascade calculations are based on the experimentally determined effective threshold energy, which may be in error, and this error may be partly the source of the factor of two discrepancy between theory and experiment in electron irradiation studies. This same discrepancy would carry over into the neutron results. Recent preliminary machine calculations indicate[57] that the scattering of the secondary and tertiary knock-ons is highly anisotropic, a factor which has not been taken into account in the cascade theory calculation (section I–12). Focusing events, which have been shown to play an important role in the dissipation of energy of collision, have not yet been incorporated into cascade calculations. Such focusing events have been seen experimentally by Wehner[58] in sputtering, and by Thompson,[59] who observed preferred ejection of silver and gold atoms from foils in prominent crystallographic directions upon irradiation with 1-MeV protons and 10-keV argon atoms. Inclusion of most of these effects in the cascade theory is expected to bring experiment and theory closer to agreement. Stored energy experiments have also been carried out on neutron irradiated copper[60] and gave a value of about 1.6 cal/g/$\mu\Omega$-cm for the stored energy to resistivity ratio during annealing of pure copper up to 60°K. This value is low compared to that observed after electron irradiation. In a more recent experiment,[61] copper doped with B^{10} was irradiated at liquid helium temperature. The purpose of the doping was to create more damage by the fissioning of the boron induced by thermal neutrons. The stored energy to resistivity ratio upon subsequent warming to about 50°K was 4 cal/g/$\mu\Omega$-cm, a value in better agreement with results of electron irradiation experiments and theoretical estimates.

Detailed studies have also been made on copper irradiated with 9-MeV deuterons.[47,55,62] A comparison of the experimental resistivity vs. exposure curve with theory indicates a discrepancy of a factor of 5 to 6. When the data are reinterpreted with the help of stored energy[63] and volume change[64,65] experiments during annealing, the discrepancy is reduced to about a factor of 4.

5. Plastic Deformation Experiments

Several mechanisms have been proposed for the production of point defects during plastic deformation (section I–11). It is not known theoretically which of these mechanisms, if any, is the dominant one, or how many and what type of defects are produced per unit strain. Since dislocations and point defects are introduced into the crystal simultaneously, the quantitative interpretation of experiments in this field is complicated and difficult. In a qualitative way it has been shown quite conclusively, however, that point defects are formed during plastic deformation.

Molenaar and Aarts[66] measured the stress-strain curve and the corresponding change in resistivity of a polycrystalline copper wire during plastic deformation in tension at $-183°C$, as shown in Fig. V–5.1. They observed that both the resistivity and stress increased continuously as a function of extension. After 8% extension, at point A in Fig. V–5.1, the specimen was annealed for 3 hours at 20°C, which caused a considerable decrease in the resistivity increment but no observable change in the stress-strain curve. This indicates that the dislocation structure could not have been altered in any important way by the annealing, and that the decrease in resistivity is probably caused by the disappearance of a point defect. Pry and Hennig[67] showed further that a constant fraction of the cold-work induced extra resistivity is recoverable, i.e., the ratio of the resistivity drop caused by the room temperature annealing to the total extra resistivity is a constant independent of the amount of straining prior to the annealing. This indicates that both point defects and dislocations are being continuously produced.

It is quite difficult, however, to obtain accurate estimates of the number of point defects produced by cold work. Fig. V–5.2 shows a collection of data on resistivity increase versus strain in copper,[68] the deformation having been performed at 78°K or less. It is seen that, although there is a general agreement in magnitude and shape of the curves, the absolute values can differ by more than a factor of 2. Peiffer[69] has shown that the rate of increase of electrical resistivity with plastic deformation in copper is highly sensitive to the initial condition of the sample. Thus, the differences shown in Fig. V–5.2 are not unexpected. The apparent similarities of the curves of Fig. V–5.2 indicate a 3/2 power law, and van

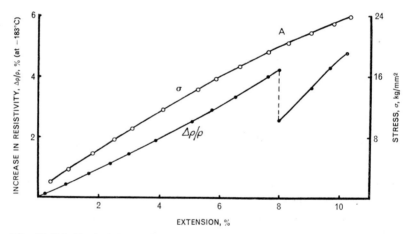

Fig. V–5.1 Resistivity and stress changes of copper deformed in tension at −183°C. At point A the sample was annealed for 3 hours at 20°C. (From reference 66.)

Bueren[70,71] has derived such a law for the production of vacancies in the early stages of cold work based on the assumption that vacancies and interstitials are formed in the wake of jogs present in the expanding dislocation rings (I–11) and that jogs are formed where the expanding dislocation rings cross the already present randomly distributed dislocations. The plastic deformation of single crystals, however, does not fit this simple law, since Blewitt et al.,[72] have shown that the resistivity of a copper single crystal deformed at liquid helium temperature increases with the second power of the strain. Other mechanisms of defect production have been examined and shown to have different power laws. The recent experimental observation of Peiffer[69] on copper shows that a given material can have a power law that changes with the state of deformation or the dislocation arrangement. Fig. V–5.3 illustrates how the behavior of a copper specimen treated as in Fig. V–5.1 changes with successive treatments and larger strains. Peiffer's analysis of these data shows that a power law is still obeyed but that the exponent changes from about 3/2 to <1 in the strain regions considered. Thus, although van Bueren's explanation may be valid at low strains, it is clear that there are several mechanisms for defect formation operative during plastic deformation in copper. Other work by Peiffer[73] and Wintenberger[74]

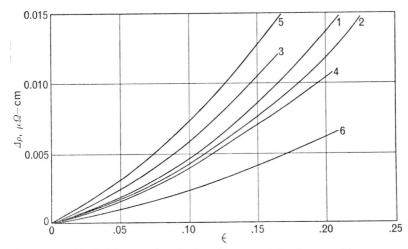

Fig. V–5.2 Resistivity-strain relations for extended polycrystalline copper wires. The absolute amount of resistivity increase is plotted versus the mean shear strain, ϵ. (1) Observations of Molenaar and Aarts; (2) of Druyvesteyn and Manintveld; (3) of Berghout; (4) of Aarts and Jarvis; (5) of Pry and Hennig; (6) of Jongenburger and van Bueren. (From reference 68.)

shows, for example, that in aluminum the resistivity increase is proportional to the strain at all values of the strain and, therefore, the dominant mechanism may well be different in different metals.

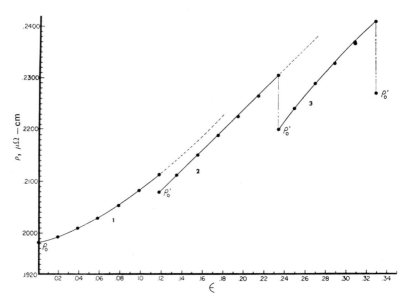

Fig. V–5.3 Electrical resistivity as a function of elongation strain for a representative copper specimen. The dashed extensions of the curves represent continuations of the data if no anneals are performed. The discontinuities arise at strains where a room temperature anneal has been performed. The resistivities after anneal, ρ_0', increase with increasing strain. (From reference 69.)

Because of the large amount of available data on copper, an estimate can be made of the number of defects formed per unit strain. If the electrical resistivity of vacancies in copper is taken as 1.5 $\mu\Omega$-cm/atomic % (IV–6), and if it is assumed that all the electrical resistivity recovery which occurs in copper between liquid nitrogen and room temperature is due to vacancies, then the atomic fraction of vacancies produced by 1% plastic strain is about 4×10^{-6} from the data of both Molenaar and Aarts[66] and Berghout.[75] Henderson and Koehler[76] have measured the stored energy released when copper deformed at −185°C is heated to 40°C. If the energy of formation of a vacancy in copper is taken as 1 eV and this figure is applied to the total energy released between −185 and 40°C, then the atomic fraction of vacancies formed per 1% plastic strain obtained is 6 × 10⁻⁶, in rather good agreement with the resistivity data, considering the uncertainties in this field.

A typical stored energy release experiment is illustrated in Fig. V–5.4, which shows two large, well-defined peaks of energy release occurring above −100°C as well as some smaller, non-systematic peaks at lower temperatures. The presence of the two large peaks suggests that two defects anneal out at these temperatures. Manintveld[77] annealed cold-worked copper isochronally and

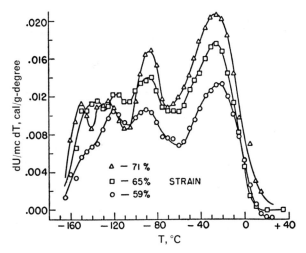

Fig. V–5.4 Energy release spectra for three high purity copper specimens deformed to the extent indicated. (U = energy released, cal; m = mass, g; c = specific heat.) (From reference 76.)

observed two decay steps in the electrical resistivity above −140°C. This is illustrated in Fig. V–5.5, which also shows similar data for gold and silver. Although Berghout also observed these steps in the resistivity decay of cold-worked copper, other investigators have been unable to find them.[78-80] In view of the disturbances in a lattice, certainly caused by cold work, which can distort annealing curves (III–4), some features of the annealing curves might be expected to be obscured. The persistence of the resolved peaks in the stored energy experiments with varying strain suggests that defects are able to anneal separately even

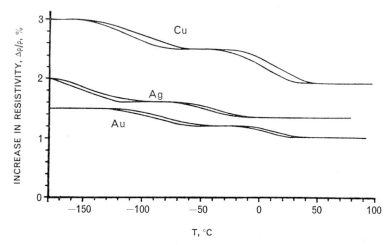

Fig. V–5.5 Isochronal recovery data for wires deformed in tension at −183°C. The resistivity was measured at −183°C. Upper and lower curves for each metal refer to annealing time of 15 and 45 minutes, respectively. (From reference 77.)

though this is not always observed in the resistivity decay. If the higher temperature decay process is assumed to be due to vacancies (the lower temperature decay may possibly be due to divacancies as suggested in I–11), then the corresponding decay step of resistivity is about half the total resistivity recovery, and the corresponding stored energy peak is about half the total stored energy recovery. Thus, although the previously estimated number of vacancies formed by cold work is reduced by a factor of 2, the rather good agreement between the resistivity and stored energy data remains. More detailed surveys of the literature on cold

worked metals show similar estimates.[81-83] Another approach to
the determination of the number of vacancies generated by cold
work could be via the analysis of accelerated diffusion during an
applied stress. Such experiments will be discussed in section V–9,
although the generation rate of vacancies has not yet been determined quantitatively.

The pioneering work of Manintveld[77] suggested that, if cold
work conditions could be controlled in such a way that the
resistivity decay steps could be resolved, then the migration
energy, kinetics, and eventually the number and identification of
point defects produced by cold work could be obtained. The
identification, of course, would rely on a comparison of the migration energy and kinetics with those obtained from inherently
simpler experiments, such as quenching and electron irradiation.
However, a search for the interstitial in copper, expected to be
produced by cold work, gave inconclusive results. Meechan and
Sosin[84] deformed copper, as well as gold and nickel, at 4.2°K
and measured the resistivity change with annealing up to about
100°K. They found the total amount of resistivity recovery in this
range, relative to that produced by the cold work, to be only
about 2%. Since, from radiation damage annealing data, interstitials are expected to be mobile in this temperature range, the
conclusion is either that interstitials are not produced by cold
work or that they interact so strongly with the dislocations, or
each other, that a much higher temperature is required to cause
them to migrate freely. Although the experiments of Takamura
et al.[85] suggest the latter case, there is at present no known way
to decide between these possibilities. Somewhat better success
has been achieved in comparing the migration energies of the
cold-work produced defects in silver[86] and gold,[87] which migrate
at about −40°C, with vacancies and their complexes produced by
quenching. Although precise agreement has not been obtained in
the case of either the migration energies or the kinetics, indications
are that vacancy-type defects migrate in these metals above
−40°C, and that they can be trapped by impurities and/or
dislocations and then appear to migrate with a higher energy,

which may be interpreted to be the sum of the migration and binding energies. Direct observation by electron microscopy, while unable to reveal single point defects, has shown the production of debris by cold work which is best interpreted as the condensation of vacancy-type defects.[88,89] Experiments on the formation and growth of voids during high temperature plastic deformation point in the same direction.[90,91]

From the above experiments combined with theoretical considerations, one may conclude that point defects are produced by plastic deformation, but a number of uncertainties remain as to the nature of these defects. One can state with some confidence that vacancies, or vacancy clusters, have been observed after plastic deformation, but the evidence for interstitials must be judged as inconclusive at the present time. Some highly suggestive similarities occur in the migration energies obtained by annealing experiments after cold work, quenching, and irradiation. However, the presence of dislocations, and particularly the changing dislocation structure and its interaction with point defects, complicates the annealing kinetics and makes it difficult even to separate out the point defect contribution to a physical property (such as electrical resistivity). The intricacies of plastic deformation are of great inherent interest, but, for investigating the basic properties of point defects themselves, plastic deformation is generally not a satisfactory method of defect production.

6. Changes in Mechanical Properties

Important changes in mechanical properties can occur when point defects are introduced into a metal. The majority of these changes depend in a complicated way on the interactions of dislocations with point defects or their clusters. These changes are not yet interpretable at the same level of sophistication as changes, for example, in electrical resistivity or lattice parameter. That is, it is usually not possible to determine the basic properties of the defects themselves from this type of experiment. The changes in many mechanical properties are often large and readily measurable and are of considerable practical importance, and a number of careful investigations have been made in this field. For these reasons a discussion of some selected typical experiments related to the theoretical discussion of Chapter IV is pertinent and is presented in this section.

a) Dislocation pinning

As pointed out in IV–7, point defects may pin dislocations and thereby reduce the internal friction and increase the elastic modulus. Conceptually, the simplest experiment is that of quenching-in vacancies, since only one type of defect is then produced. In practice, however, it has proved very difficult to obtain quantitative results from this type of experiment, although the expected effects are generally observed. Roswell and Nowick[92] measured the internal friction in quenched gold wires after quenching in water and in air and after furnace cooling. In each case they observed a decrease in internal friction, the largest change following the fastest quench. Similar results were reported by Levy and Metzger for aluminum.[93] Kamel[94] quenched gold foils from different temperatures and showed that the internal friction was not at its minimum immediately following the quench, but decreased further with time at room temperature. This implies that after the quench the vacancies must either migrate to the dislocations or form clusters in order to pin the dislocations. Kamel's initial values of the internal friction are somewhat difficult to explain, but may be related to the observations of Barnes et al.,[95] who measured the internal friction of quenched copper and noted the expected decrease at room temperature but found the initial value to be highly sensitive to the heat treatment the metal had received prior to quenching. This sensitivity can be due to the annealing or rearranging of dislocations and the extent of dispersal of vacancy clusters during the prior heat treatment. The general results of all these experiments indicate, however, that shortly after the quench vacancies or their clusters can pin dislocations and thereby decrease the internal friction. This expected pinning effect also increases the hardness of the metal, an effect discussed later in this section.

The difficulties which seem to arise from altering the dislocation content or structure by quenching strains appear to be avoidable in irradiation experiments, in which the defects are introduced without altering the bulk temperature of the sample. Thompson and Holmes[96] measured the change in modulus and internal friction during reactor irradiation at 28°C of a well-annealed single crystal of copper. The measurements were made in the kilocycle frequency range at a maximum strain amplitude of 5×10^{-8}, sufficiently small to ensure strain amplitude independence. A typical set of results is shown in Fig. V–6.1, where

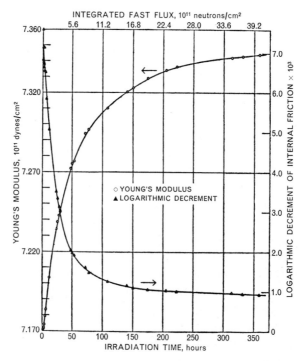

Fig. V–6.1 Young's modulus and logarithmic decrement of internal friction vs. reactor irradiation time at a flux of 3×10^6 neutrons/cm²-sec (fast) for a previously well-annealed single crystal of copper. (From reference 96.)

Young's modulus, obtained from the resonant frequency, and the logarithmic decrement of internal friction are shown as functions of radiation exposure. The modulus increase and the logarithmic decrement decrease are in agreement with a dislocation pinning mechanism. It should be noted that saturation of these changes occurs at a very low exposure, of the order of 4×10^{12} nvt. The same crystal was irradiated up to an exposure of 1.4×10^{14} nvt and the modulus showed no further change, which indicates that saturation had indeed occurred at the lower flux value. The irradiation of this particular crystal caused the modulus to increase by about 3.7% and the internal friction to decrease by a factor of 7. The modulus change was found to be proportional to the reciprocal of $(1 + \gamma t)^2$ and the change of internal friction to the reciprocal of $(1 + \gamma t)^4$, where t is the radiation time and γ is the pinning rate constant. The $(1 + \gamma t)$ terms can be related to the change in L, the average dislocation loop length between pinning points, by the introduction of the radiation produced defects, that is, $L = L_0/(1 + \gamma t)$. Thus the change in modulus is proportional to L^2 and the change in internal friction to L^4, in agreement with equations IV–7.1 and IV–7.3 of the pinning theory described in section IV–7.

Stern and Granato[97] measured the internal friction of copper in the megacycle region following gamma irradiation and found that the internal friction decreased in a manner predicted by the dislocation pinning theory. They were able to estimate the number of pinning points produced per vacancy-interstitial pair. This number is less than unity, which indicates that some of the defects migrate to sinks or traps other than the dislocations. Electron irradiation has been shown to produce similar effects. Dieckamp and Sosin[98] found that Young's modulus of copper increased to saturation upon electron bombardment, and then slowly decreased at high integrated exposures. As shown by Lomer and Niblett,[99] the internal friction is decreased by electron irradiation.

Muss and Townsend[100] have shown that deuteron irradiation of tungsten at room temperature produces very similar results. A typical result is shown in Fig. V–6.2. The characteristic rise in

R

range, as shown in Fig. V–6.3. It is clear from this figure that for efficient pinning it is necessary that the defects be mobile, i.e., be able to migrate to positions where they can serve as pinning points. Another important point is that, although the efficiency is low, pinning does occur at 20°K. This means that the defect that does the pinning at this low temperature must have moved over a long range, of the order of 150 atomic distances, in order to account for the amount of pinning observed. This pinning effect has also been observed following electron irradiation at 4.2°K.[103] Since defects are known to be immobile at 20°K, the implication is that interaction of focusing collision chains (I–12) with dislocations results in the preferential creation of a small fraction of

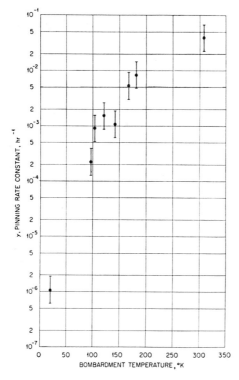

Fig. V–6.3 The pinning rate constant, γ, for copper as a function of reactor irradiation temperature. (From reference 101.)

the defects at or near the dislocations. The strong effect of permitting some defects to migrate was observed by irradiating copper with neutrons at about 20°K, measuring the modulus, warming to 47°K, and remeasuring the modulus at 20°K. As shown in Fig. V–6.4, a substantial increase is observed in the

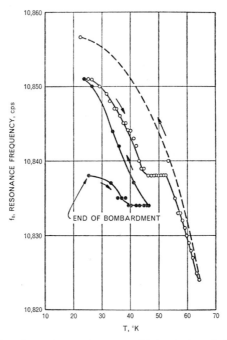

Fig. V–6.4 The effect of annealing on radiation induced pinning in a copper single crystal. The ordinate is the resonance frequency of the crystal. The solid circles represent the first warm-up and return to about 21°K and the open circles, the second warm-up. (From reference 102.)

modulus (as measured by the resonance frequency), and hence in the pinning, with a corresponding decrease (not shown in the figure) in the internal friction. Since the vacancy in copper is generally believed to migrate at a much higher temperature, the defect migrating and causing the pinning at these low temperatures is an interstitial or an interstitial type of defect. If the irradiation is done at about 170°K, then upon subsequent warming considerable additional pinning occurs at about 260°K, as shown in Fig. V–6.5.[101] Similar results have been observed with electron irradiation by Lomer et al,[99] who found a small change in internal

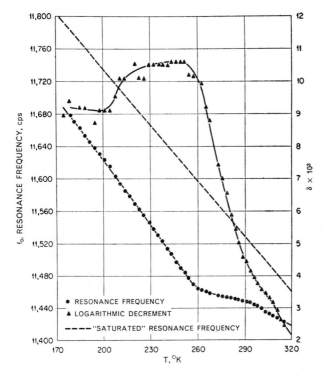

Fig. V–6.5 Logarithmic decrement and resonance frequency during initial warm-up after irradiation at 168°K. (From reference 101.)

friction in copper irradiated with electrons at 100°K followed by a large decrease in internal friction during warming at about 200°K, and again at 270°K. These experiments indicate that one or more defects migrate in the 200–270°K region in copper.

Similar effects might be expected to arise from defects created by plastic deformation. However, changes in dislocation structure, in particular in the breakaway and generation of dislocations, are found to overwhelm the effects of point defects. In fact, during plastic deformation[104,105] the modulus has been observed to decrease and the internal friction to increase, a behavior opposite that caused by the pinning effect. A study of internal friction following the annealing of cold-worked metals reveals changes which may be associated with the motion of point defects but which have not been positively identified[106] because of the complications arising from dislocation networks and defect clusters.

b) Hardening

Point defects or their clusters can interfere with the motion of dislocations at stresses higher than those used for internal friction studies; in fact, the measurements previously discussed were performed at extremely low amplitude to avoid such effects. As the strain is increased, the point defect-dislocation interaction manifests itself by changing the characteristics of the stress-strain curve. As an example, the stress-strain curves for quenched and slowly cooled aluminum single crystals[107] are shown in Fig. V–6.6. The two most important features of these curves are the much increased critical shear stress and the lower rate of work hardening of the quenched specimens. The maximum increase in the critical shear stress may not be reached immediately after quenching, but may require some time to develop. Such an effect is illustrated in Fig. V–6.7, where the yield stress of quenched copper is plotted as a function of time at $100°C$.[108] Apparently the mobility of the vacancies is sufficiently high at this temperature to permit their migration. This migration is required by both the jog and void models of dislocation anchoring given in section IV–7. These models also predict the existence of a yield point and a subsequent low rate of work hardening. These features are indicated by the stress-elongation curve of the quenched specimen in Fig. V–6.6.

Irradiation induced defects also cause hardening superficially similar to quench hardening. The effect of irradiation at ambient reactor temperature for single crystals of copper[109] is illustrated in Fig. V–6.8, which shows a rise in critical shear stress and a lowered rate of work hardening at low strains. Striking differences from the dislocation pinning effect were found, however, when copper was irradiated in a reactor at 20°K. The critical shear stress was found to have an increased value immediately after irradiation, and subsequent warming to 80°K and remeasuring at 20°K produced no apparent change. This observation implies that the defect which migrated in this region to cause changes in internal friction and modulus has a very small contribution to the critical shear stress. Clearly, the change in hardness at 20°K must arise from some other effect of neutron irradiation. This does not mean that the migrating defect has no effect, as changes in critical shear stress have been observed following electron irradiation. In fact, Makin et al.[110,111] found electron irradiation of copper at −195°C to cause a greater increase in the critical shear stress than at 30°C. This indicates that a mobile defect has caused pinning at low temperatures but has migrated away at the higher temperature. Its effect on the change of critical shear stress with low temperature neutron irradiation is probably obscured by another effect. An explanation of the major source of neutron damage hardening has been proposed by Seeger (see section IV–7). In this model, the clusters of damage associated with local zones of displaced atoms block the motion of dislocations. In a detailed study of neutron irradiated copper, Diehl[112] has shown that most of the predications of Seeger's model are obeyed.

Further information on the mechanism of radiation hardening can be obtained by the study of polycrystalline specimens since, if the Petch relation is applicable (IV–7), source hardening can be separated from lattice friction hardening. Source hardening means that the stress required to free a dislocation has been increased, and lattice friction hardening means that the resistance to the motion of dislocations on their glide planes has been increased. The Petch relation, equation IV–7.14, is expected to be applicable when a material exhibits a sharp yield point.[113,114] Copper shows such a yield point after irradiation, as illustrated in

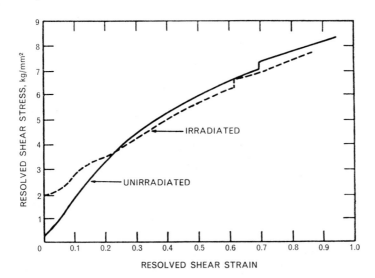

Fig. V–6.8 Stress-strain curves of unirradiated and reactor irradiated copper crystals. (From reference 109.)

Fig. V–6.9 by experiments of Adams and Higgins.[113] By investigating the critical shear stress of neutron irradiated polycrystalline copper as a function of grain size, they found that both lattice friction hardening and source hardening occur simultaneously. Further, the lattice friction component was found to be far more temperature dependent than the source hardening. It has also been observed that, upon annealing to 20°C, the lattice hardening remains unaltered but the source hardening is reduced.[114]

The above techniques have also been applied to body-centered metals, but the results indicate that the applicability of the Petch relation to these materials after irradiation is very much in doubt. For example, important deviations from the Petch relation have been observed in molybdenum[115] and iron.[116] Johnson et al.[115] have shown that if the data for molybdenum are forced to fit the Petch relation, then the lattice friction stress increases upon irradiation but the dislocation unpinning stress is decreased. This in itself would be hard to explain, but, more importantly, such a decrease in the unpinning stress would lead to a wrong prediction of the change in the ductile-brittle transition temperature with irradiation. Cottrell's theory of brittle fracture, based on the Petch relation (section IV–7), would in this case predict a substantial lowering of the transition temperature in irradiated molybdenum. Experiments have shown that, in fact, just the opposite occurs.[117,118]

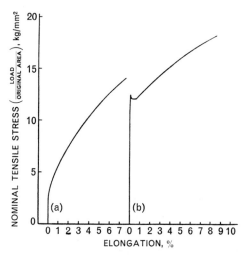

Fig. V–6.9 Stress-strain curves for (a) unirradiated and (b) irradiated [about 6×10^{17} nvt (fast)] polycrystalline copper specimens of 0.0025-cm grain diameter, tested at 20°C. (From reference 113.)

c) Excess vacancies and internal friction in alloys

As pointed out in section IV–7, stress-induced ordering in a substitutional solid solution gives rise to internal friction. The internal friction in this case is proportional to the number of vacancies present and can therefore be used to measure the lifetime of an excess number of vacancies. It should be noted that this type of internal friction has nothing to do with dislocations but arises entirely from the interchange of vacancies with adjacent atoms. In order to retain the excess vacancies it is desirable to carry out the measurements at temperatures at which the vacancies migrate slowly. At any reasonable frequency in an internal friction experiment the vacancies are moving rapidly and can anneal during the experiment. The vacancy migration can be studied, however, by the equivalent elastic aftereffect experiment, which can be carried out at the lower temperatures.

In an elastic aftereffect experiment the specimen is put under a constant stress (without causing plastic deformation) for a sufficient length of time for the strain to reach its equilibrium value. Upon removal of the stresses, the strain will slowly decay back to zero and is measured, for example, by the rate of untwisting of a twisted wire. The equation governing this situation is obtained by setting the stress, σ, equal to zero in equation IV–7.4. This gives the following differential equation for the decay of the strain:

$$d\epsilon/\epsilon = - \, dt/\tau \, , \qquad\qquad \text{V–6.1}$$

the solution of which is the equation for simple exponential relaxation

$$\epsilon = \epsilon_0 e^{-t/\tau} \, , \qquad\qquad \text{V–6.2}$$

where the relaxation time, τ, is proportional to the mean time of stay of an atom on its lattice site and is therefore inversely proportional to its jump frequency. This mean time of stay is proportional to the product of the probability that a vacancy is adjacent to an atom and the probability that an atom will jump into the vacancy. The former is simply the atomic fraction of vacancies, which has been shown to depend exponentially on E_F, the formation energy of the vacancy, and the latter is proportional to the exponential of E_M, the migration energy of a vacancy. It should be noted, however, that, whereas in a pure metal the jump of any atom nearest neighbor to a vacancy is equally probable, diffusion rates in alloys are generally unequal, so that the vacancy will have a tendency to migrate on the sublattice of the most mobile atom species. This factor must be considered in the interpretation of data on alloys with large solute concentrations.

During an elastic aftereffect, or other internal friction, measurement in an alloy containing a thermodynamic equilibrium concentration of vacancies, the relaxation time is governed by an exponential containing the sum of the activation energies for vacancy
formation and migration, which is the same as the activation
energy for atomic diffusion in the alloy. A typical example of an
equilibrium elastic aftereffect experiment on a 70–30% silver-zinc
alloy is shown in Fig. V–6.10 for three different temperatures.[119]
Such strain decay curves in alloys usually deviate somewhat from
a pure exponential, and the definition of the relaxation time, τ,
is therefore slightly ambiguous. However, the cross-cut method
of analysis (section III–2) will give the correct activation energy,
and, in order to take cross cuts at a similar point on all curves,
Nowick[119] defines an effective τ as the inflection point of the curve.

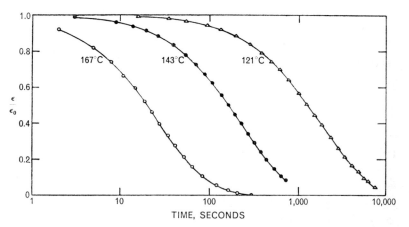

Fig. V–6.10 Typical elastic aftereffect measurements at three temperatures
on a 70–30% silver-zinc alloy. The relaxation time, in each case, is the
value of the time at the inflection point. (From reference 119.)

In principle, a measurement of the decrease of τ, i.e., the
acceleration of the strain decay at a constant temperature, with
increasing quench temperature should yield the energy of formation of the vacancies. In practice, however, the results were

unreliable, probably because the dimensions of the specimens used for elastic aftereffect studies are such that fast, strain-free quenches are not possible. The decay rate of the quenched-in vacancies can be studied with sufficient accuracy, however, by measuring τ at a series of annealing temperatures on specimens quenched from the same temperature. Figure V–6.11 illustrates such experiments[120] in a 70–30% silver-zinc alloy. The slope of the line in Fig. V–6.11 yields an activation energy of 0.86 eV, the migration energy of the vacancy. A second long-time decay with a higher activation energy was also observed,[120,121] which, the authors suggest, arises from trapped vacancies.

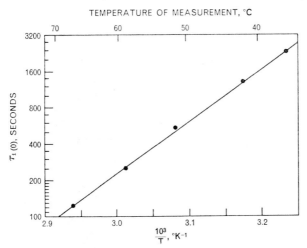

Fig. V–6.11   The initial time-to-inflection, $\tau_i(0)$, as a function of the temperature of measurement for a 70–30% silver-zinc specimen quenched from 400°C. From the slope of the straight line, $E_M = 0.86$ eV. (From reference 120.)

In view of the sensitivity of this type of measurement in the detection of excess vacancies in alloys, it seems reasonable to use this technique for the measurement of excess vacancies produced by irradiation. Unfortunately the results of existing measurements are inconclusive. Li and Nowick[122] irradiated a copper-aluminum alloy in a reactor at liquid nitrogen temperature and searched for an accelerated elastic aftereffect in steps from about 50° up to 200°C with negative results. It is possible that the vacancies migrated out of the sample at a temperature between liquid nitrogen and room temperature. Nilson[123] studied the internal friction in a precipitating aluminum-magnesium alloy after neutron irradiation at ambient reactor temperatures. He observed a shift in the internal friction peak, corresponding to a reduction of the relaxation time, which indicated the presence of an excess number of vacancies.

Excess vacancies produced by plastic deformation have also been detected by internal friction techniques.[124] The experiments were done on a silver-zinc (22% zinc) alloy using the elastic aftereffect. The rate of anelastic relaxation was found to be greatly increased by the introduction of a small plastic strain just prior to the anelasticity measurement. The effect of quenched-in vacancies was also examined for comparison. Typical relaxation curves are shown in Fig. V–6.12 together with a relaxation curve for a well-annealed specimen extrapolated to the measuring tem-

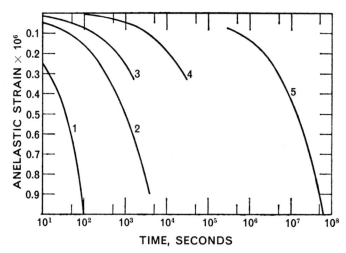

Fig. V–6.12 Typical elastic aftereffect relaxation curves at 59°C. Curves 1 and 3: deformed specimens; curves 2 and 4: quenched specimens; curve 5: equilibrium behavior. (From reference 124.)

perature of 59°C. The shape of the relaxation curve is essentially the same in all cases, which indicates that the same diffusion process is operative. The large shift in the time scale to lower values, relative to the annealed specimen, shows that a high concentration of excess vacancies was produced both by quenching and by plastic deformation. The relative excess defect concentration can be determined from the ratio of the rate of relaxation in a nonequilibrium specimen to that in a well-annealed specimen. By extrapolation of this ratio to zero time it was found that a plastic strain of about 0.005 increases the concentration of vacancies by a factor of about 10^5.

7. Annealing Experiments.
I. Annealing of Quenched-in Defects

Experiments have so far been described from which the basic static properties of point defects have been determined, such as the energy of formation and some specific physical property changes. In this section the second class of important defect properties, namely their migration characteristics, will be discussed. In annealing experiments excess defects are permitted to escape by warming the sample to a temperature high enough to provide sufficient thermal energy for the defects to migrate to sinks or to recombine. In order to follow the annealing, some characteristic physical property of the defect, usually electrical resistivity, is measured as a function of time and temperature. The central problem is the identification of the migrating defect and the measurement of the corresponding activation energy. The situation is intricate because of the interaction of the various defects, as shown in Chapter II, and unequivocal identification has been agreed upon only in a few cases.

Some carefully controlled annealing experiments on quenched-in and radiation-induced defects fall into this category, although complete interpretation of every feature of the annealing has not been achieved. Typical experiments of this type are described in this and the next section, but no attempt will be made at a complete coverage of all experiments reported in the literature. Advances in theory and experimental techniques have demonstrated the existence of many complicating factors and the need for controlling them. It is only in recent years that a sufficient degree of sophistication has been achieved to permit a quantitative determination in favorable cases. In the annealing of defects introduced by plastic deformation the necessary control has not yet been accomplished and, as already shown in section V–5, a detailed interpretation of these experiments is not yet possible. For this reason annealing experiments after cold work were briefly discussed in V–5 but will not be described further.

a) Exponential decay

The simplest annealing process, as shown in Chapter II, is the migration of a single type of point defect to a fixed number of sinks. In this case the decay in the concentration is expected to be a simple exponential. The factors which favor this type of simple annealing are known: (1) high purity to minimize defect-impurity interactions, (2) low concentration of excess defects to avoid interaction among them, and (3) a sink concentration sufficiently high relative to the defect concentration that the probability of defects encountering one another before reaching a sink is small.

These conditions have apparently been met in several experiments on pure gold for quenches at or below 700°C. A typical example[125] of the decay of the quenched-in resistivity at 60°C, following a quench from 700°C, is shown in Fig. V–7.1, which clearly shows an exponential decay over two orders of magnitude. In similar experiments Bauerle and Koehler[125] changed the temperature during the course of annealing and obtained an activation energy of 0.82 ± 0.05 eV by the change of slope method (III–2). Cattaneo and Germagnoli[126] carried out similar experiments on zone-refined gold and obtained exponential decay curves at several annealing temperatures, as illustrated in Fig. V–7.2. From a plot of the characteristic rate constant vs. the reciprocal of the absolute temperature, they obtained an activation energy of defect migration of 0.84 ± 0.03 eV. The results of these two experimental determinations are in good agreement. From the quench and equilibrium experiments discussed in previous sections, it is reasonably certain that primarily single vacancies have been quenched in and are the defects migrating to sinks in these annealing experiments. This identification is strengthened greatly by the magnitude of the measured activation energy for migration in comparison with the activation energy for self-diffusion in gold. As shown in I–7, the activation energy for self-diffusion by the vacancy mechanism is the sum of the energy of formation and the energy of migration of the vacancy. The self-diffusion activation energy in gold is accurately known[127]

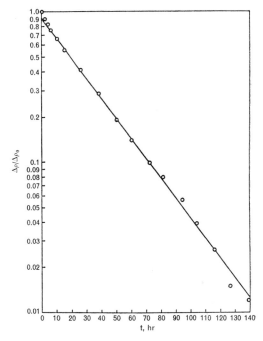

Fig. V–7.1 Decay of quenched-in resistivity illustrating exponential annealing of vacancies in gold. The specimen was quenched from 700°C and annealed at 60°C. (From reference 125.)

s

to be 1.81 $\pm$ 0.03 eV. As shown in Table V–7.1, the best values
of the energy of formation and energy of migration in gold add up
to the self-diffusion energy.

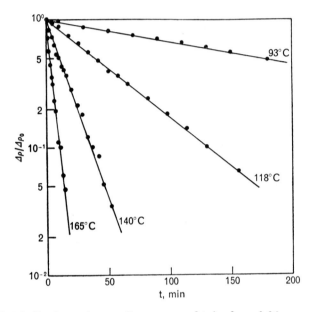

Fig. V–7.2 Isothermal annealing curves obtained on 0.04-mm pure gold
wires after quenching from 700°C. (From reference 126.)

Similar quenching and annealing experiments have been carried
out on pure copper (not zone-refined) by Airoldi, Bacchella and
Germagnoli.[39] From the increase in resistivity as a function of
quench temperature they determined a formation energy of
1.0 $\pm$ 0.1 eV. Isothermal annealing curves obtained in the 350°
to 470°C temperature range were found to be exponential. The
activation energy for migration derived from these curves was
found to be about 1.3 eV for the thinnest wire, but for larger diameter wire a somewhat larger energy was obtained. Seeger[128]
reports an activation energy of migration of 1.08 $\pm$ 0.03 eV for

TABLE V–7.1

Energies of Formation, Migration, and Self-diffusion
in Pure Gold

Type of experiment	E_F (eV/atom)	E_M (eV/atom)	$E_F + E_M = E_D$ (eV/atom)	Reference
Equilibrium	0.94 ± 0.09			Table V–2.1
Quench	0.98 ± 0.03			Table V–3.1
Annealing		0.82 ± 0.05	1.78 ± 0.08	125
Annealing		0.84 ± 0.03	1.80 ± 0.06	126
Self-diffusion			1.81 ± 0.03	127

quenched-in vacancies in copper. The activation energy for self-diffusion in copper is 2.05 ± 0.03 eV.[129] The combined results of Airoldi et al. give a value within 10% of this, and a combination of their formation energy with the Seeger migration energy is in excellent agreement with the self-diffusion data. These results are reasonable, considering that copper is much more difficult to quench than gold because of oxidation problems.

After an initial transient, exponential decay of quenched-in vacancies has also been observed in platinum quenched from temperatures between 1100° and 1400°C. An activation energy for annealing of 1.45 ± 0.05 eV was found.[37,38] The vacancy formation energy in platinum is 1.3 to 1.4 eV (see Table V–3.1) which, in combination with the above migration energy, gives about 2.8 eV for the activation energy of self-diffusion. The measured value is 2.96 ± 0.06 eV.[130] The agreement, while not perfect, is reasonable, and one may assign 1.45 eV to the migration energy of the vacancy in platinum. For quenches from above 1600°C the kinetics deviate from the pure exponential and the apparent activation energy is lower, about 1.1 eV.[131,132] A detailed study of the kinetics following such high temperature quenches has not yet been carried out. Divacancies and larger vacancy complexes may be expected to play a role.

b) *The effect of impurities*

In some recent experiments one of the parameters mentioned above, namely purity, was varied in a controlled way by purposefully doping with impurities. According to the theory discussed in II–4, if impurities are present and can trap vacancies, then the observed annealing will still be exponential but with a decreased rate and an increased effective activation energy. The decreased rate in annealing of gold doped with silver[126] is illustrated in Fig. V–7.3 at an annealing temperature of 126°C after quenching.

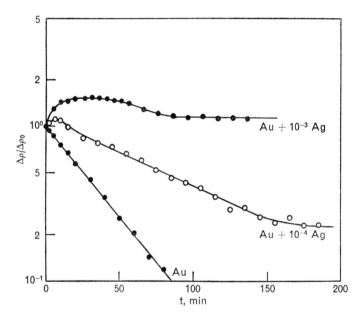

Fig. V–7.3 The influence of impurity content on the isothermal annealing curves of gold at 126°C. (From reference 126.)

A decrease in the rate of annealing with increasing impurity concentration is clearly evident. Cattaneo and Germagnoli[126] report that after the initial rise in resistivity, a complicating factor that will be discussed later, the resistivity decay curves are exponential and at the higher annealing temperature the initial disturbance in the kinetics becomes unimportant. For each of the exponential decay curves, they calculated the characteristic reaction time, τ, which is the reciprocal of the effective rate constant derived in II–4. Thus, the pertinent equation is

$$\tau = \frac{1}{K_e} = \frac{1 + 12I_0 e^{B/kT}}{K_3} = \frac{1 + 12I_0 e^{B/kT}}{K_3{}^0 e^{-E_M/kT}} . \qquad \text{II–4.12}$$

In these experiments the $12I_0 e^{B/kT}$ term dominates and therefore

$$\tau \cong (12I_0/K_3{}^0) e^{(E_M+B)/kT} .$$

Thus, when τ is plotted against $1/T$, a straight line with the above effective activation energy is expected. As illustrated in Fig. V–7.4, a straight line may be put through the experimental points,

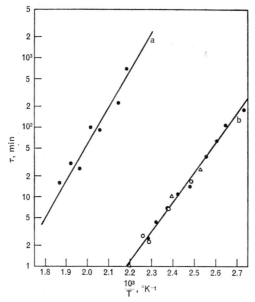

Fig. V–7.4 Characteristic recovery times of the quenched-in resistivity as a function of annealing temperature. Curve a: Au + 1.2 × 10⁻³ Ag. Curve b: pure Au; solid circle: 0.04-mm wires, air quench; open circle: 0.007-mm wires, air quench; triangle: 0.07-mm wires, water quench. (From reference 126.)

within the experimental error. The slope of this line is 1.05 $\pm$ 0.1 eV, whereas the value is 0.84 $\pm$ 0.03 eV for the zone-refined gold specimen. The difference between these two slopes, 0.22 eV, is the approximate value of the binding energy of a vacancy to the silver impurity atom. Cattaneo and Germagnoli[133] have also tried to determine the binding energy of vacancies to nickel and to antimony impurities in gold. These binding energies have not yet been determined quantitatively, but the preliminary experiments indicate that the value for nickel is small and for antimony is at least as large as for silver.

It should be noted that in the above discussion the vacancy-impurity complex was assumed to migrate much more slowly than the isolated vacancy. The opposite may also happen, in which case the presence of an impurity may increase the rate of annealing of a vacancy. This would require that the vacancy interchange positions both with the adjacent impurity and with a lattice atom adjacent to both of them faster than with a normal lattice atom.[134,135] Preliminary experiments with aluminum containing magnesium indicate that vacancies are bound to magnesium atoms[136] and that their annealing is speeded up,[137] perhaps by the above mechanism. Such an accelerated annealing would carry the impurities as well as the vacancies to the sinks, and the segregation of impurities might be observable at dislocations and grain boundaries. This type of segregation has not been sought, but Kino, Kabemoto and Yoshida[137] observed an increased rate of annealing of quenched-in defects in aluminum doped with 10^{-4} and 10^{-3} atomic fraction of magnesium. Their decay curves were approximately exponential. Cotterill and Segall[137a] have observed that upon repeated quenching and annealing a purification of aluminum occurs, presumably via vacancy-impurity complex migration to the surface. Based on the theory of section I–6, some vacancy-impurity binding energies in aluminum have been obtained directly from quenching experiments. The results indicate an approximate binding energy of 0.2 eV for magnesium[136] and 0.4 eV for tin[138].

The initial resistivity increase evident in Fig. V–7.3 has also been observed in gold by Meshii, Mori and Kauffman[139] and in silver by Quéré.[140] According to the Cattaneo and Germagnoli experiments, this initial increase is enhanced by the presence of impurities, and the other authors also suggest that this effect may arise from impurity-vacancy interaction. Quéré further points out that he has observed this effect only after a slow quench. It seems reasonable that this effect may arise from the clustering of vacancies around impurity atoms. Since the resistivity of such clusters is not known, and since very few experiments have been carried out on the kinetics associated with this effect, further interpretation is not possible at this time.

Some attempts have been made to alter another important parameter, the sink concentration, by increasing the dislocation content of the crystal by a small amount of plastic deformation prior to annealing. According to the simple theory, this treatment should result in an increased rate of annealing without any change in kinetics or activation energy. Yoshida and Koehler[141] found that, after 0.1 to 0.5% extension at room temperature of a quenched gold wire, the rate of annealing increased as expected, but, unexpectedly, there was also a decrease in the activation energy. Meshii and Kauffman[142] deformed quenched gold at 78°K prior to annealing and found that the effective activation energy was low at the beginning of the anneal but reached the normal value, characteristic of an undeformed specimen, after about 20% of the quenched-in resistivity had annealed out. The interpretation of these experiments is not clear as yet. In both, the slope change method of activation energy determination was used; therefore, the kinetics are available over only short periods of time, and, although the kinetics appears to be exponential, the data are not conclusive.

c) The role of divacancies

When quenches are carried out on pure metals from rather high temperatures, resulting in relatively high defect concentrations, the probability of interactions between defects before they reach the sinks is high, and the simple exponential annealing is no longer expected to be applicable. Bauerle and Koehler[125] found in their quench experiments on gold that when the quenches were carried out from temperatures above 700°C the annealing kinetics became complex. Koehler, Seitz and Bauerle,[143] in an interpretation of these early experiments, suggested that divacancies play an important role in the annealing process. Theory shows clearly (II–6) that the annealing kinetics are complex when both mono- and divacancies are present and are mobile. In some circumstances simple analytic approximations are applicable, and some experimental results that apparently obey these approximations have recently been reported and are discussed below.

If a steady-state approximation for the divacancy concentration can be made, and if the divacancies are much more mobile than the single vacancies, then the annealing of the vacancies follows a simple quadratic decay (equation II–6.14). The rate constant governing this decay is controlled by the activation energy for the migration of the single vacancy. Such a decay has been observed by Schüle et al.[87] in gold quenched from 1000°C, as illustrated in Fig. V–7.5, where the reciprocal of the resistivity increment is plotted against the annealing time. They found the activation energy for this process to be 0.83 ± 0.02 eV, in excellent agreement with the values quoted in Table V–7.1 for single vacancy migration. After low temperature quenches they found exponential decay, following an initial transient, which also yields the same activation energy.

In another series of experiments on gold, Cattaneo, Germagnoli and Guarini[144] demonstrated the importance of the pretreatment of the wire on the resulting kinetics. In their experiments the wire supported its own weight and was therefore under tension while being preannealed at 850°C. Extra dislocations were apparently introduced after a long period of such treatment. The samples containing the high dislocation concentration annealed more rapidly after quenching from 730°C than the others and obeyed a simple exponential decay with an activation energy of 0.83 eV. In these samples the sink concentration is high relative to the

defect concentration, and therefore the annealing is expected to
be dominated by the migration of the single vacancy. The samples
preannealed for a short time at 850°C and therefore characterized
by a lower dislocation content exhibited mixed quadratic and

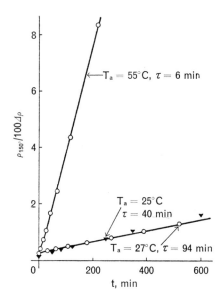

Fig. V–7.5 The percentage resistivity changes during isothermal recovery
are plotted reciprocally against the annealing time for gold quenched from
1000°C. Straight line segments imply second-order kinetics. T_a is the
annealing temperature, and τ the half-time of the decay. (From reference
87.)

first-order kinetics after quenching. This behavior is understandable on the basis of the steady-state analytical approximation if both mono- and divacancies are migrating to sinks (equation
II–6.13). The integrated form of this analytic approximation may
be written as

$$V_1 = \frac{K_3 K_2 / 2 K_1 K_4}{[1 + (K_3 K_2 / 2 K_1 K_4 V_1{}^0)] e^{K_3 t} - 1} . \qquad \text{II–6.13}$$

Cattaneo et al. separated the quadratic short-time and the exponential long-time behavior as follows:

$$\text{for } K_3 t \ll 1, \quad V_1 \simeq \frac{V_1{}^0}{1 + [K_3 + (2K_1 K_4 V_1{}^0 / K_2)] \, t}; \qquad \text{V--7.1}$$

$$\text{for } K_3 t \gg 1, \quad V_1 \simeq V_1{}^0 e^{-K_3 t}. \qquad \text{V--7.2}$$

They determined the effective rate constants of the second-order portions of the annealing curves as a function of temperature. From equation V–7.1, the effective rate constant, K, is given by

$$K = K_3 + \frac{2K_1 K_4 V_1{}^0}{K_2}$$

$$= \alpha \nu \lambda^2 \left[\exp\left(\frac{-E_M{}^{(1)}}{kT}\right) + 12 V_1{}^0 \exp\left(-\frac{E_M{}^{(2)} - B}{kT}\right) \right]. \qquad \text{V--7.3}$$

Cattaneo et al. found that a satisfactory agreement with experiment could be obtained by the following choice of parameters:

$$E_M{}^{(1)} = 0.85 \text{ eV}, \quad E_M{}^{(2)} - B = 0.5 \text{ eV}, \quad V_1{}^0 \simeq 5 \times 10^{-6},$$

$$\alpha = 4 \times 10^8 \text{ cm}^{-2}.$$

This value of the migration energy for monovacancies, $E_M{}^{(1)}$, is in good agreement with that determined from their quenches, discussed previously, and with those from other experiments (Table V–7.1), as well as with that obtained from the exponential portion fitted to equation V–7.2. It should be noted that from these experiments and this analysis the values of the divacancy migration energy, $E_M{}^{(2)}$, and of the divacancy binding energy, B, cannot be obtained separately but only as the combination $E_M{}^{(2)} - B$. At low temperatures (about 50°C) after a fast quench, Cattaneo et al. find an exponential resistivity decay which approaches a residual resistivity. The activation energy of this decay is 0.66 ± 0.05 eV, which the authors believe to be the migration energy for divacancies formed during the quench, some of which form clusters and thus account for the residual resistivity.

DeJong and Koehler[145] obtained very closely the same value for $E_M{}^{(2)} - B$, namely 0.555 ± 0.015 eV, by an entirely different method. They studied the annealing of gold wires quenched from above 700°C at 30° and at 40°C by the change of slope method, i.e., by altering the temperature quickly between 30° and 40°C frequently during the course of the anneal. If vacancies and divacancies remain in a pseudo-equilibrium during the annealing, i.e., the approximation $V_2 = KV_1^2$ (equation II–6.17) is valid, then an analytic approximation analogous, but not identical, to the steady-state one discussed above is valid, and it can be shown that an effective activation energy equal to $E_M^{(2)} - B$ was measured in these experiments (equation II–6.22). DeJong and Koehler also find that after a quench to $-35°C$ there is a small initial decrease in resistivity observable at $-3°C$ superimposed on the normal annealing. They interpret this initial decrease as the migration of monovacancies to form divacancies. From an analysis of the annealing rates and the magnitude of the decrease they arrive at a value of the binding energy $B = 0.10 \pm 0.03$ eV. Several auxiliary experiments showed that the initial resistivity decrease is due to this rearrangement. When the wire was quenched to 18°C and held there for 5 minutes, the decrease at $-3°C$ was very small but had an unaltered time constant. In another experiment a specimen was equilibrated at $-3°C$ and then pulse-heated for a few milliseconds to break up the divacancies. During a subsequent anneal at $-3°C$ the initial resistivity decrease reappeared with the same magnitude and the same time constant. These experiments indicate strongly that the equilibrium reaction between mono- and divacancies was measured. This experiment is feasible only in a well-annealed specimen of low sink concentration, because otherwise the divacancies would reach the sinks before they could break apart and thus equilibrium could not be achieved. This experiment also indicates that the resistivity of a divacancy is less than that of two monovacancies, the difference being 4.6%. With $E_M^{(2)} - B$ and B known, the value of $E_M^{(2)}$ turns out to be 0.66 ± 0.06 eV. DeJong and Koehler point out that in their specimens a direct determination of $E_M^{(2)}$ was not possible; the reason is probably the low sink concentration in their samples. In specimens of higher sink concentration $E_M^{(2)}$ may well be

Recent experiments by Seeger et al[149a] indicate that divacancies in copper play a role very similar to that in gold. With experimental and theoretical techniques analogous to those used by de Jong and Koehler they derive the following characteristic energies: $E_M{}^{(2)} - B = 0.49 \pm 0.06$ eV, $E_M{}^{(2)} = 0.68 \pm 0.05$ eV and $B = 0.19 \pm 0.06$ eV.

The annealing of quenched-in vacancies in silver is quite different from that in gold. The difference has been attributed recently to a high binding energy for divacancies in silver. This conclusion emerges from several types of experiments, which are described below. A low temperature annealing stage is invariably found when silver is quenched from above 600°C directly to liquid nitrogen temperature.[31-33] The low temperature stage has been studied by isochronal annealing[32] and also in considerable detail by isothermal annealing[31] in the neighborhood of −40°C. The activation energy of annealing for this stage is 0.57 ± 0.03 eV. From the energy of single vacancy formation, 1.1 ± 0.04 eV (Tables V–2.1 and V–3.1), and the activation energy for self-diffusion, 1.92 eV,[150] the monovacancy migration energy is deduced as 0.82 eV. Consequently, the low temperature annealing stage cannot be attributed to the energy of migration of monovacancies. The isothermal experiments also show that the kinetics of annealing of this low temperature stage is second order. The experiments show further that about half the quenched-in resistivity remains after completion of the low temperature stage. On the basis of this evidence Doyama and Koehler[31] suggested that this low temperature annealing stage arises from the migration of divacancies which form tetravacancies and perhaps some higher vacancy clusters that remain in the specimen at these low temperatures. It was assumed, of course, that the resistivity of a tetravacancy is considerably less than that of two isolated divacancies.

Further confirmation of this mechanism was obtained by Doyama and Koehler in pulse experiments. They found that the divacancies could be broken apart by pulse-heating the specimen to about 270°C for about 0.1 second. This treatment resulted in a

resistivity increment that could be annealed out in the neighborhood of 100°C with an activation energy of 0.83 $\pm$ 0.05 eV, which
indicated that the divacancies were broken into monovacancies
by the heat pulse. They also found that the kinetics of this step
was consistent with the recombination of monovacancies into
divacancies. The expected kinetics is that of the approach to
monovacancy-divacancy equilibrium, if it is assumed that no
defects are lost to sinks. This process is easily described by the
theory presented in section II–6. The reaction scheme given by
equation II–6.1 is used, since, by the above assumptions, reactions II–6.2 and II–6.3 are negligible. The appropriate differential equation is II–6.4 with $K_3 = 0$, i.e.,

$$dV_1/dt = - K_1V_1{}^2 + K_2V_2 ,\qquad\qquad \text{V–7.4}$$

which is to be integrated with the condition that

$$V_1 + 2V_2 = N_0 = \text{constant} .\qquad\qquad \text{V–7.5}$$

Elimination of V_2 from equation V–7.4 via V–7.5 and integration
results in

$$V_1 = \frac{1}{2} \frac{(2K_1K_2N_0 + \frac{1}{4}K_2{}^2)^{\frac{1}{2}}}{K_1} \tanh[\frac{1}{2}(t + t_0)(2K_1K_2N_0 + \frac{1}{4}K_2{}^2)]$$
$$- \frac{K_2}{4K_1} ,\qquad\qquad \text{V–7.6}$$

where

$$t_0 = (2K_1K_2N_0 + \tfrac{1}{4}K_2{}^2)^{-\frac{1}{2}} \ln\left[\frac{(2K_1V_1{}^0 + \frac{1}{4}K_2{}^2)^{\frac{1}{2}} + 2K_1V_1{}^0 + \frac{1}{2}K_2}{(2K_1V_1{}^0 + \frac{1}{4}K_2{}^2)^{\frac{1}{2}} - 2K_1V_1{}^0 - \frac{1}{2}K_2}\right] .$$

The equilibrium concentration of monovacancies is given by

$$V_1 = - \frac{K_2}{4K_1} + \frac{1}{2K_1}(2K_1K_2N_0 + \tfrac{1}{4}K_2{}^2)^{\frac{1}{2}} ,\qquad \text{V–7.7}$$

a relation derivable from equation V–7.4 by setting $dV_1/dt = 0$,
or from equation V–7.6 by letting $t \to \infty$. Since the kinetics following the pulse heating experiments obeyed these equations, Doyama
and Koehler were able to analyze the annealing data and obtain
0.38 $\pm$ 0.05 eV for the binding energy of a divacancy in silver.

When a quenched specimen is annealed in the neighborhood of 90°C, the activation energy for motion is again about 0.57 eV in the early stages of annealing, and very little residual resistivity remains in the sample. Doyama and Koehler suggest that the lifetime of tetravacancies is short at this temperature and that the dominant annealing process is the migration of divacancies to sinks. From this experiment, and from the low temperature annealing experiments, they bracket the binding energy of a tetravacancy, relative to two divacancies, between 0.22 and 0.38 eV. The residual resistivity finally disappears above 250°C.

Quéré,[33] following somewhat different quenching and annealing techniques, obtained activation energies of 0.58 and 0.86 eV and assigned them to divacancy and monovacancy motion, respectively, in agreement with the Doyama and Koehler results. Gertsriken and Novikov,[35] who measured the annealing of the quenched-in thermal electromotive force, also obtained 0.83 eV for the migration energy.

d) Variable sink concentration

When gold is quenched from above 800°C the annealing process becomes quite complex, since the defects are present in large enough concentration to interact with each other. These interactions are dominant if the dislocation content of the quenched specimen is low and, in order to study these processes, extra care must be exercised in the initial preparation of the samples to minimize the dislocation content. The annealing curve after such quenches exhibits a delay in the early stages of annealing and therefore has an over-all S-shape, as illustrated in Fig. V–7.6.[125] It is also known that even a small amount of deformation increases the initial rate of annealing and therefore eliminates this initial delay, in agreement with the idea that this delay arises from the interaction of the defects.

S-shaped curves can be accounted for by various theoretical descriptions, as shown in sections II–5 and II–6. The monovacancy-divacancy mechanism of II–6 can be made to fit this delay only by using rather unrealistically high values for the resistivity of divacancies compared with those of single vacancies. Recent experiments[151] on gold have shown that the application of the variable sink decay scheme of Kimura et al. (II–5) would lead to

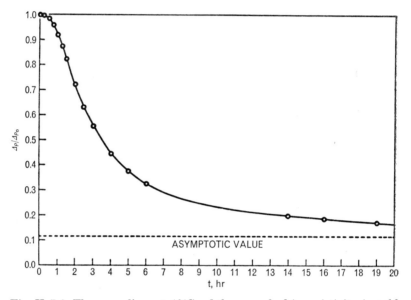

Fig. V–7.6 The annealing, at 40°C, of the quenched-in resistivity in gold when the quench is from high temperature, in this case 900°C. (From reference 125.)

a divacancy binding energy considerably higher than that derived in the previously discussed experiments on gold quenched from below 800°C. The variable sink decay scheme of deJong and Koehler (II–5) appears to be the most satisfactory at present,* on the basis of the experiments discussed below.

---

* Recent experiments by Jeanotte and Machlin[151a] indicate that oxygen may be introduced inadvertently into gold from the atmosphere used in quench experiments and that the quenched-in defects may interact with the oxygen thereby altering the kinetics and influencing the position of the S-shaped curve on the temperature scale.

DeJong and Koehler[151] studied in some detail the S-shaped annealing curves at 40°C as a function of quench temperature. They report that all the annealing curves thus obtained under these conditions can be combined into one curve by plotting the reduced variable $f = [\rho - \rho(\infty)]/[\rho_0 - \rho(\infty)]$ against the reduced time $t/t_\frac{1}{2}$, as illustrated in Fig. V–7.7. ρ is the resistivity at time t, ρ_0 is the initial quenched-in resistivity, $\rho(\infty)$ is the residual resistivity after infinite annealing time at 40°C, and $t_\frac{1}{2}$ is the time required for f to decrease to half its initial value. The curve marked "calculated," obtained from the theory as outlined in section II–5, specifically by use of equations II–5.24 and II–5.25, is obviously in good agreement with the experimental data. The dependence of $t_\frac{1}{2}$ on the initial concentration, as expressed in equation II–5.25, could be investigated from deJong and Koehler's data. They found that $1/t_\frac{1}{2}$ is proportional to N_0^p with $p = 2.6 \pm 0.2$ in comparison with the theoretical value $p = 2.5$ (where

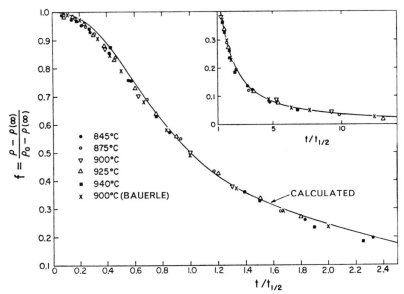

Fig. V–7.7 Normalization of the annealing data, obtained at 40°C, with respect to the quench temperatures. The full line is the calculated curve from the deJong-Koehler model. (From reference 151.)

T

N_0 is the initial concentration of defects and $N_0{}^{2.5}$ in equation II–5.25 is obtained after substitution of n_∞). The temperature dependence of $t_{\frac{1}{2}}$, which was not studied in these experiments, is seen, after this substitution into equation II–5.25, to be a very complicated function of the annealing temperature. On the basis of these experiments and the comparison with theory, deJong and Koehler suggest that the following processes take place. The quenched-in defects anneal out at the corners of tetrahedra which are formed during the annealing process itself by the clustering of vacancies. The tetravacancies are assumed to act as the nuclei for the tetrahedra, and the other defects in the crystal are assumed to remain in thermal equilibrium with each other. They further assume that after a vacancy arrives at the corner of a tetrahedron

TABLE V–7.2

Currently Available Energy Characteristics of Vacancies and Vacancy Clusters[a]

Metal	E_F (eV)	$E_M{}^{(1)}$ (eV) from quench expts.	$E_M{}^{(1)}$ (eV) from self-diffusion expts.[b]	$E_M{}^{(2)}$ (eV)	B_2 (eV)[c]	B_c (eV)[d]
Au	0.98	0.84	0.83	0.66	0.1	$\sim$0.22 (Ag) $\geqslant$0.22 (Sb) $<$0.10 (Ni)
Cu	1.0	1.08	1.05	0.68	0.19	
Pt	1.4	1.45	1.56			
Al	0.76	0.65	0.64	0.48	0.21	$\sim$0.2 (Mg) $\sim$0.4 (Sn)
Ag	1.1	0.83	0.82	0.57	0.38	
Sn	0.51	0.68	0.53			

[a] See also Tables V–2.1, V–3.1, and V–7.1.
[b] These values are obtained by subtracting E_F of column 2 from the best available self-diffusion activation energies.
[c] Binding energy of a divacancy.
[d] Binding energy of a vacancy to an impurity (the impurity is given in parentheses).

it migrates to its face, causing the tetrahedron to grow while maintaining the same shape and number of corners, i.e., number of vacancy sinks. The assumption of the growth of tetrahedra is strengthened by the direct observation of tetrahedra, from 270 to 580 Å in size, in quenched and subsequently annealed specimens of gold by transmission electron microscopy.[152,153]

The characteristic formation, migration, and binding energies for vacancies in a number of metals, as currently available, are listed in Table V–7.2. These quantities have been derived from a variety of experiments which, except for the data on tin,[44] have all been discussed in this chapter.

8. Annealing Experiments.

II. Annealing of Radiation Induced Defects

Since irradiation produces at least two primary defects in a crystal, the vacancy and the interstitial, the annealing of radiation damage is expected to exhibit stages corresponding to mutual annihilation as well as to migration to sinks. Further complications may well arise from subsidiary interactions among the defects such as clustering. Several annealing stages are clearly observable in isochronal annealing, as shown in typical plots of resistivity decay in copper, Fig. V–8.1,[2] following different types of irradiation. These curves exhibit important differences with respect to the different types of irradiation used to produce the defects but, in general, five broad stages are discernible. The region of appearance of any given stage depends on the time and temperature used in an annealing experiment, and often on the time and temperature of irradiation, and therefore cannot be defined precisely. However, it is convenient to identify the stages by the temperature range in which they usually appear, as follows: Stage I, 0° to 60°K; Stage II, 60° to 240°K; Stage III, 240° to 340°K; Stage IV, 340° to 450°K; and Stage V, >450°K. Stage I exhibits some clearly defined substages, labeled Ia to Ie (see Fig. V–8.1), most often studied after low temperature electron irradiation. Since irradiation with electrons produces the simplest type of damage (see sections I–12 and V–4), annealing after low temperature electron irradiation is best understood, although even in this case complete agreement on interpretation has not been achieved. Many carefully controlled experiments have been performed with electron irradiation, and these will be emphasized in this discussion.

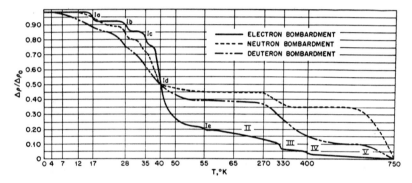

Fig. V–8.1 Schematic plot of the thermal annealing of the irradiation induced resistivity increase in copper. Note that in general the amount of resistivity recovered at any given temperature varies widely for the different types of irradiation. The fine structure at low annealing temperatures is most pronounced after electron irradiation at very low temperature, about 10°K. (From reference 2.)

a) Annealing in Stage I

The details of Stage I recovery must be studied after low temperature (~10°K) irradiation. Isochronal annealing up to 60°K following the irradiation reveals the substages in the decay spectrum. Usually the low temperature electrical resistivity is the physical property measured in these experiments. A typical isochronal recovery curve following low temperature electron irradiation of copper is shown in Fig. V–8.2.[154] The derivative of this curve is shown in Fig. V–8.3, which clearly shows the five substages referred to as Ia to Ie with increasing temperature of occurrence. Detailed isothermal kinetic studies made on Stages Ib

and Ic by Corbett, Smith and Walker[154] showed the decay to be first-order with activation energies of 0.085 and 0.095 eV respectively. Stage Ia is too small for a detailed investigation, but its activation energy is estimated to be about 0.05 eV from its relative temperature of occurrence. Altering the dose of irradiation and thereby the concentration of the defects left the kinetics and activation energies unaltered in Stages Ib and Ic as expected for a first-order reaction. Sosin and Neely[155] have shown that Stages Ia, Ib, and Ic are relatively insensitive to the presence of impurities up to about 0.1 atomic %, and Meechan et al.[156] have shown that the kinetics of these stages are unaffected by cold working the specimen prior to irradiation. Because of these characteristics it is generally accepted that Stages Ia, Ib, and Ic arise from the recombination of close vacancy-interstitial pairs that were produced in close configuration by the irradiation. Such a model conforms to the first-order kinetics discussed in sections II–2 and II–3. The three discrete activation energies associated with the above three substages arise, then, from three discrete separations involving three different configurations of the vacancy-interstitial pairs. All theoretical calculations indicate that only the interstitial-type defects can migrate, with an activation energy in the range of a few hundredths of an electron volt. Because of the low energy in the close pair annihilation process, the migrating defect is almost certainly the interstitial. The precise magnitude of the activation energy may depend on the separation of the vacancy-interstitial pair and increase with increasing separation. This is understandable if the distortions around the close pair lower the activation energy for interstitial migration.

In a detailed study of Stages Id and Ie, Corbett, Smith and Walker[157] found that all the annealing data could be superimposed on one curve by appropriate shifts of the time scale as shown in Fig. V–8.4. The time shifts needed to bring all the data together on an equivalent time scale correspond to an activation energy of 0.12 eV. Since the same energy governs both Id and Ie, it is reasonable to suppose that the free migration of an interstitial is responsible for these two stages. The separation of the two stages arises from the fact that the initial distribution of the defects is nonrandom. Thus a migrating interstitial has a higher than random probability of recombining with its own vacancy if it starts reasonably close to this vacancy. As shown in section II–3, a certain fraction of the interstitials will escape from their vacancies, and these can annihilate vacancies in a random and therefore bimolecular manner. A description of the over-all process has been given by Fletcher and Brown[158] and by Waite,[159] based on the theory of diffusion limited reactions. The kinetics is rather complicated, but Corbett, Smith and Walker, using the Waite equation, have shown good agreement for this process and concluded that Stage Id is the correlated annihilation step while Stage Ie represents the random recombination of vacancies and interstitials.

In agreement with this model, Stage Id, expressed as a fraction of Stage I, is expected to be independent of dose, while Stage Ie, since it depends on the product of the concentration of the two different defects, should be dose dependent. The experiments, as

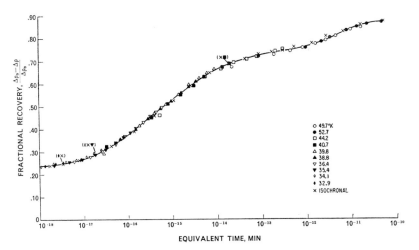

Fig. V–8.4 Isothermal and isochronal recovery curves for stages Id and Ie in copper expressed as a function of equivalent time. The shifts in the time scale leading to this normalization correspond to an activation energy of 0.12 eV. (From reference 157.)

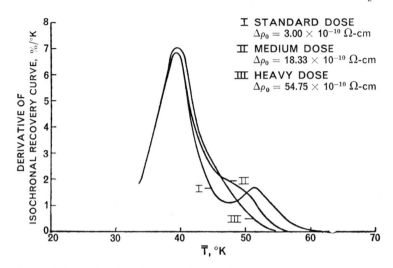

Fig. V–8.5 Differential isochronal annealing curves illustrating the dose dependence of stage I*e*. (From reference 157.)

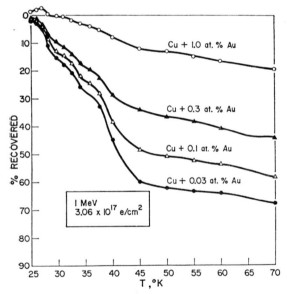

Fig. V–8.6 Isochronal resistivity recovery spectra of gold-doped copper following irradiation at 4.2°K with electrons of 1.0-MeV incident energy. (From reference 155.)

illustrated in Fig. V–8.5, show that the decay of Stage Ie is accelerated by increased dosage and therefore appears at a lower temperature.[157] At a high enough dose Ie decays in the same temperature region as Id and therefore the superposition of these two decay processes results in a broadened curve for Stage Id, as seen in the figure. The presence of impurities is also expected to influence both Id and Ie, although Ie should be more sensitive because the interstitial samples more sites before arriving at a vacancy. This sensitivity to impurities is shown in Fig. V–8.6, where the trapping of the migrating interstitial by impurities has depressed the annealing of Stages Id and Ie.[155] The liberated interstitial, which gives rise to Stage Ie, can also be expected to interact with dislocations or excess vacancies. Therefore cold work prior to irradiation should suppress the annealing of Stage Ie, as seen in Fig. V–8.7.[156] The possible fate of the interstitials will be discussed later.

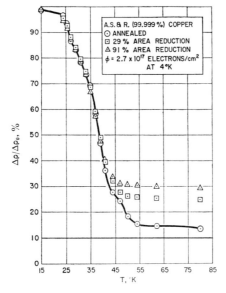

Fig. V–8.7 Isochronal recovery of resistivity of cold-worked and annealed copper following 1-MeV electron irradiation below 10°K. Note the suppression of Stage Ie. (From reference 156.)

At the end of Stage I, at about 80°K, a certain amount of residual resistivity remains. Corbett, Smith and Walker found this residual resistivity, present in samples irradiated at 20°K and annealed at 80°K for a long time, to be proportional to the total electron dose, as shown by the straight line in Fig. V–8.8 (upper

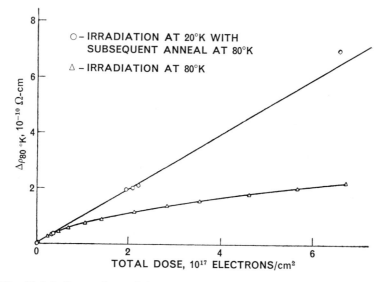

Fig. V–8.8 Comparison of the resistivity change obtained by bombarding copper with electrons directly at 80°K (lower curve) with that obtained by irradiating at 20°K and then annealing at 80°K (upper curve). (From reference 157.)

curve). Also shown is the increase in resistivity when the bombardment is performed at 80°K. The fact that residual resistivity remains in both these experiments indicates that some side reactions, in addition to simple vacancy-interstitial recombination, must have occurred. Three such side reactions were discussed theoretically in Chapter II, namely, the escape of interstitials to dislocations, the trapping of interstitials by impurities, and the association of interstitials to form di-interstitials or higher clusters. All these reactions would give rise to a growth curve similar in shape to the lower curve of Fig. V–8.8. Therefore, the irradiation experiments carried out at 80°K do not discriminate among these possibilities. The fact that the two curves of Fig. V–8.8 are different shows that the constant fractional recovery cannot be assigned solely to some other lattice defect (also produced by the radiation) which does not interact with the migrating defect, since in this case the same straight line would be obtained in both experiments. The constant fractional recovery (the straight line of Fig. V–8.8) is consistent with di-interstitial or interstitial cluster formation, but neither interstitial migration to dislocations (equation II–8.6) nor interstitial trapping at impurities (equations II–9.14 and II–9.16) leads to such a constant fractional recovery. The di-interstitial mechanism, an example of which is shown for a given di-interstitial configuration by equation II–10.9, leads to a final residual defect concentration proportional to the initial defect concentration. This result has also been shown to be independent of the di-interstitial configuration.[160] The computer calculations of Corbett, Smith and Walker also showed that tri-interstitial formation does not perturb in an important way the kinetics of annealing derived from the di-interstitial formation mechanism (II–11). A comparison of the experimental isothermal decay data with the theoretical decay curves involving di-interstitial formation is shown in Fig. V–8.9. These curves, which fit the experimental data satisfactorily, illustrate clearly the strong dependence of the rate of decay on the initial defect concentration and the dose independence of the fractional recovery. From these data and from the above analysis it may be concluded that di-interstitial formation is the most probable important side reaction occurring concurrently with vacancy-interstitial annihilation.

A type of experiment can also be done in which the initial concentration of vacancies is much higher than that of interstitials. This is the so-called "radiation doping" experiment,[157] in which a specimen is irradiated at 20°K, annealed at 80°K, and irradiated again at 20°K, and the annealing kinetics is observed after the second irradiation. The prior irradiation and anneal, according to

the model described above, leaves vacancies (and immobile di-
interstitials) in the specimen. During the second anneal, therefore,
a larger fraction of the newly introduced interstitials is expected
to be annihilated because of the simple concentration effect of
the excess vacancies. A correspondingly smaller fraction of di-
interstitials will, of course, be formed. The experiments show, in

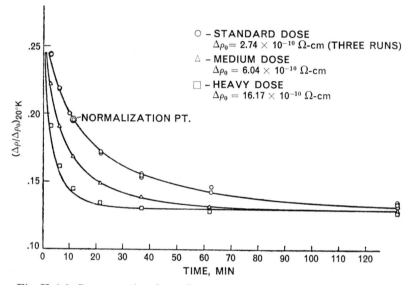

Fig. V–8.9 Concentration dependence of Stage Ie isothermal recovery. The
solid lines are the theoretical curves based on the di-interstitial formation
mechanism, normalized at one point. (From reference 157.)

agreement with the above expectations, that the rate of annealing
has increased and the residual resistivity (relative to the concentration introduced in the second irradiation) has decreased. Such
radiation doping experiments also show that the radiation induced
defects interact primarily with each other, in zone-refined copper,
rather than with impurities.

The fraction of annealing in Stage I relative to the total damage
in copper is independent of the energy of the bombarding electrons, even within a few electron volts of the threshold.[48] The

relative magnitude of the substages in Stage I is, however, quite strongly energy dependent at low electron bombarding energies, as shown in Fig. V–8.10.[48,161] As indicated in the upper part of the figure, Stages I($a + b + c$) increase relative to Stages I($d + e$) as the bombarding energy is decreased. This effect is expected on the basis of the above model, in which I($a + b + c$) are closer pairs than I($d + e$) and are therefore more easily created at low bombarding energies. The relative magnitudes of substages Ia, Ib, and Ic also vary with bombarding energy, as seen in the lower part of Fig. V–8.10, with Ic becoming more dominant as the energy is lowered. This effect is not so easily interpreted since Stage Ic represents vacancy-interstitial pairs at a presumably larger separation than those of Ia and Ib. The relative ease of formation is apparently not the same as the relative ease of migration. Since the formation is a dynamic process of an irreversible

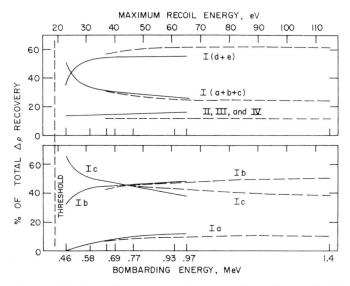

Fig. V–8.10 The dependence of the substages of Stage I annealing in copper on the electron bombarding energy. Lower figure: the relative energy dependence of substages Ia, Ib, and Ic. Upper figure: the relative energy dependence of groups of substages I($a + b + c$) and I($d + e$). The upper figure also shows the relative energy independence of Stages II, III, and IV. (Data for solid lines from reference 48; for dashed lines, from reference 161.)

nature, while the annealing is a thermally activated process, it can be concluded that some configurations may well be easier to get into than to get out of. Sosin[48] has presented some arguments that indicate that these effects may be explicable on the basis of the directionality of the primary damage event. Single-crystal experiments will be necessary to confirm these models.

Stage I annealing has also been studied after low temperature irradiation with neutrons. Annealing in this temperature range is clearly observable, as indicated in Fig. V–8.1, but the substages cannot be clearly resolved.[52,162] This is not surprising in view of the more complex nature of neutron damage (section V–4).

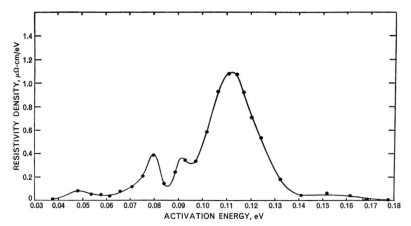

Fig. V–8.11 The activation energy spectrum for the annealing of resistivity increment induced by deuteron bombardment in pure copper. (From reference 163.)

After low temperature deuteron irradiation of copper, four of the substages, Ia to Id, have been isolated,[163] as shown in Fig. V–8.11. The resistivity activation energy spectrum was obtained from a large number of isothermal curves analyzed according to the method of section III–4 for distributed activation energies. The activation energies for the four discernible stages are 0.048, 0.08, 0.091, and 0.113 eV, respectively. These values are in good

agreement with those derived from annealing experiments following electron irradiation, and the above stages can safely be identified with Ia to Id. Stage Ie was not observed in these experiments.
Deuteron irradiation of copper at 10°K causes enough damage in
the crystal so that length changes and changes in lattice parameter can be measured with considerable accuracy. Such experiments were carried out by Vook and Wert[65] and by Simmons and
Balluffi,[64] who followed the annealing of the radiation induced
changes in length and lattice parameter, respectively. The isochronal annealing curves for resistivity, length, and lattice parameter change are almost identical, as shown in Fig. V–8.12,[62]
which indicates that these three physical parameters measure the
disappearance of the same defects. The fact that $\Delta L/L = \Delta a/a$
during annealing is highly significant. According to the theory
outlined in section IV–4, this equality means that no lattice sites

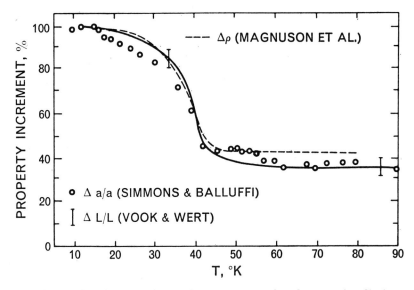

Fig. V–8.12 The isochronal annealing of copper after deuteron irradiation.
Lattice parameter, a, and length, L, were measured during warming at
about 4°K/hr. The electrical resistivity values, ρ, are residuals after 1-hr
isothermal anneals at about 1.5°K increments. (From reference 62.)

are created or destroyed, and therefore the preferential annealing of one of the defects to dislocations or surfaces cannot be an important part of the annealing process in Stage I. Thus, the deuteron experiments are in good agreement with the electron experiments and strongly support the idea that the major annealing process in Stage I is the mutual annihilation of vacancies and interstitials.

Stage I annealing processes in many other electron irradiated metals appear very similar to those in copper. Gold, however, is a striking exception. The available data, normalized in terms of an effective annealing temperature, T', are shown in Fig. V–8.13, based on the work of Lucasson and Walker[46,164] and Ward and Kauffman.[165] In this figure the reduced temperatures are rather

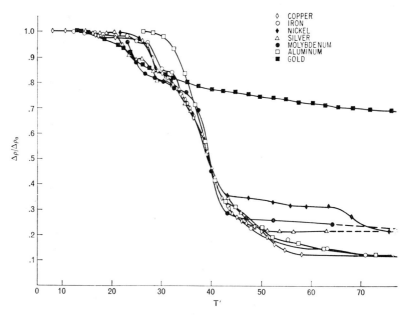

Fig. V–8.13 Normalized plot of isochronal Stage I recovery in different metals. The normalization was accomplished by requiring that the 50% recovery level occur at the same temperature as in copper. In the case of gold, which shows < 50% recovery, an arbitrary temperature shift was used. (From reference 164.)

arbitrary in that the data for all metals other than gold are required to have 50% recovery at the same temperature. Since 50%
recovery in gold does not occur until very high temperatures, an
arbitrary temperature shift (small) was used for gold. It is
apparent that not much Stage I recovery takes place in gold as
compared with the other metals, although the data of Fig. V–8.13
seem to indicate that Stages Ia, Ib, and Ic occur in gold, as in the

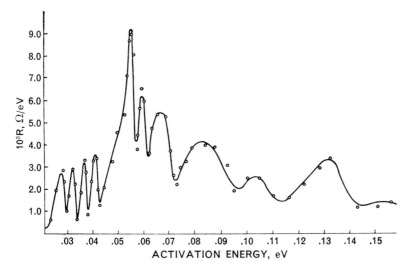

Fig. V–8.14 Activation energy spectrum for gold following low temperature
electron irradiation. (From reference 166.)

other metals, but that Stages Id and Ie are missing. The low
temperature annealing in gold following electron irradiation has
been studied in further detail by a combination of isothermal and
isochronal annealing curves.[166] An analysis of the data based on
the method of distributed activation energies reveals a larger
multiplicity of substages than observed in copper, as shown in
Fig. V–8.14. A plausible explanation for this multiplicity of substages in gold has been suggested by Koehler and Leibfried,[167]

U

who assume that the body-centered configuration of the interstitial is stable in gold rather than the split interstitial configuration applicable to copper. This is not considered to be a drastic assumption, since theoretical calculations indicate that the relative stability of these two interstitial configurations in copper is about 0.1 eV (I–7). In gold, therefore, with an interaction potential different from that in copper, the body-centered interstitial may well be more stable, although detailed calculations have not yet been made. The relative number of configurations of nearby vacancy-interstitial pairs for the two configurations of the interstitial has been analyzed by De Ford,[168] who showed that a larger number of recombination energies could result from the interstitial in the body-centered, relative to the split-interstitial, configuration. The conjecture that all these substages in gold arise from close-pair annihilation is strengthened by the observations[166] that none of the annealing peaks of the substages exhibits a dose dependence. However, recent experiments indicate that more than five substages may exist in copper also.[168a]

b) Annealing in Stages II, III, IV, and V

The characteristics of the annealing at temperatures above the range of Stage I have not been studied in nearly as much detail. Some important facts have been established, but a complete and consistent explanation of the annealing observations has not yet been achieved. A number of hypotheses have been proposed, which are still under active modification, and each of which fits many but not all of the facts. The important experimental observations and the salient features of the hypotheses are described briefly below, with emphasis on electron irradiated copper.

A significant amount of Stage V recovery appears only after bombardment with heavy particles such as neutrons, as seen in Fig. V–8.1. This annealing occurs in a temperature region associated with the recovery of cold-worked metals and is therefore generally believed to involve the breakup of large clusters of defects by self-diffusion. This belief is supported by a measurement of the energy of activation of about 2.0 eV for this stage, which is about the same as the activation energy for self-diffusion in copper. The determination of this activation energy was made by a measurement of the recovery of the critical shear stress, which was increased by the irradiation produced defects pinning the dislocations (see section V–6), and by the annealing of residual resistivity.[79,169] After electron bombardment Stage V is either unobservable or very small.

Although the values for the activation energy of Stage IV, derived from different experiments, cannot be established with high accuracy, it is generally agreed that single vacancy migration is the most likely mechanism for annealing in this temperature range. The quench experiments (Table V–7.1) have established a value for the migration energy of the vacancy in copper somewhat greater than 1 eV and a temperature of migration above room temperature. The only other method that has been used to introduce sufficient amounts of damage to cause a large Stage IV recovery has been cold work. Analysis of the annealing which occurs in this temperature region following cold work has yielded an activation energy of about 1.1 eV, in good agreement with the quench data.[170] However, for reasons already discussed, data obtained from annealing following cold work are not easily interpretable because of the lack of clearly analyzable kinetics. Yet, the agreement between the quench and cold work experiments is generally accepted as conclusive for a third, but negative reason. There is no other stage which could arise from vacancy migration in copper as long as the vacancy migration energy is accepted as >1 eV. Stage IV annealing is difficult to study after irradiation because after electron irradiation it is very small and after heavy particle bombardment it is apparently poorly defined. Some indirect experiments indicate that the temperature range and the approximate activation energy for this stage during electron irradiation are in reasonable agreement with those derived from quench and cold work experiments.[156,171]

Meanwhile, back at Stage I, vacancies, some trapped interstitials, and some di-interstitials (and perhaps a few higher clusters) were left in electron irradiated copper. Since vacancies apparently do not move until Stage IV, Stages II and III presumably arise from the migration of an interstitial type of defect. Stage II does not show up in very pure copper but is always observable when impurities are present.[46] It becomes very large, for example, when copper is doped with 0.02% cadmium, as shown in Fig. V–8.15.[172] Interstitial trapping at impurities, a process which has been shown theoretically to be plausible,[173] is therefore strongly indicated in Stage II. It is also seen in this figure that the development of an

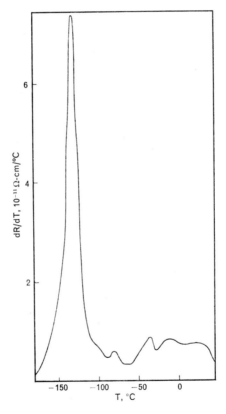

Fig. V–8.15 Isochronal annealing of 0.02 atomic % cadmium-copper after electron bombardment at −77°K. (From reference 172.)

ment with single vacancy migration energies from quench and cold work experiments, namely, about 1.1 eV for copper. Walker's objection to his second possibility may not be valid in view of the recent calculations (see I–5 and I–8) which indicate that the di-interstitial is less mobile than the single interstitial and that its binding energy is sufficiently high that its formation may be favored over the formation of interstitial-impurity complexes.

Seeger[170] and Meechan, Sosin and Brinkman[156] feel that the assignment of single vacancy migration to Stage IV is conclusive and therefore propose a different model for Stages I, II, and III. They suggest that a second type of interstitial, the crowdion (see I–4), exists in metastable form in copper at low temperatures and that its free migration is responsible for the annealing in Stage I*e* (I*b* and I*c* are still considered to be the annihilation of vacancy-interstitial pairs, and I*d* the correlated annihilation of vacancies by both interstitials and crowdions). This leaves the free interstitials to migrate in Stage III, and they explain Stage II as the annealing of vacancy-interstitial pairs through a continuum of nearest-neighbor distances up to a distance at which the interstitial migration can be considered to be free. Further, the cold-work experiments can be explained by supposing that metastable crowdions are converted into free interstitials at dislocations. In this way Stage I*e* can be depressed and Stage III enhanced. Although such a mechanism gives first-order kinetics for Stages I*a* to I*d* and second-order kinetics in Stage III, as required by the experiments, there are several difficulties with this model also. First, according to the latest theoretical calculations the crowdion is unstable rather than metastable in copper (I–4). Second, Granato and Nilan[176] have shown that free crowdion-vacancy annihilation should be a third-order process since the crowdion is restricted to migrate in one direction. Thus, the kinetics of Stage I*e* are not explainable by this process. Third, their proposal for Stage II does not take impurity trapping into account although the experiments already discussed show clearly that there is no Stage II annealing in very pure copper and that controlled doping with impurities enhances Stage II annealing and develops distinct features in it. Also, in view of the currently available theoretical calculations of interstitial migration energy in copper, 0.6 to 0.7 eV seems too high.

Clearly the situation is by no means resolved even for copper, the material investigated in greatest detail, and for the simplest type of irradiation, electron bombardment.

9. Diffusion with External Generation of Defects

The relation between the migration of thermally generated point defects and self-diffusion was discussed in section I–7. It was shown that if diffusion occurs by means of such defects the activation energy for self-diffusion is the sum of the energy of formation and the energy of migration of the defect. One can go a step further in discussing the nature of the defect responsible for diffusion by recalling that the energy of formation of an interstitial is about three times as large as that for a vacancy (I–4). It is unlikely, therefore, that interstitials could be present in sufficient concentration at thermal equilibrium to be the responsible agent for diffusion. The theoretical evidence indicates very strongly, therefore, that diffusion occurs via the vacancy mechanism, at least in the common face-centered cubic metals. There is important experimental evidence, namely the Kirkendall effect, which supports this conclusion. A brief description of this effect is given below. Once it has been shown that diffusion occurs via a defect mechanism, one can discuss the influence of non-equilibrium defect concentration on the diffusion process. A steady-state excess defect concentration may be produced by a steady generation of point defects by particle irradiation or by plastic deformation, and experiments characteristic of both processes will be described. In some other systems, when a mobile interstitial impurity is present, the interaction between this impurity and excess defects may seriously disturb the normal diffusion of the impurity atom. Experiments illustrating this effect will also be discussed in this section.

a) Kirkendall effect

In the experiments of Smigalskas and Kirkendall[177] a parallel set of fine molybdenum wires were laid along each of a pair of opposite faces of a rectangular bar of α-brass (30% Zn, 70% Cu) and the whole specimen was then plated with a thick layer of copper. After a diffusion anneal the molybdenum wire markers were found to have moved in toward one another by an amount proportional to the square root of the annealing time. This motion was much greater than could be accounted for by any density changes due to changes in composition. This shift of markers is known as the Kirkendall[178] effect, and this effect has been confirmed over a wide range of temperature and composition in a large number of f.c.c. and a few b.c.c. alloy systems by many investigators.[179] It has also been shown that the markers play an entirely passive role in this process and serve merely to reveal the relative motion of different parts of the lattice. Thus, it can safely be assumed that the markers are fixed relative to the lattice. From the copper-α-brass experiment it is concluded, therefore, that the number of zinc atoms moving from the brass toward the copper must be greater than the number of copper atoms moving in the opposite direction. The copper side of the interface must expand to accommodate the increased number of atoms, and the brass, which suffers a net loss of atoms, must shrink at the same time, as shown by the motion of the markers. Such an unequal diffusion of two constituents could not be explained if the diffusion were due to any type of direct exchange of atoms, since in that case the diffusion coefficients of the two constituents would have to be equal. The Kirkendall effect can easily be explained by a defect mechanism of diffusion, since the difference between the net rates of flow of the two atomic species can be balanced by a flow of defects. This picture requires that sources and sinks of defects be present within the system, because the Kirkendall effect is independent of the surface to volume ratio. As shown in section I–11, dislocations can act as efficient sources and sinks of point defects. On the basis of the Kirkendall-type experiments and on the basis of the energy of formation argument referred to at the beginning of this section, it can be concluded with a great deal of confidence that diffusion occurs, at least in the commonly studied f.c.c. metals, by means of the vacancy mechanism.

b) Accelerated diffusion by quench

If diffusion occurs by the vacancy mechanism, then the diffusion coefficient is proportional to the concentration of vacancies present. An excess concentration (larger than the equilibrium thermodynamic concentration at the temperature in question) of vacancies may be produced in the sample by various means, as discussed in this chapter. In an experiment following a quench, the concentration of vacancies steadily decreases toward equilibrium during an annealing treatment. During their migration, the excess vacancies, of course, cause atomic interchange. A full description of this process in terms of a time dependent diffusion coefficient has not yet been given, but some experiments have demonstrated the importance of quenched-in vacancies on diffusion controlled rate processes. An example of this effect, as revealed by internal friction, has already been discussed in section V–6. An acceleration of the ordering of Cu_3Au alloys at low temperature caused by rapid quenching from high temperature demonstrated the effect of excess vacancies on ordering, i.e., on diffusion in these alloys.[180] Some recent experiments, described below, have shown that excess vacancies also play an important role in precipitation phenomena in alloys.

In a typical experiment on a precipitating alloy, Panseri and Federighi[181] quenched aluminum-10% zinc from different temperatures and studied the subsequent low temperature resistivity changes associated with pre-precipitation clustering. This clustering effect causes the resistivity to rise to a maximum and then to decrease as a function of annealing time. The normalized maxima associated with this clustering effect are shown in Fig. V–9.1 for a series of quench temperatures. The process is clearly speeded up with increasing quenching temperature, presumably because of acceleration of the diffusion process due to the excess vacancies. Similar effects have been observed in other aluminum alloys such as aluminum-silver[182] and aluminum-copper.[43,183]

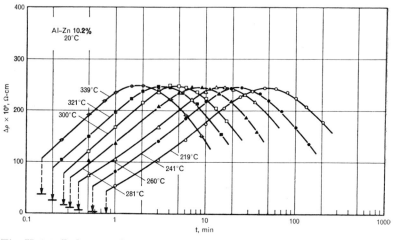

Fig. V–9.1 Influence of quench temperature on isothermal aging curves in Al-Zn (10%) at 20°C. The normalized maxima shift to shorter times with increasing quench temperature. (From reference 181.)

c) Accelerated diffusion by irradiation

If irradiation is carried out at a temperature at which the radiation produced defects are mobile, a balance will be reached between the constant rate of defect production and defect annealing. During this process an excess steady-state concentration of defects will be present in the sample, and the diffusion coefficient will be increased accordingly. This enhanced diffusion coefficient associated with irradiation in a typical reactor is only of the order of 10^{-20} cm^2/sec. Since such small diffusion coefficients cannot yet be observed with tracer atoms, radiation enhanced diffusion is not yet measurable in pure metals. However, the migration of vacancies in an alloy can cause a large number of local atomic interchanges, and such microdiffusion can often result in an appreciable change in a physical property. Changes in physical properties attributable to radiation enhanced diffusion have been observed in a number of alloys.[184] A brief description of the theory and of some typical experiments is given below.

The main features of radiation enhanced diffusion can be illustrated by a simplified theory in which it is assumed that the defects anneal at internal or external surfaces and that their mutual annihilation is unimportant. This condition is expected to be valid when the defects are present at a low concentration relative to the sink concentration. Steady-state condition can be assumed for both vacancies and interstitials if an experiment is carried out for a time much longer than the buildup time required to reach steady-state concentration. For simplicity, the development will be given for vacancy diffusion only, although identical equations are valid for interstitials moving via the interstitialcy mechanism. The results do not depend on any assumption as to whether interstitials do or do not cause any atomic interchange in alloys, and, in fact, enhanced diffusion experiments cannot distinguish between the two diffusion mechanisms. It is assumed, however, based on the discussions of this and previous chapters, that the interstitials move faster than the vacancies so that a steady-state assumption for vacancies is automatically valid for interstitials.

Under these conditions the differential equation governing the concentration of excess vacancies is[185]

$$dV/dt = K - K_v V , \qquad \text{V–9.1}$$

where K is the rate of vacancy production and is proportional to the radiation flux, and K_v is the rate constant for vacancy escape and is proportional to the vacancy sink concentration, α, and, therefore,

$$K_v = \alpha \nu_v \lambda^2 , \qquad \text{V–9.2}$$

where ν_v is the jump frequency of the vacancy and λ its jump distance. Under steady-state conditions, $dV/dt = 0$ and

$$V = \frac{K}{K_v} = \frac{K}{\alpha \nu_v \lambda^2} . \qquad \text{V–9.3}$$

The number of vacancies present in a radiation field is the sum of the thermal vacancies, V_0, and the radiation produced vacancies, V. The diffusion coefficient in the radiation field, D', is proportional to the total vacancy concentration and is given by

$$D' = (V_0 + V)\nu_v\lambda^2 = V_0\nu_v\lambda^2 + \frac{K\nu_v\lambda^2}{\alpha\nu_v\lambda^2} = D + \frac{K}{\alpha}, \quad \text{V-9.4}$$

where D is the diffusion coefficient under thermal conditions alone. The natural measure of diffusion enhancement, $D' - D$, is, therefore, the temperature-independent constant K/α. At temperatures where thermal diffusion is negligibly small, $D' = K/\alpha$, and, therefore, the radiation enhanced diffusion coefficient itself is independent of the temperature. This temperature independence is physically understandable since, as the temperature is lowered, the migration rate of the vacancies is decreased, but there is an exactly corresponding increase in the steady-state concentration of vacancies in the sample. It should also be noted that the enhanced diffusion coefficient is proportional to the flux.

If the concentration of defects is high, recombination can take place in addition to migration to sinks. In this case the differential equations governing the concentration of excess vacancies and interstitials are

$$dV/dt = K - K_v V - \nu_i(V + V_0)i,$$
$$di/dt = K - K_i i - \nu_i(V + V_0)i, \quad \text{V-9.5}$$

where i is the concentration of interstitials, ν_i is their jump frequency, and K_i is the rate constant for interstitial escape. The approximate solution of these equations shows that the enhanced diffusion coefficient has a temperature dependence with an activation energy of one-half the vacancy migration energy, $\frac{1}{2}E_M{}^v$, and is proportional to the square root of the flux.[185,186]

Short-range ordering alloys, such as α-brass and copper-aluminum, are particularly suitable for the study of enhanced diffusion, since the ordering is a diffusion process and the change of order can be conveniently followed by electrical resistivity changes. From a study of resistivity as a function of time, the characteristic relaxation time, τ, can be obtained. The experiments on 30% zinc α-brass,[185] carried out in a nuclear reactor at a total flux of about 5×10^{12} nv over a wide temperature range, showed that a large enhancement of the diffusion occurs in temperature regions where thermal diffusion is negligibly small. The data are shown in Fig. V–9.2, where $1/\tau$ (a quantity proportional to the diffusion coefficient) is plotted as a function of the reciprocal of the absolute temperature for both thermal experiments and experiments in the radiation field. The radiation enhanced rate clearly becomes independent of the temperature below about 150°C. At a sufficiently low temperature the simple theory outlined above would become invalid, because the assumption that the buildup

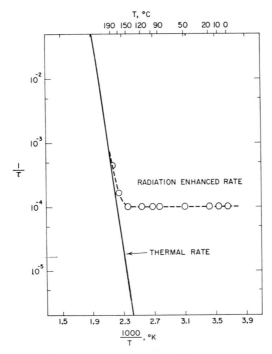

Fig. V–9.2 Radiation enhanced microdiffusion in α-brass. The rate of ordering, $1/\tau$, is plotted versus $1/T$. Dashed line: theoretical radiation enhanced rate; circles: experimental points. (From reference 185.)

time to steady state is short compared to the time of the experiment would no longer hold. When this occurs the enhancement is smaller than would be indicated by a simple extrapolation of the horizontal temperature independent line. The experiments on α-brass were not carried out to such low temperatures, but investigation of another system, iron-silicon,[187] in which the radiation enhanced diffusion behavior is completely analogous to that of α-brass, shows this expected departure at low temperature. In both these systems it appears, therefore, that the major annealing process is defect migration to fixed sinks, and that the simple theory describes adequately the process of radiation enhanced diffusion.

Experiments on 10% zinc α-brass have been done with 30-keV neon ions as the bombarding particles.[188] With such heavy charged particles the rate of defect generation is about eight orders of magnitude larger than in the reactor experiment described above. In these experiments, therefore, the steady-state concentration of defects is much higher than in the reactor experiments and considerable recombination is expected to occur. Arndt and Hines[188] found that these data could be interpreted on the basis of equations V–9.5. They showed that the enhancement was proportional to the square root of the flux, and, from the temperature dependence of the radiation induced enhancement, deduced an activation energy of vacancy motion of about 0.8 eV.

A series of reactor irradiation experiments were performed on copper-aluminum alloys by Kernohan and Wechsler.[189,190,190a] They found that in this alloy the radiation enhancement was approximately proportional to the square root of the flux and was not temperature independent. An analysis of the data by the scheme of equations V–9.5 resulted in about 1 eV for the activation energy of motion of the vacancy, in good agreement with the quenching experiments of Li and Nowick.[191] It appears, therefore, that in this alloy vacancy-interstitial recombination plays a role even in a reactor flux comparable to that in the α-brass experiments. The difference in the behavior of α-brass and copper-aluminum may well arise from a difference in sink concentration.

Because of the difficulty of annealing α-brass, the samples of α-brass studied probably had a high dislocation content, and therefore the linear annealing case is expected to dominate at the bombarding fluxes attainable in a reactor. On the other hand, copper-aluminum can be better annealed and might therefore be expected to exhibit some vacancy-interstitial recombination effects at comparable fluxes. Recent experiments on radiation enhanced diffusion in α-brass with gamma radiation have shown that the process is extremely sensitive to even small amounts of plastic deformation, the magnitude being decreased with increasing plastic deformation, in accord with the expected importance of dislocations as sinks for defects.[191a]

Radiation enhanced diffusion has also been observed in segregating and precipitating alloys. Ryan, Pugh and Smoluchowski[192] observed an increase in the magnetic susceptibility of copper-nickel alloys after neutron irradiation which could be removed by subsequent annealing in the temperature region where self-diffusion becomes important. The change in magnetic susceptibility was too large to be explained except by the clustering of the nickel atoms. Clustering of this extent cannot be achieved thermally, and only by radiation enhanced diffusion could such clustering be demonstrated, since diffusion can be stimulated this way without raising the temperature of the alloy. Kernohan, Billington and Lewis[193] have demonstrated radiation enhancement in a precipitating alloy, namely beryllium in nickel. The amount of beryllium in solution was determined by the Curie temperature of the sample, and it was shown that the rate of precipitation was appreciably increased by reactor irradiation. A similar effect was observed by Tucker and Webb[194] for the aluminum-copper system. They found that, upon irradiation with 1.4-MeV electrons at −60°C, the mobile irradiation defects promoted the low temperature clustering of copper atoms at this temperature.

d) Accelerated diffusion by plastic deformation

Plastic deformation produces point defects, but very little is known about the mechanism of generation or about the nature and number of defects produced (V–6). However, since point defects are produced, during continuous plastic deformation diffusion may be expected to be enhanced by a mechanism similar to that of radiation enhancement. A number of experiments aimed at investigating this effect in bulk diffusion by tracer techniques have been reported in the literature.[195–199] These experiments are inherently more difficult than the radiation enhanced diffusion experiments because important extraneous factors, such as distortion of the specimen, alteration of dislocation concentration and configuration, non-uniformity of strain, etc., are present and are very difficult to control. At present there is considerable controversy[200,201] concerning the conditions under which enhancement of true bulk diffusion by plastic deformation is observable. Three recent experiments, in which the various experimental parameters were carefully considered and controlled as much as possible, indicate quite convincingly that plastic deformation enhanced bulk diffusion is observable. These experiments are described briefly below.

Self-diffusion in α-iron, with radioactive Fe^{55} used as the tracer, was measured during compressive straining at various strain rates, and the resulting diffusion coefficients were compared with diffusion in the unstrained material at the same temperature.[202] The plastic deformation enhancement, expressed as $(D_s - D_u)/D_u$, where D_s and D_u are the diffusion coefficients in the strained and unstrained specimens, respectively, was found to be proportional to the strain rate, $\dot{\epsilon}$, as shown in Fig. V–9.3. Such a linearity is generally found whenever plastic deformation enhanced diffusion is observed. In the experiments on iron the enhancement was found to be independent of the total amount of strain suffered by the specimen. The diffusion enhancement shown in Fig. V–9.3 increases with decreasing temperature. However, the over-all temperature dependence, although similar, was not found to be as simple as in the case of radiation enhancement. A suggested interpretation[202] of these results involved an increased steady-state concentration of vacancies resulting from the constant generation of excess vacancies and their annealing to sinks. Very similar results were found by Shestopalov and Romashkin[203] for the diffusion of silver in copper during compressional deformation. These investigators also observed a linear enhancement of diffusion with strain rate but report a dependence on the total strain accumulated in the crystal. Their interpretation of the diffusion enhancement is also in terms of steady-state production and annealing of vacancies. They suggest that the dependence of diffusion enhancement on accumulated damage comes about because the vacancies are generated by moving dislocations, and therefore the more dislocations present, the greater the vacancy generation rate.

Recent experiments on strain enhanced diffusion in single crystals of nickel[204,205] have indicated that in this metal appreciable straining time is required to reach a steady-state enhancement. Again, once steady state is reached, the enhancement is

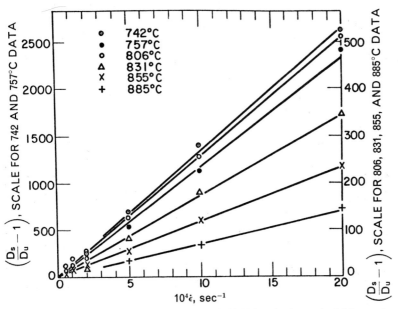

Fig. V–9.3 Plastic deformation enhanced diffusion in iron. At high strain rates the enhancement is proportional to the strain rate. (From reference 202.)

w

proportional to the strain rate. Apparently in this case a certain amount of damage must be accumulated before steady state is reached, perhaps analogously to the copper work reported above. These experiments were also analyzed on the basis of the excess vacancy mechanism, but it was further suggested that the highest concentration of excess vacancies is around the core of the dislocations and that, therefore, the enhanced diffusion effect occurs primarily along the moving dislocations.

e) *Interstitial impurity diffusion with vacancy trapping*

Many nonmetallic elements form interstitial solid solutions with body-centered cubic metals, for example, carbon and nitrogen in iron. The migration of these interstitial impurity atoms is known to occur by means of a simple thermally activated hopping process, i.e., the interstitial atom jumps from one interstice to another equivalent one. Impurity atoms and defects are known to interact, and many of the interstitial impurity atoms may be trapped if a sufficient concentration of point defects is present. Such interactions have been studied very little so far, and there is at present only one detailed study of the effect of excess vacancies on the migration history of an interstitial impurity; this is described below.

Interstitial carbon can be put into solution in iron at elevated temperatures and maintained in a supersaturated solution at lower temperatures, provided the sample is cooled sufficiently rapidly. As the temperature of the "solution quenched" sample is raised, the carbon interstitials begin to diffuse and to precipitate, first into an intermediate carbide state at around 170°C, and then into the well-known Fe_3C phase at around 260°C. When a high concentration of vacancies is introduced by a low temperature irradiation and then the sample is warmed to slightly above room temperature, the carbon is found to disappear from solution at a very high rate. The presence of carbon in solution is conveniently measured by internal friction (see IV–7). The decay in internal friction, and hence the decrease in the number of carbon atoms in solution, as a function of time following a prior low temperature irradiation, is illustrated in Fig. V–9.4.[206] Shown for comparison is the start of a decay curve in an unirradiated specimen. It is evident that irradiation accelerates this process by about three orders of magnitude. An activation energy determined from the decay curves taken at different temperatures was found to be the same as that for the diffusion of carbon in iron, namely 0.87 eV.

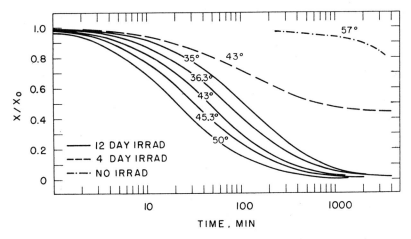

Fig. V–9.4 Normalized curves for the decay of the carbon internal friction peak. (From reference 206.)

A kinetic analysis of such internal friction as well as of the corresponding resistivity decay curves,[207] obtained after different lengths of irradiation by the method of section III–4, showed that this decay process is bimolecular with unequal concentration of reactants. The inference from these results is that interstitial carbon atoms are being trapped at radiation produced vacancies and, therefore, no longer behave as free interstitial carbon atoms.

Electron microscope examinations showed no evidence for any precipitation at this stage.[208] Calorimetric experiments[209] showed a heat release associated with this internal friction decay, indicating that the interstitial carbon is bound to vacancies with a binding energy calculated to be about 0.4 eV. This binding energy is higher than that in the intermediate carbide phase, about 0.27 eV, and when, at a sufficiently high temperature, the interstitial is untrapped it precipitates directly into the Fe_3C phase. Electron microscopy and resistivity evidence is consistent with this interpretation. Thus the final precipitation step has been unaffected, but the intermediate phase has been eliminated by the temporary trapping of the carbon by the vacancies.

References

1. *Vacancies and other Point Defects in Metals and Alloys*, The Institute of Metals, London, 1958.
2. D. S. Billington and J. H. Crawford, *Radiation Damage in Solids*, Princeton University Press, 1961.
3. *Radiation Damage in Solids*, Vols. I and II, International Atomic Energy Agency, Vienna, 1962.
4. *Recovery and Recrystallization of Metals*, L. Himmel, Editor, Interscience, New York, 1962.
5. H. G. van Bueren, *Imperfections in Crystals*, North Holland Publishing Company, Amsterdam, 1961.
6. R. O. Simmons and R. W. Balluffi, *Phys. Rev.* **125**, 862 (1962).
7. R. O. Simmons and R. W. Balluffi, *Phys. Rev.* **119**, 600 (1960).
8. R. O. Simmons and R. W. Balluffi, *Phys. Rev.* **129**, 1533 (1963).
9. R. O. Simmons and R. W. Balluffi, *Phys. Rev.* **117**, 52 (1960).
10. R. Feder and A. S. Nowick, *Phys. Rev.* **109**, 1959 (1958).
11. L. G. Carpenter, *J. Chem. Phys.* **21**, 2244 (1953).
12. D. K. C. MacDonald, *J. Chem. Phys.* **21**, 177 (1953) and in *Defects in Crystalline Solids*, pp. 383–90, The Physical Society, London, 1955.
13. F. J. Bradshaw and S. Pearson, *Proc. Phys. Soc. London* **69B**, 441 (1956).
14. J. F. Nicholas, *Acta Met.* **3**, 411 (1955).
15. C. J. Meechan and R. R. Eggleston, *Acta Met.* **2**, 680 (1954).
16. S. D. Gertsriken and B. F. Slynsar, *Phys. Metals Metallog. (USSR) (English Transl.)* **6**, No. 6, 103 (1958).
17. K. Misek and J. Polak, *J. Phys. Soc. Japan* **18**, Suppl. II (*Intern. Conf. on Crystal Lattice Defects*) 179 (1963).
18. G. Borelius, *Arkiv Fysik* **15**, 65 (1959).
19. H. U. Åström, *Arkiv Fysik* **14**, 263 (1958).
20. J. E. Bauerle and J. S. Koehler, *Phys. Rev.* **107**, 1493 (1957).
21. W. DeSorbo, *Phys. Rev.* **117**, 444 (1960).
22. T. Mori, M. Meshii and J. W. Kauffman, *J. Appl. Phys.* **33**, 2776 (1962).
23. J. Takamura, *Acta Met.* **9**, 547 (1961).
24. R. P. Huebener and C. G. Homan, *Phys. Rev.* **129**, 1162 (1963).

25. H. H. Grimes, D. Butler and P. Hoekstra, *Bull. Am. Phys. Soc.* **8**, 217 (1963).
26. R. M. Emrick, *Phys. Rev.* **122**, 1720 (1961).
27. D. Lazarus, *Solid State Physics*, Vol. 10, pp. 71–126, Academic Press, New York, 1960.
28. J. E. Bauerle, C. E. Klabunde and J. S. Koehler, *Phys. Rev.* **102**, 1182 (1956).
29. F. J. Bradshaw and S. Pearson, *Phil. Mag.* **2**, 379 (1957).
30. B. G. Lazarev and O. N. Ovcharenko, *Dokl. Akad. Nauk SSSR* **100**, 875 (1955).
31. M. Doyama and J. S. Koehler, *Phys. Rev.* **127**, 21 (1962).
32. L. J. Cuddy and E. S. Machlin, *Phil. Mag.* **7**, 745 (1962).
33. Y. Quéré, *J. Phys. Soc. Japan* **18**, Suppl. III (*Intern. Conf. on Crystal Lattice Defects*) 91 (1963).
34. O. N. Ovcharenko, *Phys. Metals Metallog.* (*USSR*) (*English Transl.*) **11**, No. 3, 78 (1961).
35. S. D. Gertsriken and N. N. Novikov, *Phys. Metals Metallog.* (*USSR*) (*English Transl.*) **9**, No. 2, 54 (1960).
36. F. J. Bradshaw and S. Pearson, *Phil. Mag.* **1**, 812 (1956).
37. A. Ascoli, M. Asdente, E. Germagnoli and A. Manara, *J. Phys. Chem. Solids* **6**, 59 (1958).
38. G. L. Bacchella, E. Germagnoli and S. Granata, *J. Appl. Phys.* **30**, 748 (1959).
39. G. Airoldi, G. L. Bacchella and E. Germagnoli, *Phys. Rev. Letters* **2**, 145 (1959).
40. F. J. Bradshaw and S. Pearson, *Phil. Mag.* **2**, 570 (1957).
41. W. DeSorbo and D. Turnbull, *Acta Met.* **7**, 83 (1959); *Phys. Rev.* **115**, 560 (1959).
42. C. Panseri and T. Federighi, *Phil. Mag.* **3**, 1223 (1958).
43. H. Kimura, A. Kimura, and R. R. Hasiguti, *Acta Met.* **10**, 607 (1962).
44. W. DeSorbo, *J. Phys. Chem. Solids* **15**, 7 (1960).
44a. C. J. Beevers, *Acta Met.* **11**, 1029 (1963).
45. P. G. Lucasson and R. M. Walker, *Discussions Faraday Soc.* **No. 31**, 57 (1961).
46. P. G. Lucasson and R. M. Walker, *Phys. Rev.* **127**, 485, 1130 (1962).
47. F. Seitz and J. S. Koehler, in *Solid State Physics*, Vol. 2, pp. 307–449, F. Seitz and D. Turnbull, Editors, Academic Press, New York, 1956.
48. A. Sosin, *Phys. Rev.* **126**, 1698 (1962).
49. A. Sosin, in *Radiation Damage in Solids*, Vol. I, pp. 223–38, International Atomic Energy Agency, Vienna, 1962.
50. R. B. Minnix and P. E. Shearin, *Bull. Am. Phys. Soc.* **8**, 196 (1963).
51. C. J. Meechan and A. Sosin, *Phys. Rev.* **113**, 422 (1959).
52. T. H. Blewitt, R. R. Coltman, C. E. Klabunde and T. S. Noggle, *J. Appl. Phys.* **28**, 639 (1957).
53. T. H. Blewitt, R. R. Coltman, D. K. Holmes and T. S. Noggle, *Creep and Recovery*, p. 84, Am. Soc. Metals, 1957.
54. D. S. Billington and J. H. Crawford, *Radiation Damage in Solids*, Chapter 5, Princeton University Press, 1961.
55. D. K. Holmes, in *Radiation Damage in Solids Course 18* (*Proceedings of the International School of Physics "Enrico Fermi", 1960*), pp. 182–227, D. S. Billington, Editor, Academic Press, New York 1962.
56. J. S. Koehler and F. Seitz, *Discussions Faraday Soc.* **No. 31**, 45 (1961).

57. C. Erginsoy, G. H. Vineyard and A. Englert, *Phys. Rev.* (in press).
58. G. K. Wehner, *Advances in Electronics*, Vol. 7, p. 239, Academic Press, New York, 1955.
59. H. W. Thompson, *Phil. Mag.* **5**, 51, 278 (1960); and in *Radiation Damage in Solids*, Vol. I, pp. 239–49, International Atomic Energy Agency, Vienna, 1962.
60. T. H. Blewitt, R. R. Coltman and C. E. Klabunde, *Phys. Rev. Letters* **3**, 132 (1959).
61. T. H. Blewitt, R. R. Coltman and C. E. Klabunde, *J. Phys. Soc. Japan* **18**, Suppl. III (*Intern. Conf. on Crystal Lattice Defects*) 288 (1963).
62. R. O. Simmons, J. S. Koehler and R. W. Balluffi, in *Radiation Damage in Solids*, Vol. I, pp. 155–204, International Atomic Energy Agency, Vienna, 1962.
63. A. V. Granato and T. C. Nilan, *Phys. Rev. Letters* **6**, 171 (1961).
64. R. O. Simmons and R. W. Balluffi, *Phys. Rev.* **109**, 1142 (1958).
65. R. Vook and C. Wert, *Phys. Rev.* **109**, 1529 (1958).
66. J. Molenaar and W. H. Aarts, *Nature* **166**, 690 (1950).
67. R. H. Pry and R. W. Hennig, *Acta Met.* **2**, 318 (1954).
68. H. G. van Bueren, Thesis, University of Leiden, 1956; *Philips Research Reports* **12**, 190 (1957).
69. H. R. Peiffer, *J. Appl. Phys.* **34**, 298 (1963).
70. H. G. van Bueren, *Acta Met.* **1**, 464 (1953).
71. H. G. van Bueren, *Acta Met.* **1**, 607 (1953).
72. T. H. Blewitt, R. R. Coltman and J. K. Redman, *Report of the Conference on Defects in Crystalline Solids*, pp. 369–82, The Physical Society, London, 1955.
73. H. R. Peiffer, *J. Appl. Phys.* **29**, 1581 (1958).
74. M. Wintenberger, *Acta Met.* **7**, 549 (1959).
75. C. W. Berghout, *Acta Met.* **4**, 211 (1956).
76. J. W. Henderson and J. S. Koehler, *Phys. Rev.* **104**, 626 (1956).
77. J. A. Manintveld, *Nature* **169**, 623 (1952).
78. R. R. Eggleston, *J. Appl. Phys.* **23**, 1400 (1952).
79. R. R. Eggleston, *Acta Met.* **1**, 679 (1953).
80. J. H. Bredt and J. S. Koehler (to be published).
81. T. Broom, *Advances in Physics* **3**, 26 (1954).
82. H. G. van Bueren, *Imperfections in Crystals*, pp. 283–315, North Holland Publishing Company, Amsterdam, 1961.
83. R. W. Balluffi, J. S. Koehler and R. O. Simmons, in *Recovery and Recrystallization of Metals*, L. Himmel, Editor, AIME (in press).
84. C. J. Meechan and A. Sosin, *J. Appl. Phys.* **29**, 738 (1958).
85. J. Takamura, K. Furukawa, S. Miura and P. H. Shingu, *J. Phys. Soc. Japan* **18**, Suppl. III (*Intern. Conf. on Crystal Lattice Defects*) 7 (1963).
86. F. Ramsteiner, W. Schüle and A. Seeger, *Physica Status Solidi* **2**, 1005 (1962).
87. W. Schüle, A. Seeger, D. Schumacher and K. King, *Physica Status Solidi* **2**, 1199 (1962).
88. R. L. Segall and P. G. Partridge, *Phil. Mag.* **4**, 912 (1959).
89. P. B. Hirsch and D. H. Warrington, *Phil. Mag.* **6**, 735 (1961).
90. P. R. Oliver and L. A. Girifalco, *Acta Met.* **10**, 765 (1962).
91. L. A. Girifalco and D. R. Behrendt, *Phys. Rev.* **124**, 420 (1961).
92. A. E. Roswell and A. S. Nowick, *Acta Met.* **5**, 228 (1957).
93. M. Levy and M. Metzger, *Phil. Mag.* **46**, 1021 (1955).

94. R. Kamel, *Acta Met.* **7**, 680 (1959).
95. R. S. Barnes, N. H. Hancock and E. C. H. Silk, *Phil. Mag.* **3**, 519 (1958).
96. D. O. Thompson and D. K. Holmes, *J. Appl. Phys.* **27**, 713 (1956).
97. R. M. Stern and A. V. Granato, *Acta Met.* **10**, 358 (1962).
98. H. Dieckamp and A. Sosin, *J. Appl. Phys.* **27**, 1416 (1956).
99. J. N. Lomer and D. H. Niblett, *Phil. Mag.* **7**, 1211 (1962).
100. D. R. Muss and J. R. Townsend, *J. Appl. Phys.* **33**, 1804 (1962).
101. D. O. Thompson and V. K. Paré, *J. Appl. Phys.* **31**, 528 (1960).
102. D. O. Thompson, T. H. Blewitt and D. K. Holmes, *J. Appl. Phys.* **28**, 742 (1957); see also G. Leibfried, *J. Appl. Phys.* **31**, 117 (1960).
103. A. Sosin, *J. Appl. Phys.* **33**, 3373 (1962).
104. A. Hikata, B. B. Chick, C. Elbaum and R. Truell, *Acta Met.* **10**, 423 (1962).
105. For a recent review, see R. Truell and C. Elbaum, in *Handbuch der Physik*, Vol. XI/2, pp. 153–258, Springer-Verlag, Berlin, 1962.
106. R. R. Hasiguti, N. Igata and G. Kamoshita, *Acta Met.* **10**, 442 (1962).
107. R. Maddin and A. H. Cottrell, *Phil. Mag.* **46**, 735 (1955).
108. H. Kimura, R. Maddin and D. Kuhlmann-Wilsdorf, *Acta Met.* **7**, 154 (1959).
109. T. H. Blewitt, R. R. Coltman, R. E. Jamison and J. F. Redman, *J. Nucl. Mater.* **2**, 277 (1960).
110. M. J. Makin, A. T. Churchman, D. R. Harries and R. E. Smallman, in *Proc. 2nd UN Intern. Conf. on Peaceful Uses of Atomic Energy*, Paper No. 80, UN, Geneva, 1958.
111. M. J. Makin and T. H. Blewitt, *Acta Met.* **10**, 241 (1962).
112. J. Diehl, in *Radiation Damage in Solids*, Vol. I, International Atomic Energy Agency, Vienna, 1962, pp. 129–54; see also J. Diehl, Chr. Leitz and W. Schilling, *Physics Letters*, **4**, 236 (1963).
113. M. A. Adams and P. R. B. Higgins, *Phil. Mag.* **4**, 777 (1959).
114. M. J. Makin and S. A. Manthorpe, *Acta Met.* **9**, 886 (1961).
115. A. A. Johnson, N. Milasin and F. N. Zein, in *Radiation Damage in Solids*, Vol. I, pp. 259–75, International Atomic Energy Agency, Vienna, 1962.
116. J. G. Y. Chow, S. B. McRickard and D. H. Gurinsky, in *Radiation Damage in Solids*, Vol. I, pp. 277–98, International Atomic Energy Agency, Vienna, 1962.
117. C. A. Bruch, W. E. McHugh and R. W. Hockenbury, *Trans. AIME* **203**, 281 (1955).
118. M. J. Makin and E. Gilles, *J. Inst. Metals* **86**, 108 (1958).
119. A. S. Nowick, *Phys. Rev.* **88**, 925 (1952).
120. A. S. Nowick and R. J. Sladek, *Acta Met.* **1**, 131 (1953).
121. A. E. Roswell and A. S. Nowick, *Trans. AIME* **197**, 1259 (1953).
122. C. Y. Li and A. S. Nowick, *Phys. Rev.* **103**, 294 (1956).
123. W. G. Nilson, *Can. J. Phys.* **39**, 119 (1961).
124. C. H. Neuman, D. Lazarus and D. B. Fitchen, *J. Phys. Chem. Solids* **20**, 170 (1961).
125. J. E. Bauerle and J. S. Koehler, *Phys. Rev.* **107**, 1493 (1957).
126. F. Cattaneo and E. Germagnoli, *Phys. Rev.* **124**, 414 (1961).
127. S. M. Makin, A. H. Rowe and A. D. LeClaire, *Proc. Phys. Soc. London* **70B**, 545 (1957).

128. A. Seeger, in *Radiation Damage in Solids*, Vol. I, p. 120, International Atomic Energy Agency, Vienna, 1962.
129. A. Kuper, H. Letaw, L. Slifkin, E. Sonder and C. T. Tomizuka, *Phys. Rev.* **96**, 1224 (1954); **98**, 1870 (1955).
130. G. V. Kidson and R. Ross, in *Radioisotopes in Scientific Research*, Vol. I, p. 185, Pergamon, New York, 1958.
131. F. J. Bradshaw and S. Pearson, *Phil. Mag.* **1**, 812 (1956).
132. G. R. Piercy, *Phil. Mag.* **5**, 201 (1960).
133. F. Cattaneo and E. Germagnoli, *Nuovo Cimento* **28**, 923 (1963).
134. For recent discussions see, A. D. LeClaire, *Phil. Mag.* **7**, 141 (1962).
135. A. Ascoli and A. C. Damask, *J. Phys. Chem. Solids* **21**, 124 (1961).
136. J. Takamura, K. Okazaki and I. G. Greenfield, *J. Phys. Soc. Japan* **18**, Suppl. III (*Intern. Conf. on Crystal Lattice Defects*) 78 (1963).
137. T. Kino, S. Kabemoto and S. Yoshida, *J. Phys. Soc. Japan* **18**, Suppl. III (*Intern. Conf. on Crystal Lattice Defects*) 85 (1963).
137a. R. M. J. Cotterill and R. L. Segall, *Phil. Mag.* **8**, 1105 (1963).
138. H. Kimura and R. R. Hasiguti, *J. Phys. Soc. Japan* **18**, Suppl. III (*Intern. Conf. on Cyrstal Lattice Defects*) 73 (1963).
139. M. Meshii, T. Mori and J. W. Kauffman, *Phys. Rev.* **125**, 1239 (1962).
140. Y. Quéré, *Compt. Rend.* **251**, 367 (1960); **252**, 2399 (1961); *J. Phys. Radium* **23**, 778 (1962); see also reference 33.
141. S. Yoshida and J. S. Koehler, *Acta Met.* **8**, 878 (1960).
142. M. Meshii and J. W. Kauffman, *Acta Met.* **8**, 815 (1960).
143. J. S. Koehler, F. Seitz and J. E. Bauerle, *Phys. Rev.* **107**, 1499 (1957).
144. F. Cattaneo, E. Germagnoli and G. Guarini (to be published).
145. M. deJong and J. S. Koehler, *Phys. Rev.* **129**, 40 (1963).
146. W. DeSorbo and D. Turnbull, *Phys. Rev.* **115**, 560 (1959).
147. J. J. Spokas and C. P. Slichter, *Phys. Rev.* **113**, 1462 (1959).
148. T. S. Lundy and J. F. Murdock, *J. Appl. Phys.* **33**, 1671 (1962).
149. M. Doyama and J. S. Koehler, *Bull. Am. Phys. Soc.* **8**, 216 (1963).
149a. A. Seeger, V. Gerold, Kin Pong Chik and M. Rühle, *Physics Letters* **5**, 107 (1963).
150. C. T. Tomizuka and E. Sonder, *Phys. Rev.* **103**, 1182 (1956).
151. M. deJong and J. S. Koehler, *Phys. Rev.* **129**, 49 (1963).
151a. D. Jeanotte and E. S. Machlin (to be published).
152. J. Silcox and P. B. Hirsch, *Phil. Mag.* **4**, 72 (1959).
153. R. M. J. Cotterill, *Phil. Mag.* **6**, 1351 (1961).
154. J. W. Corbett, R. B. Smith and R. M. Walker, *Phys. Rev.* **114**, 1452 (1959).
155. A. Sosin and H. H. Neeley, *Phys. Rev.* **127**, 1465 (1962).
156. C. J. Meechan, A. Sosin and J. A. Brinkman, *Phys. Rev.* **120**, 411 (1960).
157. J. W. Corbett, R. B. Smith and R. M. Walker, *Phys. Rev.* **114**, 1460 (1959).
158. R. C. Fletcher and W. L. Brown, *Phys. Rev.* **92**, 585 (1953).
159. T. R. Waite, *Phys. Rev.* **107**, 463, 471 (1957).
160. G. J. Dienes and A. C. Damask, *Phys. Rev.* **125**, 447 (1962).
161. J. W. Corbett and R. M. Walker, *Phys. Rev.* **115**, 67 (1959).
162. R. R. Coltman, C. E. Klabunde, D. L. McDonald and J. K. Redman, *J. Appl. Phys.* **33**, 3509 (1962).
163. G. D. Magnuson, W. Palmer and J. S. Koehler, *Phys. Rev.* **109**, 1990 (1958).

164. P. G. Lucasson and R. M. Walker, *Phys. Rev.* **127**, 1130 (1962).
165. J. B. Ward and J. W. Kauffman, *Phys. Rev.* **123**, 90 (1961).
166. W. Bauer, J. W. De Ford, J. S. Koehler and J. W. Kauffman, *Phys. Rev.* **128**, 1497 (1962); J. W. Kauffman and J. Tesk (to be published).
167. J. S. Koehler and G. Leibfried, *J. Phys. Soc. Japan* **18**, Suppl. III (*Intern. Conf. on Crystal Lattice Defects*) 266 (1963).
168. J. W. De Ford, Thesis, University of Illinois, 1962 (unpublished).
168a. J. A. Tesk, E. C. Jones and J. W. Kauffman (to be published).
169. A. W. McReynolds, W. Augustyniak, M. McKeown and D. Rosenblatt, *Phys. Rev.* **98**, 418 (1954).
170. A. Seeger, in *Radiation Damage in Solids*, Vol. I, pp. 101–27, International Atomic Energy Agency, Vienna, 1962.
171. C. J. Meechan, *J. Appl. Phys.* **28**, 197 (1957).
172. D. G. Martin, *Phil. Mag.* **6**, 839 (1961).
173. R. R. Hasiguti, *J. Phys. Soc. Japan* **15**, 1807 (1960).
174. C. J. Meechan and J. A. Brinkman, *Phys. Rev.* **103**, 1193 (1956).
175. R. M. Walker, in *Radiation Damage in Solids Course 18* (*Proceedings of the International School of Physics "Enrico Fermi", 1960*), pp. 594–630, D. S. Billington, Editor, Academic Press, New York (1962).
176. A. V. Granato and T. G. Nilan, *Bull. Am. Phys. Soc.* **6**, 419 (1961).
177. A. D. Smigalskas and E. O. Kirkendall, *Trans. AIME* **171**, 130 (1947).
178. E. O. Kirdendall, *Trans. AIME* **147**, 104 (1942).
179. For reviews, see, for example, A. D. LeClaire, in *Progress in Metal Physics*, Vol. 4, pp. 265–332, B. Chalmers, Editor, Pergamon, Oxford, 1953; and D. Lazarus, in *Solid State Physics*, Vol. 10, pp. 71–126, F. Seitz and D. Turnbull, Editors, Academic Press, New York, 1960.
180. R. A. Dugdale, *Phil. Mag.* **1**, 537 (1956).
181. C. Panseri and T. Federighi, *Acta Met.* **8**, 217 (1960).
182. D. Turnbull, H. S. Rosenbaum and H. N. Treaftis, *Acta Met.* **8**, 277 (1960).
183. W. DeSorbo, H. N. Treaftis and D. Turnbull, *Acta Met.* **6**, 401 (1958).
184. A. C. Damask, in *Radiation Damage in Solids Course 18* (*Proceedings of the International School of Physics "Enrico Fermi", 1960*), pp. 763–77, D. S. Billington, Editor, Academic Press, New York (1962); and in *Radiation Damage in Solids*, Vol. II, pp. 3–19, International Atomic Energy Agency, Vienna, 1962.
185. G. J. Dienes and A. C. Damask, *J. Appl. Phys.* **29**, 1713 (1958).
186. W. M. Lomer, AERE (Harwell) Report 1540, 1954 (unpublished).
187. H. D. Dietze and E. Balthesen, *Nukleonik* **3**, 93 (1961).
188. R. A. Arndt and R. L. Hines, *J. Appl. Phys.* **32**, 1913 (1961).
189. M. S. Wechsler and R. H. Kernohan, *J. Phys. Chem. Solids* **12**, 107 (1959).
190. R. H. Kernohan and M. S. Wechsler, *J. Phys. Chem. Solids* **18**, 175 (1961).
190a. M. S. Wechsler, *Am. Soc. Testing Mater. Spec. Tech. Publ.* **341**, 86 (1963).
191. C. Y. Li and A. S. Nowick, *Phys. Rev.* **103**, 294 (1956).
191a. R. E. Larsen and A. C. Damask (to be published).
192. F. M. Ryan, E. W. Pugh and R. Smoluchowski, *Phys. Rev.* **116**, 1106 (1959).
193. R. H. Kernohan, D. S. Billington and A. B. Lewis, *J. Appl. Phys.* **27**, 40 (1956).

194. C. W. Tucker and M. B. Webb, *Acta Met.* **7**, 187 (1959).
195. F. S. Buffington and M. Cohen, *Trans. AIME* **194**, 859 (1952).
196. N. Ujiiye, B. L. Averbach, M. Cohen and V. Griffith, *Acta Met.* **6**, 68 (1958).
197. C. H. Lee and R. Maddin, *Trans. AIME* **215**, 397 (1959); *J. Appl. Phys.* **32**, 1846 (1961).
198. A. F. Forestieri and L. A. Girifalco, *J. Phys. Chem. Solids* **10**, 99 (1959).
199. J. B. Darby, C. T. Tomizuka and R. W. Balluffi, *J. Appl. Phys.* **30**, 104 (1959); **32**, 840 (1961).
200. R. W. Balluffi and A. L. Rouff, *Appl. Phys. Letters* **1**, 59 (1962); see also *J. Appl. Phys.* **34**, 1634, 1848, 2862 (1963).
201. Yu. P. Romashkin, *Soviet Phys. Solid State (English Transl.)* **2**, 2709, 2716, 2722 (1961); a careful analysis of early experiments is given in these papers, including references to other Russian work.
202. K. Hirano, B. L. Averbach, M. Cohen and N. Ujiiye, *Acta Met.* (in press).
203. L. M. Shestopalov and Yu. P. Romashkin; *Soviet Phys. Solid State (English Transl.)* **2**, 2664 (1961).
204. A. R. Wazzan, J. Mote and J. E. Dorn, University of California, Berkeley Technical Report Series 114, April 18, 1961 (unpublished).
205. A. R. Wazzan, Thesis, University of California, Berkeley, 1962 (unpublished); UCRL-10457 (unpublished).
206. H. Wagenblast and A. C. Damask, *J. Phys. Chem. Solids* **23**, 221 (1962).
207. F. E. Fujita and A. C. Damask, *Acta Met.* (in press); see also *J. Phys. Soc. Japan* **18**, Suppl. III (*Intern. Conf. on Crystal Lattice Defects*) 105 (1963).
208. H. Wagenblast, F. E. Fujita and A. C. Damask, *Acta Met.* (in press).
209. R. A. Arndt and A. C. Damask, *Acta Met.* (in press).

Author Index

Italic numbers refer to reference citations

301

Subject Index

307